FIRST COURSE IN ABSTRACT ALGEBRA

PRENTICE-HALL MATHEMATICS SERIES
Albert A. Bennett, *Editor*

FIRST COURSE IN

ABSTRACT ALGEBRA

by

RICHARD E. JOHNSON
Associate Professor of Mathematics, Smith College

PRENTICE-HALL, INC.

Englewood Cliffs, N. J.

Library of Congress Card Catalog Number: 53-8952.

First printing .... *June, 1953*
Second printing ...... *February, 1958*
Third printing .... *May, 1959*

31827

Preface

This book is a study of various algebraic systems arising in modern mathematics. By an algebraic system we understand a set of elements together with certain operations and relations defined on the set. The first chapter is devoted to a discussion of the ingredients of an algebraic system, namely elements, sets, mappings, operations, and relations.

Clearly one of the features of modern algebra is its postulational treatment of algebraic systems. It seems historically fitting to introduce this postulational method with Peano's axioms for the natural number system. The second and longest chapter of the book is devoted to the evolution of the systems of integers, rational numbers, and real numbers from the natural number system.

It is the belief of the author that one should first develop working models of such abstract systems as integral domains, fields, and groups before defining these systems. This partially accounts for the detailed analysis of the systems of integers, rational numbers, and, to a lesser extent, real numbers carried out in the second chapter. Even without this motivation, however, these number systems are of such basic importance in all of mathematics that every student of mathematics should be exposed to a rigorous development of their properties.

The second chapter also sets a pattern for the rest of the book in its use of algebraic language and techniques. Thus, for example, the words "associative" and "commutative" arise in describing the properties of the system of natural numbers; and the technique of partitioning a set relative to an equivalence relation enters in the definition of the system of integers. It is felt that these abstract concepts are better understood if they are first encountered in a concrete example such as the real number system.

The first abstract algebraic systems introduced are the integral domain and field in Chapter III. By the time the discussion of such systems comes to an end in Chapter V, the field of integers modulo a prime p, polynomial domains, and the complex number field have been covered. Included in these chapters is much of the elementary theory of equations dealing with polynomials.

The course of the book changes in Chapter VI from integral domains and fields to groups. In keeping with the spirit of the book, with its emphasis on mappings, the first groups to be discussed are the permutation groups. Cayley's theorem that every group is isomorphic to some permutation group is proved to justify our leaning towards permutation groups. A detailed analysis of cycles and transpositions is given. The partitioning of a group into cosets of a subgroup is discussed, and the resulting quotient group of an invariant subgroup is derived.

Chapters VII to IX are concerned with vector spaces, linear transformations, matrices, determinants, and systems of linear equations. A one-to-one correspondence between the set of all linear transformations of an n-dimensional vector space and the set of all $n \times n$ matrices over a field is used to induce an algebra of matrices from the corresponding algebra of linear transformations. Matrices are used to give the theoretical solution of a system of linear equations, and then determinants are employed as a practical devise for solving such a system.

The final chapter of the book is intended to give the reader a quick look at some of the more unusual algebraic systems of modern mathematics. We have selected three such systems from among the many possible choices, namely linear algebras, rings, and Boolean algebras. The concept of an ideal is introduced in the section on rings, and the relationship between ideals and congruences as used earlier in the book is discussed. The 1904 Huntington postulates of a Boolean algebra are used, with the rest of the properties of the algebra of all subsets of a given set being derived from these postulates.

As the title indicates, this book is intended for use as a textbook in an introductory course in abstract algebra. Such a course is often given at the third or fourth year college level, although, in some schools, it is left for the first-year graduate level. Enough material has been included for a year undergraduate course meeting three hours per week. The book could be covered in a one semester graduate course meeting four or five hours per week.

Some parts of the book may be omitted without destroying its continuity. The details of Section 7 on the real number system need not be given. Section 12 on the quotient field of an integral domain and Section 22 on quotient groups may be omitted. With some filling in of Section 16, Section 15 on the field of polynomials modulo a prime may be left out. Chapter X on other algebraic systems may be omitted in its entirety. The first five chapters of the book could serve as a one semester course in abstract algebra. This part contains many of the topics usually included in a college course on the theory of equations.

It would be impossible for the author to state precisely where he first encountered each idea incorporated in this book. His partiality to linear transformations over matrices dates back to his graduate work with Professor M. H. Ingraham. Others who have had a profound influence on the author's algebraic interests are Professors N. Jacobson, F. Kiokemeister, and N. H. McCoy. The latter has also read through the final version of this book, for which the author is most grateful. Finally, the help and encouragement from my wife, Sylvia, has had much to do with the ultimate completion of the book.

R. E. JOHNSON

Northampton, Mass.

Contents

FIRST COURSE IN ABSTRACT ALGEBRA

CHAPTER I

Basic Concepts

It is the aim of this book to define and develop the elementary properties of some of the fundamental algebraic systems arising in various branches of modern mathematics. Prior to a discussion of these systems, there must come an explanation of a few of the abstract concepts used in describing these systems. While such concepts as element, set, mapping, relation, and operation might be new to the reader in their abstract formulation given here, examples of these concepts are very familiar to all of us.

1. Sets and elements

We start off with the undefined (and undefinable) notions of set and element. A *set* is made up of *elements*, though, again, the phrase "is made up of" is not definable. For example, a line is made up of points; in other words, a line is a set of elements called "points." The set of people in Montana, the set of books in the Library of Congress, and the set made up of the natural numbers 1, 2, 3, . . . are further examples of sets of elements.

For the most part, sets will be designated by italic capital letters such as "P," "T," . . ., while elements of a set will be designated by small italic letters such as "a," "n," "x," . . .. The symbol "$\in$" means "is an element of;" thus

$$a \in S$$

means* "a is an element of the set S." For example, if L is a line in a

---

*In some contexts, "$a \in S$" will mean "a in S," or "a be an element of S," or similar variations depending on the grammar involved. Thus "let $a \in S$" is read "let a be an element of S," and "for all $a \in S$" is read "for all a in S." We shall also use "$a,b \in S$" which will mean "a and b are elements of S," or "a and b in S," or other similar variations.

plane and a, b, and c are points in the same plane, then "$a \in L$" and
"$b \in L$" signify that "a and b are points on the line L," as indicated
in Figure 1. On the other hand, "$c \notin L$" means that "c is not on L."
A stroke through a symbol indicates a denial of the symbol; "$\notin$"
means "is not an element of," "$\neq$" means "is not equal to," and so on.

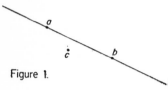

Figure 1.

For the sets S and T, we shall write
"$S = T$" if S and T are made up
of the same elements. If we use the
equality sign with elements, say
"$a = b$," it will indicate that a and
b are the same element.

In case the elements of a set S
are also elements of a set T, S is called a *subset* of T. This is indicated
by the notation

$$S \subset T.$$

("$\subset$" may be read "is contained in.") If $S \subset T$ with $S \neq T$, then S
is called a *proper subset* of T. The set of all science books in the Library
of Congress is a proper subset of the set of all books there, and the set
of all people in Texas is a proper subset of the set of all people in the
United States. Although the set of all mountains west of the Missis-
sippi and over 14,000 feet in elevation is a subset of the set of all
mountains over 14,000 feet in elevation in the United States, it certainly is not a proper subset. It is evident that for any two sets S and
T, $S = T$ if and only if $S \subset T$ and $T \subset S$.

If S and T are both subsets of a set W, that is, if $S \subset W$ and $T \subset W$,
then the *union* of S and T, designated by

$$S \cup T,$$

is the subset of W made up of all elements of W, each of which is
either in S or in T (or in both). The *intersection* of S and T, designated
by

$$S \cap T,$$

is the subset of W consisting of all elements of W, each of which is in
both S and T. Thus

while

$$a \in S \cup T \quad \text{if and only if} \quad a \in S \text{ or } a \in T,$$

$$a \in S \cap T \quad \text{if and only if} \quad a \in S \text{ and } a \in T.$$

void set = null set

Should it happen that S and T have no elements in common, then $S \cap T$ is the *void set*. The union or intersection of any collection of subsets of W may be defined similarly.

For example, let W be the set of all letters of our alphabet, and let the subsets R, S, and T be defined by their membership as follows:

$$R = \{a,e,g,k,n,p\}, \qquad S = \{b,c,e,k,n,q,w\}, \qquad T = \{c,f,h,m,q,x,z\}.$$

Then

$$R \cup S = \{a,b,c,e,g,k,n,p,q,w\}, \qquad R \cap S = \{e,k,n\},$$

$$R \cup T = \{a,c,e,f,g,h,k,m,n,p,q,x,z\}, \qquad R \cap T \text{ is void.}$$

As other illustrations, the union of the set of all senators and the set of all representatives is the set of all congressmen in the United States; the intersection of the set of all men over 25 years in age and the set of all men under 50 years in age is the set of all men between 25 and 50 years in age.

Associated with any two sets S and T is the *product* set

$$S \times T$$

consisting of all pairs (a,b), where $a \in S$ and $b \in T$. If S is a set of women and T is a set of men, then $S \times T$ is the set of all possible pairs, or mates, of a woman and a man from the given sets. An example of a product set occurring in analytic geometry is that of a rectangular coordinate system in the plane. If X and Y are the sets of all coordinates of points on the x- and y-axes respectively, then $X \times Y$ is the set of all pairs (a,b), where $a \in X$ and $b \in Y$; that is, $X \times Y$ is the set of all coordinates of points in the plane. Another example is as follows: if

$$S = \{a,b\}, \qquad T = \{p,q,r,s\},$$

then

$$S \times T = \{(a,p), (a,q), (a,r), (a,s), (b,p), (b,q), (b,r), (b,s)\}.$$

1-1 EXERCISES

1. Let S be the set of all letters appearing in the first line of this chapter, T the set in the second line. Find $S \cup T$ and $S \cap T$.

2. List all the subsets of the set $\{a,b,c,d\}$.

3. If $S = \{a,b,c,d\}$ and $T = \{x,y,z\}$, find $S \times T$ and $T \times T$.

4. If S and T are lines in a plane (that is, sets of points on lines), what are $S \cup T$ and $S \cap T$? *Set of all coordinate points in the plane*

5. If R, S, and T are any subsets of a set W, prove that:

   (i) $(R \cup S) \cup T = R \cup (S \cup T)$;

   (ii) $(R \cap S) \cap T = R \cap (S \cap T)$;

  (iii) $(R \cup S) \cap T = (R \cap T) \cup (S \cap T)$;

  (iv) $(R \cap S) \cup T = (R \cup T) \cap (S \cup T)$.

2. Mappings and operations

Examples of correspondences between sets are extremely common in our everyday life. Thus to each card in the index file of a library, there corresponds a book of the library; to each day, there corresponds a date on the calendar; to each city, there corresponds a name; and so on. In mathematics, the concept of a correspondence between two sets is of fundamental importance. The reader probably is familiar with the mathematical notion of a function. For example, the equation $y = x^2$ defines a function; that is, to each number x there corresponds a unique number y given by this equation.

We shall find it convenient to use the word "mapping" to describe a particular type of correspondence* between two sets.

1-2 DEFINITION. If S and T are two sets (not necessarily distinct), then a *mapping* of S into T is a correspondence between S and T that associates with each element of S a unique element of T.

It is convenient to use a notation for mappings similar to the familiar $f(x)$ notation for functions. We shall use small Greek letters such as "α," "θ," ... to designate mappings. If α is a mapping of the set S into the set T, then for each $a \in S$, the corresponding element of T is designated by "$a\alpha$." We shall use the the notation

$$\alpha: \quad a \to a\alpha$$

to indicate that under the mapping α of S into T, a is mapped into $a\alpha$; that is, $a\alpha$ is the element of T corresponding to the element a of S.

For example, let $S = \{a,b,c,d,e\}$ and $T = \{s,t,u,v,w,x,y,z\}$, and let α be the mapping of S into T defined below:

$$\alpha: \quad a \to u, \quad b \to w, \quad c \to s, \quad d \to u, \quad e \to t.$$

An equivalent way of defining α is as follows:

$$\alpha: \quad a\alpha = u, \quad b\alpha = w, \quad c\alpha = s, \quad d\alpha = u, \quad e\alpha = t.$$

*We have not attempted to define a correspondence between two sets.

The mapping θ of the set N of natural numbers into itself defined by

$$\theta: \quad 1 \to 1, \quad 2 \to 4, \quad 3 \to 9, \quad 4 \to 16, \quad \ldots$$

associates with each natural number n its square n^2; that is,

$$n\theta = n^2$$

for each $n \in N$.

As another example of a mapping, let L be the set of all books in the Library of Congress and let N be the set of natural numbers. For each $a \in L$, let "$a\gamma$" designate the number of pages in the book a. Then the correspondence

$$\gamma: \quad a \to a\gamma$$

is a mapping of L into N.

Two mappings α and β of S into T are equal, $\alpha = \beta$, if and only if $a\alpha = a\beta$ for each $a \in S$.

A mapping α of S into T is a mapping of S *onto* T if for each $b \in T$, there exists an $a \in S$ such that $a\alpha = b$. Thus if α is a mapping of S onto T, each element of T corresponds to some element of S.

A type of mapping of particular importance is the so-called "1–1 mapping" ("one-to-one mapping") of one set onto another.

1-3 Definition. The mapping α of S onto T is a 1–1 *mapping of* S onto T if for each $a,b \in S$,

$$a \neq b \quad \text{implies} \quad a\alpha \neq b\alpha.$$

If a classroom is full of students, all seated in chairs, then there exists a 1–1 mapping of the set of students onto the set of chairs in the room. As another illustration, let S be the set of all husbands in Chicago and T be the set of all wives of these men. Then the correspondence that associates with each man in S his wife in T is a 1–1 mapping of S onto T.

An equivalent way of defining a 1–1 mapping α of S onto T is that for each $a,b \in S$, if $a\alpha = b\alpha$ then $a = b$.

The concept of a 1–1 mapping is closely related to that of counting. Two sets S and T are said to have the same *number of elements* if and only if there exists a 1–1 mapping of S onto T. For example, the set of all fingers on the right hand has the same number of elements as the set of all fingers on the left hand, since there clearly exists a 1–1 mapping of one of these sets onto the other. If n is a natural number, it is customary to say that a set S has n elements if it has the same number of elements as the set $\{1,2, \ldots,n\}$. We shall have more to say about this in the succeeding chapters.

If α is a 1–1 mapping of the set S onto the set T, then for each $c \in T$ there is a unique element $a \in S$ such that $c = a\alpha$. We see therefore that α induces in a natural way a mapping of T onto S for which $c \to a$.

1-4 DEFINITION. If α is a 1–1 mapping of S onto T, then the *inverse*, α^{-1}, of α is the mapping of T onto S defined by

$$\alpha^{-1}: \quad (a\alpha)\alpha^{-1} = a, \qquad a \in S.$$

The mapping α^{-1} is well-defined by the above definition, since each element of T can be written uniquely in the form $a\alpha$. Furthermore, α^{-1} is a 1–1 mapping of T onto S. To prove this, we have only to observe that if $a\alpha \neq b\alpha$ then $a \neq b$.

If S is the set of all husbands, T of wives, in Chicago as given above, and if α is the mapping of S onto T that associates with each man in S his wife in T, then α^{-1} is the mapping of T onto S that associates with each woman in T her husband in S. Another example is as follows. If $S = \{a,b,c,d,e\}$ and $T = \{v,w,x,y,z\}$, and α is the mapping of S onto T defined by

$$\alpha: \quad a\alpha = x, \quad b\alpha = v, \quad c\alpha = w, \quad d\alpha = z, \quad e\alpha = y,$$

then clearly α is a 1–1 mapping of S onto T. The inverse α^{-1} of α is then defined by

$$\alpha^{-1}: \quad v\alpha^{-1} = b, \quad w\alpha^{-1} = c, \quad x\alpha^{-1} = a, \quad y\alpha^{-1} = e, \quad z\alpha^{-1} = d.$$

Let S, T, and U be three (not necessarily distinct) sets, and α be a mapping of S into T, β be a mapping of T into U. Then each element $a \in S$ is mapped into an element $a\alpha \in T$, and, in turn, $a\alpha$ is mapped into an element $(a\alpha)\beta \in U$. Hence α and β induce in a natural way a mapping of S into U, by which $a \to (a\alpha)\beta$.

1-5 DEFINITION. Let α be a mapping of set S into set T and β be a mapping of set T into set U. Then the *product*, $\alpha\beta$, of α by β is the mapping of S into U defined by

$$\alpha\beta: \quad a\alpha\beta = (a\alpha)\beta, \qquad a \in S.$$

If, for example, $S = \{a,b,c\}$, $T = \{p,q,r,s\}$, and $U = \{w,x\}$, and α and β are defined by

$$\alpha: \quad a\alpha = q, \quad b\alpha = r, \quad c\alpha = p,$$

$$\beta: \quad p\beta = x, \quad q\beta = w, \quad r\beta = w, \quad s\beta = x,$$

then $\alpha\beta$ is the mapping of S into U given by

$$\alpha\beta: \quad a\alpha\beta = w, \quad b\alpha\beta = w, \quad c\alpha\beta = x.$$

The word "operation" is used in mathematics to indicate a special kind of mapping. Addition and multiplication as used in elementary algebra are examples of operations as we shall presently see.

1-6 Definition. A (binary) *operation* on the set S is a mapping of $S \times S$ into S.

In case α is an operation on S, so that α is a mapping of $S \times S$ into S, the element of S corresponding to each element (a,b) of $S \times S$ will be designated by "$a \; \alpha \; b$" rather than "$(a,b)\alpha$" as heretofore. If, for example, S is the set of numbers used in elementary algebra, then to each pair (a,b) of numbers of S corresponds a number $a + b$, their sum. Since $+: (a,b) \to a + b$ is a mapping of $S \times S$ into S, addition is an example of an operation on S. Similarly, $\cdot: (a,b) \to a \cdot b$ is a mapping of $S \times S$ into S, and multiplication is an operation on S.

Another quite different example of an operation is the following. Let P be the set of all points in a plane, and for each pair (a,b) of elements of P, let $a \; \alpha \; b$ be the point of trisection nearer a of the segment connecting a to b. Then the mapping $\alpha: (a,b) \to a \; \alpha \; b$ is an operation on P.

1-7 Exercises

1. Let $\alpha: n \to n^2$ and $\beta: n \to 2n + 3$ be mappings of the set N of natural numbers into itself. Since $n\alpha\beta = n^2\beta = 2n^2 + 3$, the mapping $\alpha\beta$ of N into N is given by $\alpha\beta: n \to 2n^2 + 3$. Find $\alpha\alpha$, $\beta\beta$, $\beta\alpha$, $(\alpha\beta)\alpha$, and $\alpha(\beta\alpha)$.

2. Let S, T, U, V be sets, α be a mapping of S into T, β of T into U, and γ of U into V. Prove that $\alpha(\beta\gamma) = (\alpha\beta)\gamma$.

3. If α is a 1–1 mapping of set S onto set T and β is a 1–1 mapping of set T onto set U, prove that $\alpha\beta$ is a 1–1 mapping of S onto U. Also prove that $(\alpha\beta)^{-1} = \beta^{-1}\alpha^{-1}$ and that $(\alpha^{-1})^{-1} = \alpha$.

4. An operation α on a set S is said to be "commutative" if $a \; \alpha \; b = b \; \alpha \; a$ for each $a,b \in S$. Give an example of a commutative operation; also of a non-commutative operation.

3. Relations

To illustrate the final concept to be discussed in this chapter, let L be the set of all lines in a plane, and let the symbols "$\perp$" and "$\parallel$" mean "is perpendicular to" and "is parallel to" respectively. We know that for any two lines m and n, either m is perpendicular to n ($m \perp n$) or m is not perpendicular to n ($m \not\perp n$). Likewise, for each $m,n \in L$, either $m \parallel n$ or $m \not\parallel n$. If $m \perp n$, then m has the relation of being perpendicular to n; if $m \parallel n$, then m has the relation of being parallel to n. We say that $\perp$ and $\parallel$ are relations on L.

1-8 DEFINITION. The set S is said to have $\mathcal{R}$ as a _relation_* if for each pair (a,b) of elements of S, the phrase "a is in the relation $\mathcal{R}$ to b" is meaningful, being true or false depending solely on the choice of a and of b.

If $\mathcal{R}$ is a relation on the set S, then the notation

$$a \mathcal{R} b$$

will be used to signify that "a is in the relation $\mathcal{R}$ to b," while

$$a \not\mathcal{R} b$$

will be used to signify that "a is not in the relation $\mathcal{R}$ to b." This conforms with the notation used for parallel and perpendicular lines in the example above. One must remember that for each pair (a,b) of elements of S, we have either $a \mathcal{R} b$ or $a \not\mathcal{R} b$ (but not both). Further examples of relations are given below.

Let S be the set of all books in the Library of Congress, and "$\mathcal{R}$" be the phrase "has more pages than." For each $a,b \in S$, either $a \mathcal{R} b$ (a has more pages than b) or $a \not\mathcal{R} b$ (a does not have more pages than b). Thus $\mathcal{R}$ is a relation on S. Note that if a and b have the same number of pages, then $a \not\mathcal{R} b$. Certainly, then, $a \not\mathcal{R} a$ for each $a \in S$.

Let M be the set of all men in Montana, and let "$\mathcal{F}$" be the phrase "is a father of." For each $m,n \in M$, either $m \mathcal{F} n$ (m is a father of n) or $m \not\mathcal{F} n$ (m is not a father of n). Clearly $\mathcal{F}$ is a relation on M.

As a final example, let K be the set of all people in Kansas, and let "$\mathcal{S}$" be the phrase "has the same surname as." For each $a,b \in K$, either $a \mathcal{S} b$ (a has the same surname as b) or $a \not\mathcal{S} b$ (a does not have the same surname as b). Again, $\mathcal{S}$ is an example of a relation on K.

---

*Let $T = \{$"true," "false"$\}$, a set with two elements. Then a _relation_ is a mapping $\mathcal{R}$ of $S \times S$ into T. In case $(a,b)\mathcal{R} =$ "true" (that is, if (a,b) is mapped into the element "true" of T by $\mathcal{R}$), we say "a is in the relation $\mathcal{R}$ to b," while if $(a,b)\mathcal{R} =$ "false," we say "a is not in the relation $\mathcal{R}$ to b."

1-9 Definition. A relation $\Re$ on the set S is:

  (i) *reflexive* if $a \; \Re \; a$ for each $a \in S$;

  (ii) *symmetric* if whenever $a \; \Re \; b$, then also $b \; \Re \; a$;

  (iii) *transitive* if whenever $a \; \Re \; b$ and $b \; \Re \; c$, then also $a \; \Re \; c$.

A relation on S that is reflexive, symmetric, and transitive is an *equivalence relation* on the set.

Equality $(=)$ is always an equivalence relation, as is suggested by the similarity of the words "equals" and "equivalence." Let us look at our previous examples of relations and see which are equivalence relations.

If L is the set of all lines in a plane, the relation $\perp$ on L is not reflexive, since no line is perpendicular to itself. However, the relation $\perp$ is symmetric, since if $a \perp b$, then certainly $b \perp a$. Finally, the relation $\perp$ is not transitive, for if $a \perp b$ and $b \perp c$, then $a \parallel c$ rather than $a \perp c$.

The relation $\parallel$ on L is an equivalence relation if we consider any line as being parallel to itself.

If S is the set of all books in the Library of Congress, and $\Re$ is the relation "has more pages than," then $\Re$ is neither reflexive nor symmetric. However, $\Re$ is transitive, since $a \; \Re \; b$ and $b \; \Re \; c$ clearly imply $a \; \Re \; c$.

If M is the set of all men in Montana, and $\mathfrak{F}$ is the relation "is a father of," then $\mathfrak{F}$ is not reflexive, since a is not the father of a; $\mathfrak{F}$ is not symmetric, since $a \; \mathfrak{F} \; b$ implies b is the son of a; $\mathfrak{F}$ is not transitive, since $a \; \mathfrak{F} \; b$ and $b \; \mathfrak{F} \; c$ imply that a is the grandfather of c.

Finally, if K is the set of all people in Kansas, and $\mathcal{S}$ is the relation "has the same surname as," then it is easily seen that $\mathcal{S}$ is an equivalence relation on K. We note that the relation $\mathcal{S}$ essentially segregates the people of Kansas into non-overlapping subsets, one subset containing all the people of Kansas with the surname "Smith," another subset containing all the people with the surname "Jones," and so on.

1-10 Definition. A set $\{T, U, V, \ldots\}$ of subsets of a set S is a *partition* of S if the following conditions are satisfied:

  (i) S is the union of the subsets T, U, V, $\ldots$;

  (ii) the intersection of any two distinct subsets in the set $\{T, U, V, \ldots\}$ is the void set.

If $\{T, U, V, \ldots\}$ is a partition of the set S, then for each $a \in S$, there exists a unique subset X in the partition such that $a \in X$. The partitioning of a set into subsets is analogous to the partitioning of a house into rooms. Note that nothing is said about the number of subsets in the partition. This number might be one (in which case $\{S\}$ is the partition of S), it might be any finite number, and it might be infinite.

A partition $\{T,U,V,\ldots\}$ of the set S induces an equivalence relation $\mathcal{R}$ on S. Roughly speaking, two elements of S are in the relation $\mathcal{R}$ to each other if they belong to the same subset of the partition. To be more precise, for each $a,b \in S$, $a \mathcal{R} b$ if and only if there is an X in the given partition such that $a,b \in X$. Since $a \mathcal{R} a$, and whenever $a \mathcal{R} b$ then also $b \mathcal{R} a$, the relation $\mathcal{R}$ evidently is reflexive and symmetric. In order to prove that $\mathcal{R}$ is transitive, assume that $a \mathcal{R} b$ and $b \mathcal{R} c$. Then, by the very definition of $\mathcal{R}$, there exist subsets X and Y (not necessarily distinct) in the given partition such that $a,b \in X$ and $b,c \in Y$. Since $b \in (X \cap Y)$, clearly $X \cap Y$ is not void; hence, by 1-10, (ii), $X = Y$. Thus $a,c \in X$ and $a \mathcal{R} c$. This proves that $\mathcal{R}$ is transitive, and completes the proof that $\mathcal{R}$ is an equivalence relation on S.

For example, if S is the set of chairs in a given house, let "$a \mathcal{R} b$" mean that "the chairs a and b are in the same room of the house." Then $\mathcal{R}$ is the equivalence relation on S induced by the partitioning of the house (and hence of S) into rooms.

The converse of the result above is also true, that is, if $\mathcal{R}$ is an equivalence relation on a set S, then $\mathcal{R}$ induces a partition of S. In order to prove this, let

$$X_a = \{c; c \in S, a \mathcal{R} c\},$$

which is read "X_a is the set of all elements c such that $c \in S$ and $a \mathcal{R} c$." Let us show that the set $\{X_a, X_b, \cdots\}$, where $a, b, \ldots$ are the elements of S, is a partition of S. Since $\mathcal{R}$ is reflexive, $a \in X_a$ for each $a \in S$; thus it is clear that S is the union of all subsets in the set $\{X_a, X_b, \ldots\}$.

The set $\{X_a, X_b, \ldots\}$ has been shown to satisfy 1-10, (i). We will have proved 1-10, (ii) for this set when we have shown that for each $a,b \in S$ such that $X_a \cap X_b$ is not void, $X_a = X_b$. If $X_a \cap X_b$ is not void, let $c \in X_a \cap X_b$. Then

$$
\begin{array}{ll}
a \mathcal{R} c \quad \text{and} \quad b \mathcal{R} c & \text{(by definition of } X_a \text{ and } X_b\text{),} \\
a \mathcal{R} c \quad \text{and} \quad c \mathcal{R} b & \text{(since } \mathcal{R} \text{ is symmetric),} \\
a \mathcal{R} b & \text{(since } \mathcal{R} \text{ is transitive).}
\end{array}
$$

Now for each $d \in X_b$, $b \mathcal{R} d$; thus, since $a \mathcal{R} b$ and $b \mathcal{R} d$, $a \mathcal{R} d$. This shows that $d \in X_a$, and proves that $X_b \subset X_a$. A similar argument proves that $X_a \subset X_b$. Together, these imply that $X_a = X_b$ as desired. We conclude that $\{X_a, X_b, \ldots\}$ is a partition of S. It is obvious that the relation on S induced by this partition is $\mathfrak{R}$.

The subsets X_a of S induced by the equivalence relation $\mathfrak{R}$ on S are called the "equivalence sets" related to $\mathfrak{R}$. We have proved the following result.

1-11 Theorem. If $\mathfrak{R}$ is an equivalence relation on the set S, then the set of all equivalence sets related to $\mathfrak{R}$ is a partition of S. Conversely, for any given partition of S, there exists an equivalence relation $\mathfrak{R}$ on S such that the set of all equivalence sets related to $\mathfrak{R}$ is the given partition of S.

If, for example, K is the set of all people in Kansas and S is the relation "has the same surname as," then K is partitioned by S into subsets containing all the people of Kansas with the same surname. Thus B, S, J, ... are in the partition of K, where B is the set of all people in Kansas with the surname Brown, S is the set of all people in Kansas with the surname Smith, J is the set of all people in Kansas with the surname Jones, and so on.

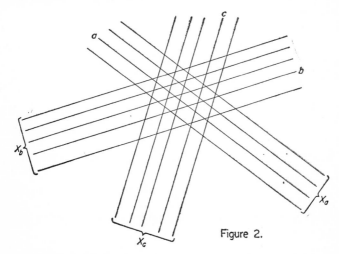

Figure 2.

Another illustration of the partitioning of a set by an equivalence relation is afforded by the equivalence relation $\parallel$ on the set L of all lines in a plane. For each $a \in L$, X_a is the set of all lines in the plane parallel to a. The set L is partitioned into sets of parallel lines, as indicated in Figure 2.

1-12 EXERCISES

1. Let $\mathcal{R}$ be a relation on the set S that is symmetric and transitive. Prove that if for each $a \in S$ there is some $b \in S$ such that $a \mathcal{R} b$, then $\mathcal{R}$ is an equivalence relation.

2. Give an example of a relation that is reflexive and symmetric but not transitive.

3. Give an example of a relation that is reflexive and transitive but not symmetric.

4. Give an example of a relation that is symmetric and transitive but not reflexive. (Hint: use the results of Exercise 1 above.)

5. If $\mathcal{R}$ is a relation on the set S that is reflexive and is such that whenever $a \mathcal{R} b$ and $a \mathcal{R} c$, then $b \mathcal{R} c$, prove that $\mathcal{R}$ is an equivalence relation.

6. Let $\mathcal{R}$ be a relation on the set S. Define the relation S on S as follows: for each $a,b \in S$, $a \mathcal{S} b$ if and only if there exists a finite set $\{c_1, c_2, \ldots, c_n\}$ of elements of S such that $a \mathcal{R} c_1, c_1 \mathcal{R} c_2, \ldots, c_{n-1} \mathcal{R} c_n, c_n \mathcal{R} b$. Prove that S is a transitive relation. What is the relation S in case $\mathcal{R}$ is the relation "is a father of" on the set M of all men in Montana? What is the relation S in case $\mathcal{R}$ is the relation $\perp$ on the set L of all lines in a plane?

CHAPTER II

The Real Number System

The number system underlying elementary calculus is the so-called system of real numbers. To get an idea of the complexity of the real number system, one has only to note that much of the mathematical research undertaken in the present century is directly or indirectly concerned with the properties of this system. We cannot possibly hope to do any more in this book than to define this system and give its more elementary properties. Contained in the real number system are the important subsystems of natural, integral, and rational numbers. These subsystems are discussed in some detail, since they play a fundamental role in the remainder of the book. They are used not only to aid in the analysis of the abstract algebraic systems to be presented, but also to yield actual examples of these systems.

4. The natural numbers

Everyone of us is acquainted with the natural numbers 1, 2, 3, and so on, used in counting. We realize that in the set N of all natural numbers there is a first number, namely 1; and that 1 has a successor, namely 2; and that 2 has a successor, namely 3; and, generally, that any natural number n has a successor $n + 1$. Furthermore, we know that any given natural number n can be arrived at by starting with 1 and proceeding step by step through successors (that is, by counting in order $1, 2, 3, \ldots, n$). We are familiar with the operations of addition and multiplication on the set N, and with their many properties (such as: $a + b = b + a$, $a(b + c) = ab + ac$, and so on).

What the reader might not realize is that the familiar arithmetical properties of the set N can be deduced from a few relatively simple assumptions, or axioms, about N, just as, for example, all the theorems of Euclidean geometry can be derived from a few axioms. While the development of geometry axiomatically dates back to the time of Euclid, the axiomatic foundations of arithmetic are quite recent, being first given by the Italian mathematician G. Peano in 1889. We shall use, in essence, Peano's axioms for our starting point.

2-1 Axiom. The set N of natural numbers is made up of the element 1 and at least one other element.

Designate by "M" the set of all elements of N other than 1. In view of the axiom above, M has at least one element.

2-2 Axiom. There exists a 1–1 mapping $*: n \to n^*$ of N onto M.

The reader should think of the mapping $*: n \to n^*$ of N onto M as the mapping that associates with each natural number n its *successor* n^*. Thus, according to 2-2, every natural number has a unique successor, since the mapping $*$ is 1–1, and every natural number other than 1 (that is, in M) is the successor of some natural number, since the mapping $*$ is of N onto M.

2-3 Axiom. Any subset S of N with the following two properties is necessarily equal to N:

(i) $1 \in S$;
(ii) for each $n \in S$, $n^* \in S$ also.

This axiom essentially states that every natural number can be reached by starting with 1 and counting the numbers in succession.

Let us now see how the arithmetical properties of the natural numbers can be derived from these three axioms. In what is to follow, no properties of the natural numbers will be used except the axioms above and those theorems derived from the axioms.

A method of proof to be used extensively throughout this book is that of mathematical induction. Before stating what this is, we remark that the word *statement* is used to designate a sequence of words and symbols declaring something to be a fact, about which we can assert either "it is true," or "it is false."

2-4 Principle of mathematical induction

If with each natural number n is associated a statement E_n, then all statements E_n are true provided

(i) E_1 is true, and,
(ii) for each n such that E_n is true, E_{n^*} is also true.

The proof of 2-4 is as follows. Let S be the set of all $n \in N$ for each of which E_n is true. By (i), $1 \in S$; by (ii), for each $n \in S$, $n^* \in S$ also.

Thus S has the two properties of 2-3. Hence $S = N$, and all statements E_n are true.

A definition in which a property is defined for the natural number n^* whenever it is defined for n is called a *recursive definition*. Examples of recursive definitions are to be found in the following definitions of addition and multiplication on N.

In line with our policy of using no properties of the natural numbers except those derived from the axioms, we must in some way define the operations of addition and multiplication on N, and then prove the expected properties of these operations from the axioms. How is addition defined on N? We know that as it is usually defined, $1 + 1 = 2$, $2 + 1 = 3, 3 + 1 = 4$, and so on; that is, n plus 1 is the successor of n. Then $n + 2 = (n + 1) + 1$, that is, $n + 2$ is the successor of $n + 1$; and $n + 3$ is the successor of $n + 2$; and so on. These ideas are embodied in the following recursive definition.

2-5 DEFINITION. The operation of addition ($+$) is defined recursively on N as follows:

   (i) $n + 1 = n^*$;

   (ii) whenever $n + m$ is defined, define $n + m^*$ such that $n + m^* = (n + m)^*$.

Let n be any fixed natural number, and E_m be the statement "$n + m$ is defined by 2-5." Certainly E_1 is true by (i), and whenever E_m is true, E_{m^*} is true by (ii). By mathematical induction, E_m is true for all numbers m (and n). Thus 2-5 defines the addition of each pair of elements of N.

The operation of multiplication on N with which we are familiar is closely related to addition. Thus, for example, we are used to the following rules of multiplication: $3 \cdot 1 = 3$, $3 \cdot 2 = 3 + 3$, $3 \cdot 3 = 3 \cdot 2 + 3$, and so on. The following definition is based on this interpretation of multiplication as a repeated sum.

2-6 DEFINITION. The operation of multiplication ($\cdot$) is defined recursively on N as follows:

   (i) $n \cdot 1 = n$;

   (ii) whenever $n \cdot m$ is defined, define $n \cdot m^*$ such that $n \cdot m^* = n \cdot m + n$.

The familiar rules of composition are given by the theorem that follows.

2-7 THEOREM. The following laws are valid for the operations $+$ and $\cdot$ on N:

(i) the ASSOCIATIVE LAWS: for each $k,m,n \in N$,

$$k + (m + n) = (k + m) + n; \quad k\cdot(m\cdot n) = (k\cdot m)\cdot n.$$

$2\cdot(3\cdot 4) = (2\cdot 3)\cdot 4$

(ii) the COMMUTATIVE LAWS: for each $m,n \in N$,

$$m + n = n + m; \quad m\cdot n = n\cdot m.$$

(iii) the DISTRIBUTIVE LAW: for each $k,m,n \in N$,

$$(k + m)\cdot n = k\cdot n + m\cdot n.$$

$(2+3)\cdot 4 = 2\cdot 4 + 3\cdot 4$

(iv) the CANCELLATION LAWS: for each $k,m,n \in N$,

if $m + k = n + k$, then $m = n$;

if $m\cdot k = n\cdot k$, then $m = n$.

Some of these will be proved now, some will be proved later, and the remaining ones will be left as exercises for the reader. Since the cancellation laws are natural consequences of a later result (the trichotomy law), their proofs will be postponed until then. As one might expect, the proofs of the other laws are by mathematical induction.

First, let us prove the associative law of addition. If for any given $k,m \in N$, E_n is the statement

$$k + (m + n) = (k + m) + n,$$

$2 + (3+4) = (2 +3) + 4$

then what we wish to prove is that all statements E_n are true. We first check to see if E_1 is true, that is, if

$$k + (m + 1) = (k + m) + 1.$$

In view of 2-5, (i), the left side of this equation equals $k + m^*$ while the right side equals $(k + m)^*$. However, by 2-5, (ii),

$$k + m^* = (k + m)^*.$$

We conclude that E_1 is true.

Next, let n be any natural number for which E_n is true. We shall show that E_{n*} also is true, which will prove that all statements E_n are true by mathematical induction, and will verify the associative law of addition. Now

$$(k + m) + n^* = ((k + m) + n)^*$$

by 2-5, (ii), while

$$k + (m + n^*) = k + (m + n)^* = (k + (m + n))^*$$

for the same reason. Since $(k + m) + n = k + (m + n)$, these two equations show that

$$(k + m) + n^* = k + (m + n^*),$$

that is, that E_{n^*} is true.

We shall now prove the commutative law of addition. For any given $m \in N$, let E_n be the statement

$$m + n = n + m.$$

If we wish to verify that all E_n are true, we first must verify that E_1 is true, that is, that

$$m + 1 = 1 + m.$$

The truth of this statement is not at all evident from 2-5 if $m \neq 1$, so we resort to mathematical induction to prove E_1. Let F_m be the statement "$m + 1 = 1 + m$." Certainly F_1 is true. Also,

$$m^* + 1 = (m + 1) + 1,$$

while $$1 + m^* = 1 + (m + 1) = (1 + m) + 1$$

using the associative law of addition. If F_m is true, that is, if $m + 1 = 1 + m$, the equations above then show that $m^* + 1 = 1 + m^*$, that is, that F_{m^*} is true. By mathematical induction, all statements F_m are true, and hence E_1 is true for each $m \in N$.

To continue the proof of the commutative law of addition, let n be any natural number such that E_n is true, that is, such that

$$m + n = n + m.$$

In order to show that E_{n^*} also is true, we note that

$$m + n^* = (m + n)^*$$

by 2-5, (ii), while

$$n^* + m = (n + 1) + m = n + (1 + m),$$

and since $1 + m = m + 1 = m^*$,

$$n^* + m = n + m^* = (n + m)^*.$$

Clearly, then, $m + n^* = n^* + m$ in view of our assumption that $m + n = n + m$. Hence E_{n^*} is true, and the commutative law of addition follows by mathematical induction.

Since the distributive law follows readily by mathematical induction from the two laws proved above, its proof is left as an exercise for the reader. We will point out, however, that its proof begins as follows: for any given $k,m \in N$, let E_n be the statement "$(k + m) \cdot n = k \cdot n + m \cdot n$." Clearly E_1 is true; and so on. Remember, the associative and commutative laws of addition may be used in the proof.

Finally, let us prove the commutative law of multiplication. That $1 \cdot m = m$ for each $m \in N$ follows by mathematical induction from the equations below:

$$1 \cdot m^* = 1 \cdot m + 1 = (1 \cdot m)^*.$$

If E_n is the statement "$m \cdot n = n \cdot m$," m any fixed element of N, then E_1 is true. Since

$$m \cdot n^* = m \cdot n + m,$$

while the distributive law yields

$$n^* \cdot m = (n + 1) \cdot m = n \cdot m + 1 \cdot m = n \cdot m + m,$$

evidently E_{n^*} is true if E_n is true. This proves the commutative law of multiplication.

The order in which we establish the laws of 2-7 is quite important. The reader would find it difficult, for example, to establish the associative law of multiplication without the aid of the distributive law.

2-8 EXERCISES

1. Prove that $n^* \neq n$ for each $n \in N$. (Hint: let S be the set of all n for which $n^* \neq n$. Use 2-1 to 2-3 to prove that $S = N$.)

2. Prove that $n + m \neq n$ for each $m,n \in N$. (Hint: for any given m, let S be the set of all n such that $n + m \neq n$.)

3. Complete the proof, started in the text, of the distributive law.

4. Prove the associative law of multiplication, using any of the other laws except the cancellation laws.

5. Prove that for each $m,n \in N$,

$$(m^* \cdot n^*)^* = (m^* + n^*) + m \cdot n.$$

Having successfully introduced the operations of addition and multiplication on N, and having proved their more elementary properties, we turn now to the definition of the familiar order relations "less than" and "greater than" on N.

2-9 DEFINITION. The order relation "less than" ($<$) is defined on N as follows: for each $m,n \in N$,

$$m < n \quad \text{if and only if} \quad m + k = n \quad \text{for some} \quad k \in N.$$

Let us check to see if the relation $<$ is reflexive, symmetric, or transitive. Since $n + k \neq n$ for each $k,n \in N$ by 2-8, Exercise 2, evidently n is not less than n for any $n \in N$. Thus the relation $<$ is not reflexive. If m, n, and p are natural numbers for which $m < n$ and $n < p$, then $m + k = n$ and $n + j = p$ for some $j,k \in N$. Hence $m + (k + j) = p$ and therefore $m < p$. Thus the relation $<$ is transitive. The relation $<$ is not symmetric, for if $m < n$ and $n < m$ were true, then $m < m$ would also be true by the transitivity of $<$, contrary to previous results.

The number 1 is the least natural number, that is,

$$1 < n$$

for each $n \neq 1$ (why?). It is evident also that

$$n < n^*$$

for each $n \in N$.

little theorem

The order relation "greater than" ($>$) is defined in the usual way: for each $m,n \in N$,

$$m > n \quad \text{if and only if} \quad n < m.$$

An important property of the order relation $<$ is that each two unequal natural numbers are comparable relative to $<$; that is, one of the given numbers is necessarily less than the other. We state this property in the following form.

2-10 TRICHOTOMY LAW. For any two natural numbers m and n, one and only one of the following three statements is true:

(i) $m = n$;   (ii) $m < n$;   (iii) $m > n$.

The proof of 2-10 is broken up into two parts. First, let us prove that only one of the three statements can hold for any given m and n. If $m = n$, then (ii) and (iii) cannot hold by 2-8, Exercise 2. If $m < n$, then $m + k = n$ for some $k \in N$; and therefore $m \neq n$ by 2-8, Exercise 2. If $m < n$, then $n \not< m$ according to our previous remarks. Thus it is clear that only one of (i), (ii), and (iii) can hold for any given m and n.

There remains to be proved that one of the three statements must hold for any given m and n. If $m = 1$, clearly either $n = m$ or $n > m$.

If $m \neq 1$, let S be the set of all $n \in N$ for each of which $n < m$; and let T be the set of all $n \in N$ for each of which $n > m$ or $n = m$. The sets S and T have elements, for $1 \in S$ and $m^* \in T$. If $n \in S$, let us prove that either $n^* \in S$ or $n^* = m$. By assumption, $n + k = m$ for some $k \in N$. If $k = 1$, then $n^* = m$; if $k \neq 1$, then $k > 1$ and $k = 1 + j$. Thus $(n + 1) + j = m$, $n^* + j = m$, $n^* < m$, and $n^* \in S$. If $n \in T$, then $n^* \in T$ since $n^* > n$. We have proved that $1 \in S \cup T$, and for each $n \in S \cup T$, also $n^* \in S \cup T$. Therefore $S \cup T = N$ by 2-3, and we conclude that for each $n \in N$, either $n < m$, $n = m$, or $n > m$. This completes the proof of 2-10.

The order relations $<$ and $>$ are compatible with the operations of N; that is, for each $k \in N$, m and n are in the same order relation as $m + k$ and $n + k$, and also as $m \cdot k$ and $n \cdot k$. We shall state the compatibility of the order relations with the operations of N in the following form.

2-11 THEOREM. If $m < n$, then for each $k \in N$,

$$\text{(i)} \quad m + k < n + k, \quad \text{and} \quad \text{(ii)} \quad m \cdot k < n \cdot k.$$

Conversely, if for some $m, n, k \in N$ either (i) or (ii) holds, then $m < n$.

Naturally, the theorem remains true if $<$ is replaced by $>$.

To prove 2-11, assume that $m < n$, so that $m + j = n$ for some $j \in N$. Then $(m + j) + k = n + k$, $(m + k) + j = n + k$, and therefore $m + k < n + k$; also $(m + j) \cdot k = n \cdot k$, $m \cdot k + j \cdot k = n \cdot k$, and therefore $m \cdot k < n \cdot k$.

The proof of the converse uses the trichotomy law. Let us assume for some $m, n, k \in N$ that $m + k < n + k$. Certainly either $m = n$, $m < n$, or $m > n$. If $m = n$, then $m + k = n + k$ contrary to assumption. If $m > n$, then $m + k > n + k$ by the first part of the theorem. However, this again contradicts the assumption. We conclude therefore that $m < n$. The proof of the rest of the theorem is similar.

The cancellation laws 2-7, (iv), are easily proved at this point. Assume, for example, that $m \cdot k = n \cdot k$. The alternatives $m < n$ and $m > n$ of the trichotomy law imply $m \cdot k < n \cdot k$ and $m \cdot k > n \cdot k$ respectively by the theorem just proved. Since these contradict the hypothesis that $m \cdot k = n \cdot k$, necessarily the third alternative of the trichotomy law holds for m and n, that is, $m = n$. A similar proof holds for the other cancellation law.

Other useful relations on N are "less than or equal to" ($\leq$), and "greater than or equal to" ($\geq$). As the reader might guess, $m \leq n$ if either $m < n$ or $m = n$; and $m \geq n$ if either $m > n$ or $m = n$.

2-12 EXERCISES

1. Prove 2-11 with the relation $<$ replaced by $\leq$.
2. If $j < k$ and $m < n$, prove that $j + m < k + n$ and $j \cdot m < k \cdot n$.
3. Prove that $n < m < n^*$ for no $n, m \in N$.
4. If $n = k \cdot m$ and $k \neq 1$, prove that $m < n$.
5. Prove the cancellation law of addition. (*last part of theorem then #3 page 16*)

If S is any set of natural numbers, the element n of S is called the *least element* of S if $n \leq m$ for each $m \in S$. We have already observed that N has a least element, namely 1. That any nonvoid subset of N has a least element is one of the important properties of the set of natural numbers.

2-13 THEOREM. Any nonvoid subset S of N has a least element.

If $1 \in S$, obviously 1 is the least element of S and the theorem is proved. If $1 \not\in S$, the proof proceeds as follows. Certainly $1 < n$ for all $n \in S$. Let T be defined by

$$T = \{k; \, k \in N, \, k \leq n \quad \text{for each} \quad n \in S\}.$$

If $n \in S$, then $n^* > n$ and $n^* \not\in T$. Thus, while $1 \in T$, T is a proper subset of N. By 2-3, there must exist an element $m \in T$ such that $m^* \not\in T$ (if such an m did not exist, T would equal N). The element m is in S, for otherwise, we would have $m < n$ for each $n \in S$, and therefore $m^* \leq n$ for each $n \in S$, contrary to the assumption that $m^* \not\in T$. The element m is the least element of S as asserted in the theorem.

The set N is called *well-ordered* (relative to $<$) because of this property of every subset having a least element.

We conform with the usual practice of designating

$$1^* = 2, \quad 2^* = 3, \quad 3^* = 4, \quad 4^* = 5, \quad \ldots.$$

A geometric realization of the natural numbers is as equispaced points on a line as indicated in Figure 3. The mapping $*: n \to n^*$

Figure 3.

can be thought of as a translation of this line one unit to the right.

The set N of natural numbers along with the operations of addition and multiplication and the order relation $<$ (and all operations and relations implied by them) is called the *algebraic system of natural numbers*. We shall use the notation

$$\{N; +, \cdot, <\}$$

to designate this system. More generally, a set S along with any operations and relations defined on the set is called an *algebraic system*. If $\alpha, \beta, \gamma, \ldots$ are the operations and relations on S, then

$$\{S; \alpha, \beta, \gamma, \ldots\}$$

will designate this algebraic system.

5. The integers

One is not content to work with the system of natural numbers alone in elementary algebra. An algebraic weakness of this system is that not all equations of the form $m + x = n$, $m, n \in N$, can be solved for x, Thus, if $m \geq n$, there is no natural number x such that $m + x = n$. As we all know, the introduction of zero and the negative natural numbers overcomes this particular shortcoming. A method of extension of the system of natural numbers to a larger system, called the integers, that contains zero and the negative natural numbers will be given in this section.

Let

$$D = N \times N,$$

that is, D is the set of all pairs (m, a) of natural numbers. For convenience, the elements of D will be designated by "m–a" rather than "(m, a)." We must realize that

$$m\text{–}a$$

does not mean "m minus a," for no operation "minus" has been introduced: "m–a" is just another way of writing "(m, a)." However, as we shall soon see, an operation of "minus" will be introduced in an algebraic system containing the system of natural numbers, and in this new system "m–a" will mean "m minus a."

In keeping with our regular practice, equality of elements of D is the same as identity; that is, for each m–a, n–$b \in D$,

$$m\text{–}a = n\text{–}b \quad \text{if and only if} \quad m = n \quad \text{and} \quad a = b.$$

Now D is much too big a set to serve our purpose. So we shall introduce an equivalence relation on D, and then we shall use the partition of D introduced by the equivalence relation for our set of "integers."

2-14 DEFINITION. The relation "wave" ($\curvearrowright$) is defined on D as follows; for each $m\text{-}a$, $n\text{-}b \in D$,

$$m\text{-}a \curvearrowright n\text{-}b \quad \text{if and only if} \quad m + b = n + a.$$

If the reader will reflect for a moment, it will be clear that the two elements $m\text{-}a$ and $n\text{-}b$ of D are in the "wave" relation to each other if the "difference" between the natural numbers m and a is the same as the "difference" between n and b. We shall not define the word "difference," but rather leave its meaning to the imagination of the reader. Thus, for example,

$$3\text{-}1 \curvearrowright 6\text{-}4; \quad 7\text{-}2 \curvearrowright 9\text{-}4; \quad 1\text{-}4 \curvearrowright 4\text{-}7.$$

On the other hand, $3\text{-}1 \not\curvearrowright 4\text{-}6$, since $3 + 6 \neq 4 + 1$. Of course, if $m\text{-}a = n\text{-}b$, then, trivially, $m\text{-}a \curvearrowright n\text{-}b$. Certainly the converse is not true; that is, we might have $m\text{-}a \curvearrowright n\text{-}b$ although $m\text{-}a \neq n\text{-}b$.

The wave relation on D is actually an equivalence relation, as we shall now prove. That $\curvearrowright$ is both reflexive and symmetric is immediate. In order to prove that $\curvearrowright$ is transitive, assume that $m\text{-}a \curvearrowright n\text{-}b$ and $n\text{-}b \curvearrowright k\text{-}c$; then

$$m + b = n + a \quad \text{and} \quad n + c = k + b.$$

Clearly then

$$(m + b) + c = (n + a) + c \quad \text{and} \quad (n + c) + a = (k + b) + a,$$

and since $(n + a) + c = (n + c) + a$ (why?),

$$(m + c) + b = (k + a) + b.$$

Using the cancellation law, this equation yields $m + c = k + a$, which proves that $m\text{-}a \curvearrowright k\text{-}c$ as desired. Hence the relation $\curvearrowright$ on D is transitive, and therefore $\curvearrowright$ is an equivalence relation.

According to 1-11, D is partitioned into equivalence sets by the equivalence relation $\curvearrowright$. Rather than using the notation "X_u" to designate the equivalence set of D containing u, we shall use the simpler convention of placing square brackets around an element to designate the equivalence set containing the element. Thus, for the element m–$a \in D$, "[m–a]" designates the equivalence set related to $\cap$ that contains m–a:

$$[m\text{–}a] = \{n\text{–}b; n\text{–}b \in D, n\text{–}b \cap m\text{–}a\}.$$

The above equation is read as follows: "[m–a] is the set of all elements n–b in D such that n–$b \cap m$–a."

2-15 DEFINITION. The equivalence sets of D related to $\cap$ are called *integers*. The partition of D induced by $\cap$ is the set of all integers, and is designated by "I."

A geometric representation of the elements of D and the equivalence sets related to $\cap$, that is, of the integers, is given in Figure 4. In this figure, the horizontal line L and the vertical line L' have the

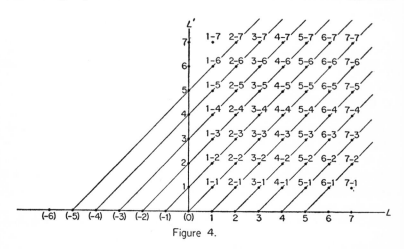

Figure 4.

natural numbers represented on them as equispaced points. The elements of D are represented as lattice points in the plane; such as, for example, 1–1, 3–2, 2–4, and so on, as indicated in the figure. The integers are the diagonal lines in the figure; that is, the integers are the sets of elements of D lying on these diagonal lines. For example, the integer [3–1] is the set {3–1, 4–2, 5–3, . . .} of elements of D on the diagonal meeting the line L at 2.

2-16 LEMMA. If m–$a \cap j$–c and n–$b \cap k$–d, then

$$(m + n)\text{–}(a + b) \cap (j + k)\text{–}(c + d).$$

By assumption, we have $m + c = j + a$ and $n + d = k + b$. Thus

$$(m + c) + (n + d) = (j + a) + (k + b).$$

This can be rewritten, using the associative and commutative laws, in the form

$$(m + n) + (c + d) = (j + k) + (a + b).$$

Hence $(m + n)$–$(a + b) \curvearrowright (j + k)$–$(c + d)$, and the lemma is proved.

Operations of addition and multiplication may be defined on I due to the existence of such operations on N. An inspection of the following definition shows that the operations are introduced as if m–a really meant "m minus a" (naturally on the assumption that we are familiar with the way such expressions are added and multiplied in elementary algebra).

2-17 DEFINITION. The operations of *addition* $(+)$ and *multiplication* $(\cdot)$ are defined on the set I of integers as follows: for each $[m$–$a]$, $[n$–$b] \in I$,

  (i) $[m$–$a] + [n$–$b] = [(m + n)$–$(a + b)]$;
  (ii) $[m$–$a] \cdot [n$–$b] = [(m \cdot n + a \cdot b)$–$(m \cdot b + a \cdot n)]$.

First of all, we should verify that these operations are well-defined. The need for this verification is that sums and products of two sets have been defined in terms of elements of these sets. Perhaps, if we chose different elements from these two sets, the sum would turn out differently. Assume, for example, that j–$c \in [m$–$a]$ (that is, j–$c \curvearrowright m$–a) and that k–$d \in [n$–$b]$. According to the definition above,

$$[j$–$c] + [k$–$d] = [(j + k)$–$(c + d)].$$

Since $[j$–$c] = [m$–$a]$ and $[k$–$d] = [n$–$b]$, we must have

$$[j$–$c] + [k$–$d] = [m$–$a] + [n$–$b]$$

if addition is to be well-defined; that is, we must have

$$[(j + k)$–$(c + d)] = [(m + n)$–$(a + b)].$$

That this equation is true is an immediate consequence of 2-16. In a similar way, the other operation on I can be shown to be well-defined.

We digress momentarily now to define what is meant by an identity element relative to an operation on a set.

If γ is an operation on a set S, so that to each pair (a,b) of elements of S corresponds a unique element $a \gamma b$ of S, then an element e of S is called an *identity element* relative to γ if

$$e \gamma a = a \quad \text{and} \quad a \gamma e = a$$

for each $a \in S$. By its very definition, an identity element must be unique (what would $e \gamma f$ be if both e and f were identity elements?). If e is an identity element relative to γ in S, then the element b is called an *inverse element* of a relative to γ if

$$a \gamma b = e \quad \text{and} \quad b \gamma a = e.$$

To get back to the set I, let us define the elements *zero* (0) and *one* (1) in I as follows:

$$0 = [n\text{–}n]; \qquad 1 = [n^*\text{–}n].$$

For each $x \in I$, define the *negative* of x $(-x)$ as follows:

$$\text{if } x = [m\text{–}a], \quad \text{then} \quad -x = [a\text{–}m].$$

The properties of the operations of I are given in the following theorem. Note that all the properties of the operations of N are included (see 2-7).

2-18 THEOREM. The following laws are valid for the operations of I: for each $x,y,z \in I$,

(i) the ASSOCIATIVE LAWS:

$$x + (y + z) = (x + y) + z, \qquad x\cdot(y\cdot z) = (x\cdot y)\cdot z;$$

(ii) the COMMUTATIVE LAWS:

$$x + y = y + x, \qquad x\cdot y = y\cdot x;$$

(iii) the DISTRIBUTIVE LAW:

$$(x + y)\cdot z = x\cdot z + y\cdot z;$$

(iv) 0 and 1 are IDENTITY ELEMENTS relative to $+$ and $\cdot$ respectively:

$$0 + x = x + 0 = x, \qquad 1\cdot x = x\cdot 1 = x;$$

(v) $-x$ is the ADDITIVE INVERSE of x:

$$x + (-x) = (-x) + x = 0;$$

(vi) the CANCELLATION LAWS:

$$\text{if } x + z = y + z, \quad \text{then} \quad x = y;$$
$$\text{if } x\cdot z = y\cdot z \text{ and } z \neq 0, \quad \text{then} \quad x = y.$$

For the most part, these laws are straightforward consequences of 2-7. We shall prove some of them, and leave the rest as exercises for the reader.

The associative law of addition is proved as follows. If $x,y,z \in I$, say $x = [k\text{--}a]$, $y = [m\text{--}b]$, and $z = [n\text{--}c]$, then

$$(x + y) + z = [(k + m)\text{--}(a + b)] + [n\text{--}c]$$
$$= [((k + m) + n)\text{--}((a + b) + c)],$$
$$x + (y + z) = [k\text{--}a] + [(m + n)\text{--}(b + c)]$$
$$= [(k + (m + n))\text{--}(a + (b + c))].$$

Since $(k + m) + n = k + (m + n)$ and $(a + b) + c = a + (b + c)$, evidently $(x + y) + z = x + (y + z)$.

Next, let us prove part of (iv), namely that $1 \cdot x = x \cdot 1 = x$. By definition, $1 = [n^*\text{--}n]$; if $x = [m\text{--}a]$, then

$$1 \cdot x + [(n^* \cdot m + n \cdot a)\text{--}(n^* \cdot a + n \cdot m)] = [((n \cdot m + m) + n \cdot a)\text{--}$$
$$((n \cdot a + a) + n \cdot m)].$$

Now $((n \cdot m + m) + n \cdot a)\text{--}((n \cdot a + a) + n \cdot m) \cap m\text{--}a$, and therefore $1 \cdot x = x$. That $x \cdot 1 = x$ follows similarly.

Finally, we shall prove the additive cancellation law. The other cancellation law will be proved later. If

$$[k\text{--}a] + [n\text{--}c] = [m\text{--}b] + [n\text{--}c],$$

then $$[(k + n)\text{--}(a + c)] = [(m + n)\text{--}(b + c)].$$

This implies that

$$(k + n) + (b + c) = (m + n) + (a + c).$$

The cancellation law in N (along with the associative and commutative laws) allows us to cancel off the n and c, leaving $k + b = m + a$. Thus $[k\text{--}a] = [m\text{--}b]$ as desired.

Such expressions as $x + y + z$, $x + y + z + w$, $x \cdot y \cdot z$, $x \cdot y \cdot z \cdot w$, and so on, are not as yet defined for the simple reason that $+$ and $\cdot$ are binary operations, that is, they combine two elements. However, it is an easy matter to define these expressions; thus we could define $x + y + z = (x + y) + z$, $x \cdot y \cdot z \cdot w = (x \cdot y) \cdot (z \cdot w)$, and so on. Note that in $(x + y) + z$ and $(x \cdot y) \cdot (z \cdot w)$ the elements are combined two at a time. One could just as well define $x + y + z = x + (y + z)$ and

$x \cdot y \cdot z \cdot w = x \cdot (y \cdot (z \cdot w))$. In view of the associative laws, the definitions in each case are the same. We shall henceforth use such expressions without defining them explicitly, since all sensible definitions lead to the same result. Formal proof of this is contained in the next chapter.

2-19 EXERCISES

1. Prove the associative law of multiplication in I.
2. Prove the commutative laws in I.
3. Prove the distributive law in I.
4. Prove that 0 is the identity element of addition in I.
5. Prove that every element of I has a unique additive inverse.
6. Prove that $0 \cdot x = 0$ for each $x \in I$.
7. Show that for each $x, y \in I$,
   (i) $-(-x) = x$;   (ii) $(-x) \cdot y = -(x \cdot y)$;
   (iii) $(-x) \cdot (-y) = x \cdot y$;   (iv) $(-x) + (-y) = -(x + y)$;
   (v) $(-x) + y = -(x + (-y))$.
8. Show that for each integer $x \neq 0$, there exists a unique natural number k such that either $x = [k^*–1]$ or $x = [1–k^*]$.

Let us now introduce the "less than" order relation on I.

2-20 DEFINITION. The order relation "less than" ($<$) is defined on I as follows: for each $[m–a]$, $[n–b] \in I$,

$$[m–a] < [n–b] \quad \text{if and only if} \quad m + b < n + a.$$

Is this relation $<$ well-defined? That is, if $m + b < n + a$ and $j–c \in [m–a]$, $k–d \in [n–b]$, is $j + d < k + c$? By assumption, $j + a = m + c$ and $k + b = n + d$. Hence, by 2-11,

$$(m + b) + (j + k) < (n + a) + (j + k).$$

On replacing $k + b$ by $n + d$ and $j + a$ by $m + c$, this becomes

$$m + j + n + d < n + k + m + c.$$

When $m + n$ is cancelled out, this reduces to $j + d < k + c$. Thus $<$ is well-defined.

The dual relation $>$ may be introduced on I just as it was on N.

2-21 THEOREM. The following properties are enjoyed by the order relation $<$ on I:

(i) the TRICHOTOMY LAW. One and only one of the following holds for each $x, y \in I$: $x = y$; $x < y$; $x > y$.

(ii) $x + z < y + z$ if and only if $x < y$.
(iii) if $z > 0$, then $x \cdot z < y \cdot z$ if and only if $x < y$.
(iv) if $z < 0$, then $x \cdot z < y \cdot z$ if and only if $x > y$.

We start off the proof of this theorem by proving the trichotomy law. If $x = [m\text{-}a]$ and $y = [n\text{-}b]$, then one and only one of the three possibilities $m + b = n + a$, $m + b < n + a$, and $m + b > n + a$ holds according to 2-10. This obviously proves (i).

To prove (iii), let x and y be as given above, and $z = [k\text{-}c]$. Since $z > 0$, we have $[k\text{-}c] > [j\text{-}j]$, $k + j > j + c$, and hence $k > c$. Thus there exists $p \in N$ such that $c + p = k$. Let us assume that $x \cdot z < y \cdot z$. Then

$$[(m \cdot k + a \cdot c) - (m \cdot c + a \cdot k)] < [(n \cdot k + b \cdot c) - (n \cdot c + b \cdot k)],$$

and

$$(m \cdot k + a \cdot c) + (n \cdot c + b \cdot k) < (n \cdot k + b \cdot c) + (m \cdot c + a \cdot k).$$

If we replace k by $c + p$ in this expression and cancel like terms, we obtain

$$m \cdot p + b \cdot p < n \cdot p + a \cdot p.$$

This reduces to $m + b < n + a$ if we cancel out the p, and yields the desired result that $[m\text{-}a] < [n\text{-}b]$. The other half of (iii) is proved by retracing the steps above.

The proofs of (ii) and (iv) are left as exercises.

At this point, the multiplicative cancellation law stated in 2-18 is easily proved. If $x \cdot z = y \cdot z$ and $z \neq 0$, then $x = y$ is the only conclusion compatible with Theorem 2-21.

2-22 DEFINITION. An integer x is a *positive integer* if $x > 0$. The set of all positive integers is designated by "P."

If $[m\text{-}a] \in P$, then $[m\text{-}a] > [n\text{-}n]$, $m + n > n + a$, and $m > a$. Thus

$$[m\text{-}a] \in P \quad \text{if and only if} \quad m = a + k \text{ for some } k \in N.$$

The natural number k associated with the positive integer $[m\text{-}a]$ is unique; that is, for each $n\text{-}b \cap m\text{-}a$, also $n = b + k$. It is clear that $m\text{-}a \cap k^*\text{-}1$, since $m + 1 = k^* + a = (a + k) + 1$. Hence the elements of P are precisely the elements of the form $[k^*\text{-}1]$, that is,

$$P = \{[k^*\text{-}1]; k \in N\}.$$

If $m \cdot n = 0$ *then either* m *or* $n = 0$

The set P is closed relative to the operations $+$ and $\cdot$; that is, the sum or product of two positive integers is a positive integer. To see this, note that if $x > 0$ and $y > 0$, then $x \cdot y > 0 \cdot y$ and therefore $x \cdot y > 0$; also $x + y > 0 + y > 0$. Actually, the reader may verify that (see 2-8, Exercise 5)

2-23
$$[m^*{-}1] + [n^*{-}1] = [(m + n)^*{-}1],$$
$$[m^*{-}1] \cdot [n^*{-}1] = [(m \cdot n)^*{-}1].$$

If x is a *negative integer*, that is, if $x < 0$, then $x = [m{-}a]$ with $m < a$. Hence $-x = [a{-}m]$, and since $a > m$, $-x > 0$. Similarly, if x is a positive integer, then $-x$ is a negative integer. Thus, for each integer $x \neq 0$, either $x \in P$ or $-x \in P$.

The system of positive integers, $\{P; +, \cdot, <\}$, is a carbon copy of the system of natural numbers, $\{N; +, \cdot, <\}$, developed in the preceding section. Precisely what we mean by this will now be shown.

The first observation we make is that there is a 1–1 mapping θ of P onto N defined by

2-24
$$\theta: \quad [k^*{-}1]\theta = k, \qquad k \in N.$$

Next, in view of 2-23, we see that

$$([m^*{-}1] + [n^*{-}1])\theta = [(m + n)^*{-}1]\theta = m + n,$$
and
$$([m^*{-}1] \cdot [n^*{-}1])\theta = [(m \cdot n)^*{-}1]\theta = m \cdot n.$$

Since $m = [m^*{-}1]\theta$ and $n = [n^*{-}1]\theta$, the equations above may be written in the form (letting $x = [m^*{-}1]$ and $y = [n^*{-}1]$),

2-25 $(x + y)\theta = x\theta + y\theta;$ $(x \cdot y)\theta = x\theta \cdot y\theta,$ $x,y \in P.$

Since $[m^*{-}1] < [n^*{-}1]$ if and only if $m < n$, we also have

2-26 $x\theta < y\theta$ if and only if $x < y,$ $x,y \in P.$

It is evident from 2-25 and 2-26 that θ is not an ordinary 1–1 mapping of P onto N. For, according to 2-25, the mapping θ actually preserves the operations of P in N: that is, the element of N corresponding to the sum of the two elements x and y in P is just the sum of the two elements of N corresponding to x and y; and the element of N corresponding to the product of x and y in P is just the product of the two elements of N corresponding to x and y. Also, by 2-26, the order relation $<$ on P and N is preserved by the mapping θ of P onto

N. Such a mapping as θ is called an *isomorphism* of the algebraic system $\{P; +, \cdot, <\}$ onto the system $\{N; +, \cdot, <\}$.

More generally, if $\{S; \alpha_1, \beta_1, \ldots\}$ and $\{T; \alpha_2, \beta_2, \ldots\}$ are two algebraic systems having corresponding operations and relations, a 1–1 mapping θ of S onto T is an *isomorphism* of $\{S; \alpha_1, \beta_1, \ldots\}$ onto $\{T; \alpha_2, \beta_2, \ldots\}$ provided that corresponding operations and relations are preserved under the mapping θ. The two algebraic systems are said to be *isomorphic* if such a mapping θ exists. Many examples of isomorphic algebraic systems will be seen on the pages that follow. We state the results proved above in the form of a theorem.

2-27 Theorem. The 1–1 mapping θ of P onto N defined in 2-24 is an isomorphism of the algebraic system $\{P; +, \cdot, <\}$ of positive integers onto the system $\{N; +, \cdot, <\}$ of natural numbers.

The fact that the systems of positive integers and natural numbers are isomorphic implies that they are algebraically equivalent. That is, the properties of these two systems related to their operations and relations are the same. However, one realizes that these two systems are not identical, for their elements are not identical; in one case, the elements are natural numbers, while in the other case, the elements are sets of pairs of natural numbers.

From now on, we shall use the system $\{P; +, \cdot, <\}$ of positive integers in place of the system $\{N; +, \cdot, <\}$ of natural numbers. Naturally, all the properties developed for the system of natural numbers hold for the system of positive integers. We shall henceforth use the symbols "1," "2," "3," and so on, previously used for natural numbers, to designate the integers [1*–1], [2*–1], [3*–1], and so on. Thus the set I is made up of the positive integers 1, 2, 3, $\ldots$, the zero integer 0, and the negative integers $-1, -2, -3, \ldots$. If $x \in I$, say $x = [m-a]$ in the old notation, then x is the unique solution of the equation $a + x = m$. Geometrically, we are identifying the diagonal lines in Figure 4 with the numbers at which they intersect the horizontal line L.

The *absolute value* $|x|$ of the integer x is defined to be:

$$|x| = x \quad \text{if} \quad x \geq 0; \qquad |x| = -x \quad \text{if} \quad x < 0.$$

Thus for each $x \in P$, $|x| = x$; $|0| = 0$; and for each negative integer x, $|x| = -x$ (a positive integer). Note that for each nonzero $x \in I$, $|x| \in P$, and also

$$-|x| \leq x \leq |x|.$$

The operation of *subtraction* $(-)$ can be introduced on I as follows:

$$x - y = x + (-y).$$

Remember, $-y$ is the additive inverse of y.

2-28 EXERCISES

1. Prove that for each $x,y,z \in I$,
   (i) $z \cdot (x - y) = z \cdot x - z \cdot y$;
   (ii) if $x = y + z$, then $y = x - z$;
   (iii) if $x < y + z$, then $x - z < y$.
2. Let S be a subset of I. Prove that S has a largest (least) element if there exists an integer x such that $x \geq y$ ($x \leq y$) for each $y \in S$.
3. Prove that for each $a,b \in I$, $|a| \leq |b|$ if and only if $-|b| \leq a \leq |b|$.
4. For each $x,y \in I$, prove that
   (i) $|x \cdot y| = |x| \cdot |y|$;   (ii) $|x + y| \leq |x| + |y|$.
5. If $x \in I$, $x \neq 0$, prove that $x^2 > 0$.
6. If $x,y \in I$, and $x \cdot y = 1$, prove that x and y are both 1 or both -1.
7. If $a \in I$, $b \in P$, prove that $a + b \cdot |a| \geq 0$.

We turn now to the development of some of the elementary factorization properties of the integers, the so-called "arithmetic" of the integers. The basic "division" process familiar to all of us comes first. This states roughly that an integer a can be "divided" by a nonzero integer b yielding a "quotient" q and a "remainder" r smaller than b. For example,

$$17 = 5 \cdot 3 + 2,$$

that is, 17 divided by 5 gives a quotient of 3 and a remainder of 2 $(2 < 5)$;

$$-73 = 11 \cdot (-7) + 4,$$

that is, -73 divided by 11 gives a quotient of -7 and a remainder of 4 $(4 < 11)$. That such a process always exists will be proved now.
For any fixed $a \in I$, $b \in P$, let

$$S = \{a + b \cdot x; x \in I, a + b \cdot x \geq 0\}.$$

Since $a + b \cdot |a| \in S$ (see 2-28, Exercise 7), S has at least one element. Now either $0 \in S$, or all elements of S are positive. In the latter case,

S has a least element by 2-13. Thus, in either case, S has a least element $r \geq 0$, and, by the definition of S,

$$r = a + b \cdot x$$

for some $x \in I$.

In order to show that $r < b$, note that

$$r - b = a + b \cdot (x - 1),$$

that is, $r - b$ has the correct form to be in S if $r - b \geq 0$. But $r - b < r$ and r is the least element of S. Thus $r - b \not\subseteq S$, $r - b < 0$, and therefore $r < b$. Replacing x by $-q$, we have proved that $a = b \cdot q + r$, $0 \leq r < b$. Since $a = (-b) \cdot (-q) + r$, this division process applies to negative as well as positive integers. This proves part of the following theorem.

2-29 THEOREM. For each $a, b \in I$, $b \neq 0$, there exist unique elements $q, r \in I$ such that

$$a = b \cdot q + r, \qquad 0 \leq r < |b|.$$

The element q is called the *quotient* and r is called the *remainder* of a divided by b.

All that remains to be proved in 2-29 is that q and r are unique. Is it possible to have

$$a = b \cdot q + r, \qquad 0 \leq r < |b|,$$

and

$$a = b \cdot q' + r', \qquad 0 \leq r' < |b|,$$

with q' and r' different from q and r? No, for suppose that these two equations are valid, and that $r \leq r'$. Then $b \cdot q' + r' = b \cdot q + r$, and

$$r' - r = b \cdot (q - q') \geq 0.$$

It is evident then that $r' - r < |b|$; and hence that $0 \leq b \cdot (q - q') < |b|$ and

$$|b| \cdot |q - q'| < |b| \cdot 1.$$

Cancelling $|b|$, a positive integer, we obtain $|q - q'| < 1$. Since 1 is the least positive integer, $|q - q'| = 0$ and $q = q'$. It follows that $r = r'$, and, therefore, that the quotient and remainder of a divided by b are unique.

We shall not attempt to teach the reader the familiar "long division" process for finding the quotient and remainder of a divided by b, but rather we shall assume it to be known by all.

If for the integers a and b there exists an integer x such that $b = a \cdot x$, then a is called a *factor* of b, and b is called a *multiple* of a.

Begin

2-30 Definition. The relation "is a factor of" ($|$) is defined on I as follows: for each $a,b \in I$,

$$a \mid b \quad \text{if and only if} \quad b = a \cdot x \quad \text{for some} \quad x \in I.$$

Since $a = a \cdot 1$, clearly $a \mid a$. If $a \mid b$ and $b \mid c$, then $b = a \cdot x$ and $c = b \cdot y$ for some $x,y \in I$. Hence $c = a \cdot (x \cdot y)$ and $a \mid c$. Thus the relation "$|$" is reflexive and transitive. Since $|$ is not symmetric, the relation $|$ is not an equivalence relation.

Any integer a may be factored trivially as $a = a \cdot 1$ or $a = (-a) \cdot (-1)$. Thus 1, -1, a, and $-a$ all are factors of a. An integer p, different from 1 and -1, is called a *prime number* if 1, -1, p, and $-p$ are its only factors. Certainly 2 and 3 are prime; 4 is not prime since $2 \mid 4$; 5 is prime; 6 is not prime since $3 \mid 6$; 7 is prime; 403 is not prime since $13 \mid 403$; and so on.

An integer c is a *highest common factor* (abbreviated HCF) of the integers a and b if:

(i) $c \mid a$ and $c \mid b$; and

(ii) if $x \mid a$ and $x \mid b$, then $x \mid c$.

For example, 8 is a HCF of 24 and 32 since (i) $8 \mid 24$ and $8 \mid 32$, and (ii) ± 1, ± 2, ± 4, and ± 8 are the only common factors of 24 and 32, and all of these are factors of 8.

The study of the factorization properties of the integers is contained in a branch of mathematics known as "number theory." For many centuries, both amateur and professional mathematicians have been fascinated by such problems in number theory as the finding of a general rule for determining prime numbers and the distribution of the prime numbers. The greatest of the amateurs was Fermat, a French lawyer of the seventeenth century. He conjectured, for example, that all integers of the form

$$2^{2^n} + 1$$

are prime. While this conjecture was shown to be false by the Swiss mathematician Euler, still the study of such Fermat numbers has proved fruitful in mathematics. The greatest of the professionals in number theory was the nineteenth century German mathematician and astronomer, Gauss. His book on number theory, *Disquisitiones*

Arithmeticae, published in 1801 when Gauss was twenty-four, is a classic of mathematics.

2-31 EXERCISES

1. Find the quotient and remainder of 1224 divided by 126. Use these to find a HCF of 1224 and 126.

2. List all the positive primes less than 100.

3. Prove that both $a \mid b$ and $b \mid a$ hold if and only if $a = b$ or $a = -b$.

4. Prove that $x \mid a$ for each $x \in P$ if and only if $a = 0$.

5. Prove that if c and d both are HCF of a and b, then $c = d$ or $c = -d$.

6. Prove that if $c \mid a$ and $c \mid b$, then $c \mid (a \cdot x + b \cdot y)$ for each $x, y \in I$. Also prove that $c \mid r$ where r is the remainder of a divided by b.

7. If n is any positive integer, and S is any set of $n + 1$ distinct positive integers, each less than or equal to $2n$, prove that there exist two distinct elements a and b of S such that $a \mid b$.

In view of Exercise 5 above, the positive HCF of the integers a and b is unique, provided that a and b have a HCF. This unique positive HCF of a and b, if it exists, is designated by

$$(a,b).$$

For example, $(8,12) = 4$, $(7,15) = 1$, $(-24,36) = 12$, $(-6,-35) = 1$, and $(0,-7) = 7$. Evidently $(a,0) = |a|$ for each nonzero $a \in I$.

2-32 THEOREM. Any two nonzero integers a and b have a HCF. Furthermore, there exist integers u and v such that

$$(a,b) = a \cdot u + b \cdot v.$$

To prove this, let

$$S = \{a \cdot x + b \cdot y; \, x, y \in I, \, a \cdot x + b \cdot y \in P\}.$$

Since $|a| = a \cdot x + b \cdot 0$, where $x = 1$ or -1 depending on whether $a \in P$ or $-a \in P$, $|a| \in S$. Similarly, $|b| \in S$. By 2-13, S has a least element c; and since $c \in S$,

$$c = a \cdot u + b \cdot v$$

for some $u, v \in I$. Let us prove that $c = (a,b)$.

By 2-29, there exist $q, r \in I$ such that

$$a = c \cdot q + r, \qquad 0 \le r < c.$$

Replacing c by $a \cdot u + b \cdot v$ in this equation and solving for r, we obtain

$$r = a \cdot (1 - u \cdot q) + b \cdot (-v \cdot q).$$

Now r has the right form to be an element of S; but since $r < c$ and c is the least element of S, $r \not\subset S$. Hence $r = 0$, $a = c \cdot q$, and $c \mid a$. In a like manner, we can show that $c \mid b$. If $d \mid a$ and $d \mid b$, then $d \mid (a \cdot u + b \cdot v)$ by 2-31, Exercise 6. Thus, $d \mid c$ and c is a HCF of a and b. This completes the proof of 2-32.

2-33 THEOREM. If p is a prime number and $p \mid a \cdot b$, then

$$p \mid a \quad \text{or} \quad p \mid b.$$

Let us assume that $p \nmid a$ (p is not a factor of a). Then $(p,a) = 1$, and there exist $u,v \in I$ by 2-32 such that

$$1 = a \cdot u + b \cdot v. \qquad \longleftarrow \text{misprint}$$

By assumption, $a \cdot b = p \cdot x$ for some $x \in I$. Since $b = b \cdot a \cdot u + b \cdot p \cdot v$,

$$b = p \cdot (x \cdot u + b \cdot v),$$

and $p \mid b$. This proves 2-33.

2-34 EXERCISES

1. Prove that if p is prime and $p \mid a \cdot b \cdot c$, then p is a factor of a, b, or c. Extend this result to a product of n factors.

2. Prove that if $c \mid a \cdot b$ and $(c,a) = 1$, then $c \mid b$.

3. Another form of the principle of mathematical induction is as follows. If a statement E_n is associated with each positive integer $n \geq a$, where a is some fixed positive integer, then all E_n are true provided

(i) E_a is true,

(ii) if each E_k, $k < m$, is true, then E_m is true.

Prove this. (Hint: assume that the theorem is false. Let m be the least integer such that E_m is false. How does this contradict (ii)?)

4. The integers u and v of 2-32 are not unique. How small, in terms of a and b, can u and v be taken?

If a is an integer with $|a| > 1$, then a has at least one prime factor. For among the elements in the set of all integers $x > 1$ such that $x \mid a$ is a least element $c \leq |a|$; this element can have no positive factors other than 1 and c, since a factor of c is also a factor of a. Thus c is a prime factor of a.

Let a be an integer greater than 1, and p_1 be a positive prime factor of a. Then

$$a = p_1 \cdot a_1$$

for some $a_1 \in P$. Certainly $a > a_1$. If $a_1 > 1$, then a_1 has a positive prime factor p_2, so that $a_1 = p_2 \cdot a_2$. Substituting this in the equation above, we obtain

$$a = p_1 \cdot p_2 \cdot a_2.$$

Again, $a_1 > a_2$. If $a_2 > 1$, then $p_3 \mid a_2$ for some prime p_3, and $a_2 = p_3 \cdot a_3$ for some $a_3 \in P$. Thus

$$a = p_1 \cdot p_2 \cdot p_3 \cdot a_3.$$

If we continue this process of factorization of a, we obtain successive quotients $a_1, a_2, a_3, \ldots, a_k, \ldots$ with

$$a_1 > a_2 > a_3 > \ldots > a_k > \ldots.$$

This set of positive quotients has a least element a_n. Necessarily $a_n = 1$, for otherwise $a_n = p \cdot a'$, p prime, and a' is a quotient smaller than a_n contrary to the choice of a_n. Thus

$$a = p_1 \cdot p_2 \cdot \ldots \cdot p_n,$$

and a is factored into a product of prime numbers. Evidently $-a = -p_1 \cdot p_2 \cdot \ldots \cdot p_n$. This proves part of the following theorem.

2-35 The fundamental theorem of arithmetic. Every integer a for which $|a| > 1$ has a unique factorization (except for order)

$$a = \pm p_1 \cdot p_2 \cdot \ldots \cdot p_n$$

into a product of positive **prime numbers.**

The uniqueness of the factorization is all that remains to be proved in 2-35. For each $n \in P$, $n \geq 2$, let E_n be the statement "n has a unique factorization into a product of positive prime numbers." Certainly E_2 is true. Assume that all E_k are true for $k < m$. Suppose that

$$m = p_1 \cdot p_2 \cdot \ldots \cdot p_r \quad \text{and} \quad m = q_1 \cdot q_2 \cdot \ldots \cdot q_s$$

are two factorizations of m into products of positive prime numbers. Since $p_1 \mid a$, evidently $p_1 \mid q_1 \cdot q_2 \cdot \ldots \cdot q_s$, and therefore (2-34, Exercise 1) $p_1 \mid q_i$ for some i. Assume for the sake of simplicity that $p_1 \mid q_1$. Then necessarily $p_1 = q_1$ since both are prime. If $m = k \cdot p_1$, then

$$k = p_2 \cdot p_3 \cdot \ldots \cdot p_r = q_2 \cdot q_3 \cdot \ldots \cdot q_s.$$

Now $k < m$, so either $k = 1$, in which case m is prime and E_m is true, or $1 < k < m$ and E_k is true by assumption. Hence the primes $p_2, p_3, \ldots, p_r$ are just the primes $q_2, q_3, \ldots, q_s$, though possibly in a different order. Since $p_1 = q_1$, we conclude that the two factorizations of m are the same, that is, that E_m is true. By mathematical induction (2-34, Exercise 3), all E_n, $n \geq 2$, are true. If a is a negative integer, one factors $|a|$ to obtain the desired result. This proves 2-35.

For example, $4 = 2 \cdot 2$; $6 = 2 \cdot 3$; $8 = 2 \cdot 2 \cdot 2$; $10 = 2 \cdot 5$; $12 = 2 \cdot 2 \cdot 3$; $14 = 2 \cdot 7$. As a more complicated example, let us factor 12870. Certainly $2 \mid 12870$, and

$$12870 = 2 \cdot 6435.$$

Now $2 \nmid 6435$, but $3 \mid 6435$; thus

$$12870 = 2 \cdot 3 \cdot 2145.$$

Again $3 \mid 2145$, $2145 = 3 \cdot 715$, and

$$12870 = 2 \cdot 3 \cdot 3 \cdot 715.$$

Now $3 \nmid 715$, but $5 \mid 715$; $715 = 5 \cdot 143$ and

$$12870 = 2 \cdot 3 \cdot 3 \cdot 5 \cdot 143.$$

Now $5 \nmid 143$, $7 \nmid 143$, but $11 \mid 143$ and $143 = 11 \cdot 13$. Thus

$$12870 = 2 \cdot 3 \cdot 3 \cdot 5 \cdot 11 \cdot 13.$$

Since 13 is prime, the above is the prime factorization of 12870. Notice that we tried the primes 2, 3, 5, 7, 11, 13, 17, ... in the order of their size. Such a scheme will factor any number, although the labor involved might be great.

It is apparent that the HCF of two integers may be found by factoring the integers into primes, and picking out the like prime factors.

However, a better way of finding the HCF of two integers is by a division process known as *Euclid's algorithm*. In order to find the HCF of two given positive integers a and b by this process, first divide a by b as follows:

$$a = b \cdot q_1 + r_1, \qquad 0 \leq r_1 < b.$$

Next, divide b by r_1 to obtain

$$b = r_1 \cdot q_2 + r_2, \qquad 0 \leq r_2 < r_1,$$

and continue the procedure as follows:

$$r_1 = r_2 \cdot q_3 + r_3, \qquad 0 \le r_3 < r_2,$$
$$r_2 = r_3 \cdot q_4 + r_4, \qquad 0 \le r_4 < r_3,$$

. . . .

. . . .

$$r_{n-2} = r_{n-1} \cdot q_n + r_n, \qquad 0 \le r_n < r_{n-1},$$
$$r_{n-1} = r_n \cdot q_{n+1}.$$

Since the successive remainders r_1, r_2, ... are getting smaller and smaller, some one of them eventually must equal zero. We have assumed above that r_n is the last nonzero remainder, so that $r_{n+1} = 0$.

If $c = (a,b)$, then $c \mid a$ and $c \mid b$, and since $r_1 = a - b \cdot q_1$, also $c \mid r_1$. By the same line of reasoning, $c \mid r_2$, $c \mid r_3$, . . ., $c \mid r_n$. On the other hand, $r_n \mid r_{n-1}$, as is seen by the last equation in Euclid's algorithm. Now $r_n \mid (r_{n-1} \cdot q_n + r_n)$, and therefore $r_n \mid r_{n-2}$. Continuing up the set of equations, we see in order that $r_n \mid r_{n-3}$, . . . , $r_n \mid r_2$, $r_n \mid r_1$, $r_n \mid b$, and $r_n \mid a$. Thus also $r_n \mid c$, and this along with our previous result that $c \mid r_n$ proves that $r_n = c$, that is, that

$$r_n = (a,b).$$

For example, let us find $(108{,}966, 76{,}219)$ by Euclid's algorithm. The successive steps of the process are listed below.

$$108{,}966 = 76{,}219 + 32{,}747,$$
$$76{,}219 = 2 \cdot 32{,}747 + 10{,}725,$$
$$32{,}747 = 3 \cdot 10{,}725 + 572,$$
$$10{,}725 = 18 \cdot 572 + 429,$$
$$572 = 429 + 143,$$
$$429 = 3 \cdot 143.$$

It follows that

$$(108{,}966, 76{,}219) = 143.$$

Euclid's algorithm may also be used to express the HCF of two integers in the form of 2-32. Let us illustrate this fact with the example above. We start off by solving the next to the last equation of the algorithm for 143:

$$143 = 572 - 429.$$

We then replace 429 in this equation by an equivalent expression from the third from the last equation of the algorithm:

$$143 = 572 - (10{,}725 - 18 \cdot 572),$$

$$143 = 19 \cdot 572 - 10{,}725.$$

Next, we replace 572 in this equation by the proper expression from the algorithm:

$$143 = 19 \cdot (32{,}747 - 3 \cdot 10{,}725) - 10{,}725,$$

$$143 = 19 \cdot 32{,}747 - 58 \cdot 10{,}725.$$

Continuing the process, we have the following successive steps:

$$143 = 19 \cdot 32{,}747 - 58 \cdot (76{,}219 - 2 \cdot 32{,}747),$$

$$143 = 135 \cdot (108{,}966 - 76{,}219) - 58 \cdot 76{,}219,$$

$$143 = 135 \cdot 108{,}966 - 193 \cdot 76{,}219.$$

The last equation expresses the HCF of 108,966 and 76,219 in the desired form.

Any two integers a and b have a common multiple; for example, $a \cdot b$ is a multiple of both a and b. An integer m is a _least common multiple_ (abbreviated LCM) of the integers a and b if: (i) $a \mid m$ and $b \mid m$; and, (ii) if $a \mid x$ and $b \mid x$, then $m \mid x$.

For example, a LCM of 24 and 32 is 96, since (i) $24 \mid 96$ and $32 \mid 96$, and (ii) if $24 \mid x$ and $32 \mid x$, then, in particular, $3 \mid x$ and $32 \mid x$, so that $96 \mid x$.

For any two nonzero integers a and b, there is a unique positive LCM. That this is so may be seen as follows: let S be the set of all positive common multiples of a and b. The least element of S, which exists by 2-13, may be shown to be the only positive LCM of a and b. This unique positive LCM of a and b is designated by

$$[a,b].$$

2-36 EXERCISES

1. Factor 54,740 into a product of prime numbers.
2. Find the HCF of the following pairs of integers:
    (i) 4,284 and 14,586;   (ii) 18,336 and 29,412;
    (iii) 5,809 and 11,729;   (iv) 125,836 and 47,527.
3. Let $n \in P$ have p as a positive prime factor, say $n = p \cdot k$. Prove

that if $p^2 > n$, then for any prime factor q of k, $q^2 < n$. Hence prove that the method of factorization given in the text (by an example) need be carried only to the largest prime p such that $p \leq \sqrt{n}$ (that is, such that $p^2 \leq n$).

4. Let $m,n,p \in P$, p prime. Use 2-35 to prove that the equation $m^2 = p \cdot n^2$ cannot possibly be correct. More generally, prove that the equation $m^2 = k \cdot n^2$ can hold only if k is the square of an integer.

5. If $n \in P$ and $p \mid (n! + 1)$, p a positive prime, prove that $p > n$. Use this fact to prove that there exists an infinite number of primes.

6. Prove that for any two positive integers a and b,

$$(a,b) \cdot [a,b] = a \cdot b.$$

7. For any two elements a and b in P, (a,b) and $[a,b]$ also are in P. Thus HCF and LCM are operations on P. Prove that these operations have the following properties.

(i) ASSOCIATIVE LAWS:

$$((a,b),c) = (a,(b,c)); \qquad [[a,b],c] = [a,[b,c]].$$

(ii) COMMUTATIVE LAWS:

$$(a,b) = (b,a); \qquad [a,b] = [b,a].$$

(iii) IDEMPOTENT LAWS:

$$(a,a) = a; \qquad [a,a] = a.$$

(iv) ABSORPTION LAWS:

$$[a,(a,b)] = a; \qquad (a,[a,b]) = a.$$

Does either of these operations have an identity element?

6. The rational numbers

The system of integers has practical as well as algebraic deficiencies. From a practical standpoint, no matter how small a unit we adopt to describe length, for example, we will at times desire to subdivide this unit in describing the length of a particular object. The inch is a convenient unit of length. However, in certain precision measurements, integral multiples of the inch are not sufficiently accurate descriptions of length, and one must resort to half inches, quarter inches, and so on. An algebraic shortcoming of the system of integers is that not all equations of the form $a \cdot x = b$, $a,b \in I$, $a \neq 0$, can be solved for x. Thus, if $a \nmid b$, there is no integer x such that $a \cdot x = b$.

These difficulties are overcome by the introduction of the fractional numbers, the so-called rational numbers. In this section, the system of integers will be enlarged so as to contain the system of rational numbers. The procedure for doing this is much the same as that for deriving the system of integers from the system of natural numbers.

Let "F" designate the set of all ordered pairs (m,a), $m,a \in I$, with $a \neq 0$. For convenience, the elements of F will be designated by "m/a" rather than "(m,a)." The symbol "$/$" does not mean "divided by," since no such operation has been defined on I. However, we shall show eventually that $/$ may be thought of as division on a larger set containing the integers.

2-37 DEFINITION. The relation "curl" ($\cap$) is defined on F as follows: for each $m/a,n/b \in F$,

$$m/a \cap n/b \quad \text{if and only if} \quad m \cdot b = n \cdot a.$$

We note that $\cap$ is defined precisely as was $\cap$ in 2-14, with the operation $+$ in 2-14 replaced by $\cdot$ in 2-37. Just as $\cap$ was shown to be an equivalence relation on D, so can $\cap$ be shown to be an equivalence relation on F. Being an equivalence relation, $\cap$ partitions F into equivalence sets. Again, the notation "$[m/a]$" is used to designate the equivalence set containing m/a:

$$[m/a] = \{n/b; n/b \in F, n/b \cap m/a\}.$$

Thus, for example, the equivalence set $[1/2]$ contains the elements $1/2, 2/4, 3/6, \ldots, -1/-2, -2/-4, -3/-6, \ldots$.

2-38 DEFINITION. The equivalence sets of F related to $\cap$ are called *rational numbers*. The set of all rational numbers is designated by "R."

Operations of addition and multiplication will be introduced on R at this point. Naturally, the definitions will be the familiar ones for adding and multiplying fractions.

2-39 DEFINITION. The operations of addition ($+$) and multiplication ($\cdot$) are defined on the set R of rational numbers as follows: for each $[m/a],[n/b] \in R$,

(i) $[m/a] + [n/b] = [(m \cdot b + n \cdot a)/a \cdot b]$,

(ii) $[m/a] \cdot [n/b] = [m \cdot n/a \cdot b]$.

Since, again, the sum and product of sets are defined in terms of elements of sets, we must verify that these operations are well-defined. In the first place, $a \neq 0$ and $b \neq 0$ imply that $a \cdot b \neq 0$; thus $(m \cdot b + n \cdot a)/a \cdot b$ and $m \cdot n/a \cdot b$ are elements of F. Suppose that $j/c \cup m/a$ and $k/d \cup n/b$. Then the operations $+$ and $\cdot$ will be well-defined provided that

$$(m \cdot b + n \cdot a)/a \cdot b \cup (j \cdot d + k \cdot c)/c \cdot d$$

and

$$m \cdot n/a \cdot b \cup j \cdot k/c \cdot d.$$

To prove these, we have by assumption that $m \cdot c = j \cdot a$ and $n \cdot d = k \cdot b$. Hence $m \cdot c \cdot b \cdot d = j \cdot a \cdot b \cdot d$ and $n \cdot d \cdot a \cdot c = k \cdot b \cdot a \cdot c$, and

$$m \cdot c \cdot b \cdot d + n \cdot d \cdot a \cdot c = j \cdot a \cdot b \cdot d + k \cdot b \cdot a \cdot c,$$

$$(m \cdot b + n \cdot a) \cdot (c \cdot d) = (j \cdot d + k \cdot c) \cdot (a \cdot b).$$

This proves that $+$ is well-defined. That $\cdot$ is well-defined is proved similarly.

2-40 EXERCISES

1. Verify that $\cup$ is an equivalence relation on F.
2. Verify that $\cdot$ is well-defined by 2-39, (ii).
3. Give a geometric description of F (as the set of lattice points (a,b) in the plane) and R (as certain lines in the plane) analogous to that for D and I as illustrated in Figure 4.

The special rational numbers *zero* (0) and *one* (1) are defined by

$$0 = [0/a]; \qquad 1 = [m/m].$$

For each $r \in R$, define the *negative* of r $(-r)$ as follows:

$$\text{if } r = [m/a], \quad \text{then} \quad -r = [(-m)/a].$$

If $m \neq 0$, the multiplicative *inverse* of r (r^{-1}) is defined as follows:

$$\text{if } r = [m/a], \quad \text{then} \quad r^{-1} = [a/m].$$

The restriction $m \neq 0$ is necessary, for otherwise $a/m \not\subseteq F$.

2-41 THEOREM. The following properties hold for the operations $+$ and $\cdot$ on R: for each $r,s,t \in R$,

    (i) the ASSOCIATIVE LAWS:

$$r + (s + t) = (r + s) + t, \qquad r \cdot (s \cdot t) = (r \cdot s) \cdot t;$$

    (ii) the COMMUTATIVE LAWS:

$$r + s = s + r, \qquad r \cdot s = s \cdot r;$$

(iii) the DISTRIBUTIVE LAW:

$$(r + s) \cdot t = r \cdot t + s \cdot t;$$

(iv) 0 and 1 are IDENTITY ELEMENTS relative to $+$ and $\cdot$ respectively:

$$0 + r = r + 0 = r, \qquad 1 \cdot r = r \cdot 1 = r;$$

(v) $-r$ and r^{-1} are the INVERSE ELEMENTS of r relative to $+$ and $\cdot$ respectively:

$$r + (-r) = (-r) + r = 0, \qquad r \cdot r^{-1} = r^{-1} \cdot r = 1 \ (r \neq 0).$$

The important new property possessed by the rational numbers but not by the integers is that every nonzero rational number has a multiplicative inverse.

Since the proofs of the various parts of 2-41 are straightforward, they will be omitted for the most part. Let us prove part of (iv): if $r = [m/a]$, $0 = [0/b]$, then

$$r + 0 = [(m \cdot b + 0 \cdot a)/a \cdot b] = [m \cdot b/a \cdot b] = [m/a] = r$$

since $m \cdot b/a \cdot b \curlywedge m/a$. If $r = [m/a]$, $m \neq 0$, then $r^{-1} = [a/m]$ and

$$r \cdot r^{-1} = [m/a] \cdot [a/m] = [m \cdot a/a \cdot m] = 1.$$

This proves part of (v). We omit the remaining proofs.

New operations of *subtraction* $(-)$ and *division* $(\div$ or $/)$ are defined on R as follows:

$$r - s = r + (-s),$$

$$r \div s = r \cdot s^{-1} \quad \text{if} \quad s \neq 0.$$

The order relation "less than" is introduced on R in a slightly different way from that on I. We shall first define the concept of being positive, and then define the relation "less than."

2-42 DEFINITION. An element $[m/a] \in R$ is called *positive* if and only if $m \cdot a > 0$. The set of all positive elements of R is designated by "R_p."

Is this concept well-defined, that is, if $r = [m/a]$ and $m \cdot a > 0$, is $n \cdot b > 0$ for each $n/b \curlywedge m/a$? We first note that if $n/b \curlywedge m/a$, then $n \cdot a = m \cdot b \neq 0$, and $(n \cdot a)^2 = (m \cdot b) \cdot (n \cdot a) = (m \cdot a) \cdot (n \cdot b)$. Since $(n \cdot a)^2 > 0$, evidently $(m \cdot a) \cdot (n \cdot b) > 0$; and since $m \cdot a > 0$, also $n \cdot b > 0$. This shows that the concept of being positive is well-defined by 2-42.

2-43 THEOREM. The set R_p of positive rational numbers has the following properties:

(i) the TRICHOTOMY LAW: for each $r \in R$, one and only one of the following hold:

$$r = 0; \qquad r \in R_p; \qquad -r \in R_p.$$

(ii) R_p is closed under addition and multiplication.

(iii) if $r \in R_p$, then $r^{-1} \in R_p$.

If $r \in R$, say $r = [m/a]$, then $m \cdot a = 0$, $m \cdot a < 0$, or $m \cdot a > 0$ by 2-21, (i). This proves (i) of 2-43. If $r,s \in R_p$, say $r = [m/a]$ and $s = [n/b]$, then $m \cdot a > 0$ and $n \cdot b > 0$. Now $r + s = [(m \cdot b + n \cdot a)/a \cdot b]$, and since

$$(m \cdot b + n \cdot a) \cdot (a \cdot b) = (m \cdot a) \cdot b^2 + (n \cdot b) \cdot a^2 > 0,$$

$r + s \in R_p$. This proves that R_p is closed under addition. The other parts of 2-43 are just as easily established.

Having identified the positive elements of R, it is an easy matter to introduce the order relation "less than" on R.

2-44 DEFINITION. The order relation *less than* ($<$) is defined on R as follows: for each $r,s \in R$,

$$r < s \quad \text{if and only if} \quad s - r \in R_p.$$

If $r < s$ and $s < t$, then $s - r, t - s \in R_p$. By 2-43, (ii), $(s - r) + (t - s) = t - r \in R_p$. Thus $r < t$, and we conclude that $<$ is transitive. Obviously $r \in R_p$ if and only if $r > 0$.

We have just barely touched on the many properties of the operations and relations on R, since it is clear that the properties of the system of integers carry over onto the system of rational numbers. We shall have more to say about the close relationship between the systems of integers and rational numbers in a moment.

2-45 EXERCISES

1. Use the results of 2-41 to prove the two cancellation laws in $\{R; +, \cdot\}$.

2. State and prove the trichotomy law for $\{R; <\}$.

3. Prove that for each $r,s,t \in R$,

    (i) $r + t < s + t$ if and only if $r < s$.

    (ii) if $t \in R_p$, $r \cdot t < s \cdot t$ if and only if $r < s$.

    (iii) if $-t \in R_p$, $r \cdot t < s \cdot t$ if and only if $r > s$.

4. Prove that for each $r,s \in \boldsymbol{R}$,
   (i) $-(r + s) = -r - s$.
   (ii) $(r \cdot s)^{-1} = r^{-1} \cdot s^{-1}$, $r,s \neq \boldsymbol{0}$.
   (iii) $(r^{-1})^{-1} = r$, $r \neq \boldsymbol{0}$.
   (iv) $-(-r) = r$.

5. Prove that for each $r,s,t,u,v \in \boldsymbol{R}$, with $u,v \neq \boldsymbol{0}$,
   (i) $r \cdot (s - t) = r \cdot s - r \cdot t$.
   (ii) $(r \div u) \cdot (s \div v) = (r \cdot s) \div (u \cdot v)$.
   (iii) $(r \div u) + (s \div v) = (r \cdot v + s \cdot u) \div (u \cdot v)$.

The set J of all rational numbers of the form $[m/1]$ is essentially the set $\boldsymbol{I}$ of integers. By this we mean that the mapping θ of J onto $\boldsymbol{I}$ defined by

2-46 $$\theta: \quad [m/1]\theta = m, \qquad m \in \boldsymbol{I},$$

is an isomorphism. In the first place, θ is a 1–1 mapping of J onto $\boldsymbol{I}$, for if $[m/1]\theta = [n/1]\theta$, then, by 2-46, $m = n$. Thus $[m/1] = [n/1]$. Since

$$[m/1] + [n/1] = [(m + n)/1],$$

$$[m/1] \cdot [n/1] = [(m \cdot n)/1],$$

$([m/1] + [n/1])\theta = m + n$ and $([m/1] \cdot [n/1])\theta = m \cdot n$. That is, if we let $r = [m/1]$ and $s = [n/1]$,

2-47 $\quad (r + s)\theta = r\theta + s\theta; \qquad (r \cdot s)\theta = (r\theta) \cdot (s\theta), \qquad r,s \in J.$

It is clear also that

2-48 $\qquad r\theta < s\theta \quad$ if and only if $\quad r < s, \qquad r,s \in J.$

This proves the following theorem.

2-49 THEOREM. The mapping θ of J onto $\boldsymbol{I}$ defined by 2-46 is an isomorphism of the algebraic system $\{J; +, \cdot, <\}$ onto the system of integers.

Since the systems $\{J; +, \cdot, <\}$ and $\{\boldsymbol{I}; +, \cdot, <\}$ are isomorphic, the former system has all the algebraic properties of the system of integers. We shall actually identify J with $\boldsymbol{I}$ in the sense that we shall designate the element $[m/1]$ of J by m:

$$m = [m/1].$$

Any rational number $[m/a]$ may be written in the form

$$[m/a] = [m/1] \cdot [a/1]^{-1},$$

and therefore any rational number may be put in the form

$$[m/a] = m \cdot a^{-1} = m \div a, \qquad m, a \in J.$$

In this sense, we finally arrive at the conclusion that any rational number is actually the quotient of two integers.

The set R is *dense* relative to the relation "less than." That is, for any two distinct elements r and s of R, with $r < s$, there exists an element t of R between them,

$$r < t < s.$$

It is left as an exercise for the reader to verify that such a rational number as t exists. Note that the set I of integers is not dense relative to the relation "less than," for there is no integer between n and $n + 1$ (see 2-12, Exercise 3). The density of a set of numbers relative to an order relation plays an important role in mathematical analysis, but is not of primary importance in algebra.

2-50 EXERCISES

1. Prove that R is dense relative to the relation "less than" by showing that if $r < s$, then the arithmetical average of r and s, namely $(r + s)/2$, is between r and s.

2. Prove that the relation "less than" is *Archimedean* (relative to $+$). That is, for each $r, s \in R_p$, there exists a positive integer n such that the sum of n s's exceeds r, that is, such that $n \cdot s > r$.

3. Give a geometric description of the set of rational numbers as a set of points on a line.

7. The real numbers

The rational numbers suffice in the everyday use of numbers for measuring. Thus, for example, a blueprint of a house describes the various lengths in rational multiples of feet; the results of a physical experiment are recorded in rational multiples of the units concerned; the budget of our nation is described in rational multiples of dollars; etc.

Mathematically, however, the rational number system has many shortcomings. As simple examples, there are no rational numbers that exactly describe the length of a diagonal of a unit square or the circumference of a unit circle in terms of the given unit of measure. The root of the difficulty appears when one introduces the concept of limit in the calculus. A sequence of rational numbers that converges* need not converge to a rational number. Mathematical analysis as it is today is built on the real number system, an extension of the rational number system in which each converging sequence has a limit. In this section, we shall sketch one way of describing this extension of the rational numbers.

The method we are about to describe is due to the German mathematician R. Dedekind, a leading mathematician of the nineteenth century. We have selected Dedekind's method for this book because of its algebraic nature. Let us fix our attention on the set R_p of positive rational numbers.

2-51 DEFINITION.† A subset A of R_p is a *Dedekind cut* (D-cut) in R_p if the following conditions are satisfied by A:

   (i) A is a proper subset of R_p (that is, $A \neq R_p$).
   (ii) if $a \in A$, $r \in R_p$, and $r < a$, then $r \in A$.
   (iii) for each $a \in A$, there exists $b \in A$ such that $b > a$.

The most obvious example of a D-cut is the set C_t, t any element of R_p, defined by

$$2\text{-}52 \qquad C_t = \{a; a \in R_p, a < t\},$$

that is, C_t consists of all positive rational numbers less than t. The density of the set R implies that there is an element a such that $0 < a < t$; thus C_t has elements. However, since $t \not\subset C_t$, $C_t \neq R_p$. If $a \in C_t$, $r \in R_p$, and $r < a$, then $r < t$ (since $<$ is transitive) and $r \in C_t$. Finally, if $a \in C_t$, then there exists some $b \in R_p$ such that $a < b < t$ due to the density of R. We have shown that C_t is a D-cut. The D-cut C_t is *the cut at* t.

A more complicated example of a D-cut is as follows. Let

$$2\text{-}53 \qquad B = \{a; a \in R_p, a^2 < 2\},$$

---

*The sequence a_1, a_2, ... of rational numbers is said to converge if for each positive (rational) number e there exists a positive integer N_e such that $|a_n - a_m| < e$ for all integers m and n greater than N_e.

†This definition differs from Dedekind's original one in that we are considering only the set R_p of positive rational numbers while he considered the whole set R, and also in that we are considering the cut as being defined by one set rather than by a set and its complement as Dedekind did.

that is, B consists of all positive rational numbers a for which $a^2 < 2$. Certainly $1 \in B$ and $2 \notin B$; thus B is a proper subset of R_p. If $r \in R_p$, $a \in B$, with $r < a$, then $r^2 < a^2 < 2$ and $r \in B$. To show that 2-51, (iii), holds, we first note that if $a \in B$ and $a < 1$, then there exists some $b \in B$, namely $b = 1$, such that $b > a$. If $a \in B$ and $a \geq 1$, let s be any element of R_p such that

$$s < (2 - a^2) \cdot (4 \cdot a)^{-1}.$$

Then
$$4 \cdot a \cdot s < 2 - a^2 < 2,$$

so that $s < 2 \cdot a \cdot s < 1$ and $s^2 < s$. Hence

$$s^2 + 2 \cdot a \cdot s + a^2 < s + 2 \cdot a \cdot s + a^2 < 4 \cdot a \cdot s + a^2 < 2,$$

and, therefore, $s + a \in B$. Since $s + a > a$, property (iii) has been shown to hold. Thus B is a D-cut of R_p: B is called the *cut at* $\sqrt{2}$.

For any D-cut A of R_p, let A' be the *complement* of A, that is,

$$A' = \{r; r \in R_p, r \notin A\}.$$

In view of 2-51, (i), A' is a proper subset of R_p; also

$$A \cup A' = R_p, \qquad A \cap A' \quad \text{is void}.$$

This partition $\{A, A'\}$ of R_p has the property that each element $a \in A$ is less than every element $a' \in A'$; that is,

$$a < a' \quad \text{for each} \quad a \in A, a' \in A'.$$

This is clear in view of 2-51, (ii). In other words, each $a' \in A'$ is an *upper bound* of the set A in the sense that $a' > a$ for each $a \in A$. As a matter of fact, A' is the set of all upper bounds of A, since, by 2-51, (iii), no element of A is an upper bound of A.

Returning to the D-cut C_t at t (2-52), C'_t consists of all elements $r \in R_p$ such that $r \geq t$. Note that in this example C'_t has a least element, namely t; that is, t is the *least upper bound* of the set C_t. It is quite evident that these are the only D-cuts having least upper bounds, for if the D-cut A has t as a least upper bound, then $A = C_t$.

The D-cut B defined by 2-53 has no least upper bound, that is, the set B' has no least element. Suppose, on the contrary, that $s \in R_p$, s the least upper bound of B. Then $s \in B'$, and $s^2 \geq 2$. If the equation $s^2 = 2$ held, there would exist integers m and n ($s = m/n$) such that

$$m^2 = 2 \cdot n^2.$$

This is impossible by 2-36, Exercise 4. If, on the other hand, $s^2 > 2$, then

$$(s - r)^2 > 2, \quad \text{where} \quad r = (s^2 - 2)/(2 \cdot s).$$

Thus $s - r \in B'$ and $s - r < s$. This contradicts the choice of s as the least upper bound of B. We have proved that the D-cut B has no least upper bound.

A geometric description of the D-cuts will make clear the reason for the name "cut." The elements of R_p can be represented as points on a line L, as indicated in Figure 5. Not all points on L are rational (that is, have rational numbers assigned to them). If P is any point

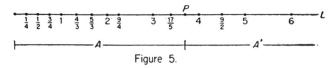

Figure 5.

on this line, then P "cuts" the line into two parts and hence partitions the set R_p into two subsets A and A'; the element $r \in R_p$ is in A if it is a point on L to the left of P, while r is in A' if it is to the right of P (or at P in case P is a rational point). Then A is a D-cut, *the cut at* P, and A' is the complement of A.

Let us designate by "Q" the set of all D-cuts of R_p. Observe that the elements of Q are themselves sets of rational numbers. An order relation "less than" can be introduced on Q in the obvious way.

2-54 DEFINITION. The order relation "less than" ($<$) is defined on Q as follows: for each $A,B \in Q$,

$$A < B \quad \text{if and only if} \quad A \subset B, A \neq B.$$

Thus $A < B$ if and only if A is a proper subset of B. It is immediate that $<$ is transitive, but neither reflexive nor symmetric.

If $A,B \in Q$ and $A \not< B$, $A \neq B$, then for some $a \in A$, we have $a \in B'$, the complement of B. Hence $b < a$ for all $b \in B$, and by 2-51, (ii), $B \subset A$. This establishes the following law.

2-55 THE TRICHOTOMY LAW. For each $A,B \in Q$, one and only one of the following statements is true:

$$\text{(i)} \ A = B; \quad \text{(ii)} \ A < B; \quad \text{(iii)} \ A > B.$$

The usual operations are introduced on Q as follows.

2-56 Definition. The operations of addition ($+$) and multiplication
($\cdot$) are defined on Q as follows: for each $A, B \in Q$,

$$A + B = \{a + b; a \in A, b \in B\};$$

$$A \cdot B = \{a \cdot b; a \in A, b \in B\}.$$

objection
← NOT
proved yet

By this definition, $r \in A + B$ if and only if $r = a + b$ for some
$a \in A$, $b \in B$; and $r \in A \cdot B$ if and only if $r = a \cdot b$ for some $a \in A$,
$b \in B$. The verification that $A + B$ and $A \cdot B$ are D-cuts (2-51) will
be omitted.

A lemma to aid in the proof of some of the theorems to follow will
now be given. Let us first illustrate the lemma geometrically. Suppose
that A is the D-cut at P (Figure 6), and r is any given positive rational

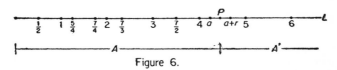

Figure 6.

number. Then no matter how small r might be, there always exists
an $a \in A$ such that $a + r \in A'$; that is, such that a is to the left of P
and $a + r$ is to the right of P.

2-57 Lemma. For each $A \in Q$, $r \in R_p$, there exists an $a \in A$ such
that $a + r \in A'$.

In case $r \in A'$, $r + a \in A'$ for all $a \in A$ and the lemma is proved.
If $r \in A$, $c \in A'$, there exists a positive integer n such that $n \cdot r > c$ by
the Archimedean property in R (see 2-50, Exercise 2). Let k be the
least positive integer such that $k \cdot r \in A'$. Certainly $1 < k \leq n$, and
$(k - 1) \cdot r \in A$. This proves the lemma, since

$$(k - 1) \cdot r \in A, \quad \text{and} \quad (k - 1) \cdot r + r \in A'.$$

2-58 Exercises

1. Let A be the set of all $a \in R_p$ such that $a^2 < 5$. Prove that A is a
D-cut. Show that A has no least upper bound in R_p.

2. Let A be the set of all $a \in R_p$ such that $a^3 < 2$. Prove that A is
a D-cut. Show that A has no least upper bound.

3. Prove that (2-52) for each $r, s \in R_p$,
    (i) $C_r + C_s = C_{r+s}$;   (ii) $C_r \cdot C_s = C_{r \cdot s}$;
    (iii) $C_r < C_s$ if and only if $r < s$.

4. Verify that for each $A,B \in Q$, $A + B$ and $A \cdot B$ are also in Q.

5. Prove that for each $A \in Q$, $s \in R_p$ with $s > 1$, there exists an $a \in A$ such that $a \cdot s \in A'$. (Hint: select $n \in P$ so that $n \cdot c > 1$ for some $c \in A$, and let $r = (s - 1)/n$. Then use 2-57, being careful to select $a > 1/n$.)

6. Prove that for each $A \in Q$, $C_1 \cdot A = A$. (C_1 is defined in 2-52.)

The order relation $<$ was introduced on Q in a much different way than it was on the other number systems of this chapter. Let us show now that it could have been introduced in exactly the same way as previously.

2-59 THEOREM. For each $A,B \in Q$, $A < B$ if and only if there exists some $C \in Q$ such that $A + C = B$.

If $A + C = B$, then for each $a \in A$, $c \in C$, evidently $a + c = b$, an element of B. Thus $a < b$ and $A \leq B$. Since for each $r \in C$ there exists an $a \in A$ (by 2-57) such that $a + r \in A'$, evidently $A \neq B$. Thus $A < B$.

On the other hand, if $A < B$, define C as the set of all elements of the form $b_2 - b_1$, where $b_1,b_2 \in B \cap A'$ and $b_2 > b_1$. The proof that $C \in Q$ is omitted. For each $a \in A$, $b_2 - b_1 \in C$, we have $a + (b_2 - b_1) = b_2 - (b_1 - a) < b_2$, and hence $a + (b_2 - b_1) \in B$. Thus $A + C \leq B$. If $b \in B$, then either $b \in A$ or $b \in A'$. If $b \in A \cap B$, then for each $c \in C$ such that $c < b$, $b = (b - c) + c \in A + C$. If $b \in A' \cap B$ and $b' > b$, where $b' \in A' \cap B$, then there exists an $a \in A$ by 2-57 such that $a + (b' - b) \in A'$. Since $a + (b' - b) = b' - (b - a) < b'$, evidently $a + (b' - b) \in B$. Thus $a + (b' - b) = b'' \in A' \cap B$, and $b = a + (b' - b'') \in A + C$. This proves that $B \leq A + C$, which together with $A + C \leq B$ proves that $B = A + C$. This completes the proof of 2-59.

Let the D-cut C_1 (2-52) be designated by "I;" thus I is the set of all positive rational numbers less than 1. For each $A \in Q$, define A^{-1} by

$$A^{-1} = \{a; a \in R_p, a < b^{-1} \text{ for some } b \in A'\}.$$

If $c \in A$, then $c < b$ for each $b \in A'$, and, therefore, $c^{-1} > b^{-1}$ for each $b \in A'$. Thus, if $c \in A$, then $c^{-1} \not\subset A^{-1}$. This shows that $A^{-1} \neq R_p$. Properties 2-51, (ii) and (iii) follow easily for A^{-1}. Hence A^{-1} is a D-cut.

2-60 THEOREM. The following properties hold for the operations $+$ and $\cdot$ on Q: for each $A,B,C \in Q$,

(i) the ASSOCIATIVE LAWS:

$$A + (B + C) = (A + B) + C; \qquad A \cdot (B \cdot C) = (A \cdot B) \cdot C.$$

(ii) the COMMUTATIVE LAWS:

$$A + B = B + A; \qquad A \cdot B = B \cdot A.$$

(iii) the DISTRIBUTIVE LAW:

$$(A + B) \cdot C = A \cdot C + B \cdot C.$$

(iv) I is the MULTIPLICATIVE IDENTITY element:

$$A \cdot I = I \cdot A = A.$$

(v) A^{-1} is the MULTIPLICATIVE INVERSE of A:

$$A \cdot A^{-1} = A^{-1} \cdot A = I.$$

(vi) the additive CANCELLATION LAW:

$$A + C = B + C \quad \text{if and only if} \quad A = B.$$

The proofs of (i) to (iv) are simple and hence are omitted. To prove (v), let $a \in A$, $b \in A^{-1}$. Then $b < c^{-1}$ for some $c \in A'$, and $b \cdot c < 1$. Since $a < c$, evidently $a \cdot b < 1$. Thus $A \cdot A^{-1} \le I$. If $r \in I$, so that $r < 1$, then $r^{-1} > 1$ and by 2-58, Exercise 5, there exists an $a \in A$ such that $r^{-1} \cdot a \in A'$. For each $b \in A$ such that $b > a$, we have $r \cdot b^{-1} < (r^{-1} \cdot a)^{-1}$, and therefore $r \cdot b^{-1} = c$, an element of A^{-1}. Thus $r = b \cdot c$, $r \in A \cdot A^{-1}$, and so $I \le A \cdot A^{-1}$. Hence $A \cdot A^{-1} = I$. Part (vi) follows easily from 2-59 and the trichotomy law. understatement

It is now possible to extend Q to a larger system in which each element has an additive inverse in exactly the same way the natural number system was extended to the system of integers.

To this end, let S be the set of all formal differences $A-C$, where $A, C \in Q$. Define the equivalence relation $\sim$ on S as follows: $A-C \sim B-D$ if and only if $A + D = B + C$. The equivalence relation $\sim$ partitions S into equivalence sets $[A-C]$, where $[A-C] = \{B-D; B-D \in S, B-D \sim A-C\}$.

2-61 DEFINITION. The equivalence sets $[A-C]$ of S are called *real numbers*. The set of all real numbers is designated by "$R^{\#}$."

The operations and order relation on Q are extended to $R^{\#}$ in the usual way:

$$[A-C] + [B-D] = [(A + B)-(C + D)],$$

$$[A-C] \cdot [B-D] = [(A \cdot B + C \cdot D)-(A \cdot D + C \cdot B)],$$

$$[A-C] < [B-D] \quad \text{if and only if} \quad A + D < B + C.$$

The associative, commutative, and distributive laws hold in R^s, as does the trichotomy law for the relation $<$. The real number $[A–A]$, designated by "0," is the additive identity element of R^s, and $[C–A]$ is the additive inverse of $[A–C]$. The properties of R^s relative to the operations $+$ and $\cdot$ are precisely the same as those of R given in 2-41.

The mapping α,

$$\alpha: \quad A\alpha = [(A + I)–I], \quad A \in Q,$$

of Q onto the subset Q_1 of R^s made up of all real numbers of the form $[(A + I)–I]$ is an isomorphism of $\{Q; +,\cdot,<\}$ onto $\{Q_1; +,\cdot,<\}$, as was the analogous mapping of the set of natural numbers into the set of integers. We may think of R^s as being made up of the elements of Q_1, the zero element, and the negatives of elements of Q_1. It is convenient for us to consider Q and Q_1 as being identical; either one will be thought of as the set of positive real numbers.

For each $t \in R_p$, C_t, defined by 2-52, is a positive real number. Let $R_a = \{C_t; t \in R_p\}$; then the mapping β,

$$\beta: \quad t\beta = C_t, \quad t \in R_p,$$

is an isomorphism of $\{R_p; +,\cdot,<\}$ onto $\{R_a; +,\cdot,<\}$. That is, for each $r,s \in R_p$,

$$(r + s)\beta = r\beta + s\beta,$$

$$(r\cdot s)\beta = r\beta \cdot s\beta,$$

$$r < s \quad \text{if and only if} \quad r\beta < s\beta.$$

These follow directly from 2-58, Exercise 3. This isomorphism extends in a natural way to one of R into R^s. Thus the system of rational numbers is contained in the system of real numbers in the sense that it is isomorphic to a subsystem of the real number system. As is our usual practice, we identify these isomorphic systems.

We saw in an example above that a set of positive rational numbers could have an upper bound without having a least upper bound. Thus the D-cut B at $\sqrt{2}$ (2-53) has an upper bound without having a least upper bound.

However, and this is the most important additional property possessed by R^s, any set of positive real numbers that has an upper bound has a least upper bound. To see this, suppose that S is a set of positive real numbers having an upper bound. Thus $S \subset Q$, and there exists some $C \in Q$ such that $A \leq C$ for each $A \in S$. Each element

$A \in S$ is a set of rational numbers. Define the set B of rational numbers as follows:

$$B = \{r; r \in R_p, r \in A \quad \text{for some} \quad A \in S\}.$$

Thus B is the set of all rational numbers belonging to some element of S. It is easily verified that B is a D-cut, and from its very definition, $A \leq B$ for each $A \in S$. Let us show that B is the least upper bound of S. If $D \in Q$ and $D < B$, then some element a of a D-cut $A \in S$ is in B but not in D; hence $A \nleq D$. Thus no D-cut smaller than B is an upper bound of S. This proves that B is the least upper bound of S. The element B might or might not be in S.

If S is any subset of Q, an element $A \in Q$ is a *lower bound* of S if $A \leq B$ for each $B \in S$. A lower bound A of S is a *greatest lower bound* of S if each other lower bound of S is smaller than A. In case no element of Q is a lower bound of S, then evidently the real number 0 (not in Q) is the greatest lower bound of S in R^*.

Assume now that the subset S of Q has lower bounds in Q, and let T be the set of all lower bounds of S in Q. Evidently each element of S is an upper bound of T. By remarks above, the set T has a least upper bound, say B, in Q. Certainly $B \leq A$ for each $A \in S$, while $B \geq C$ for each $C \in T$. Thus B is a greatest lower bound of S. We conclude that every subset of Q has a greatest lower bound.

It is an easy matter to extend these results to the set R^* of all real numbers. If S is any subset of R^* having an upper bound, then S has a least upper bound, and similarly for lower bounds.

2-62 THEOREM. The set R^* of real numbers is *complete* relative to the order relation "less than;" that is, every subset of R^* having an upper bound has a least upper bound, and every subset of R^* having a lower bound has a greatest lower bound.

That R^* is dense relative to $<$ is also easily established. If $A,B \in Q$, with $A < B$, and r is any rational number in B but not in A, then (2-52) $A < C_r < B$. If A is a negative real number and B is a positive real number, then 0 is between them. If both A and B are negative, then $-A$ and $-B$ are both positive, and an element C_r may be found between them. Certainly, then, $-C_r$ is between A and B. Such a line of reasoning proves that R^* is dense relative to $<$. Similarly, the Archimedean property can be established for R^*.

In concluding this chapter, let us give a brief resume of the four systems studied, namely, the system of natural numbers $\{N; +, \cdot, <\}$, the system of integers $\{I; +, \cdot, <\}$, the system of rational numbers $\{R; +, \cdot, <\}$, and the system of real numbers $\{R^\#; +, \cdot, <\}$. In all these systems, there are two operations $+$ and $\cdot$, and a transitive order relation $<$. We proved that (in the sense of isomorphism)

$$N \subset I \subset R \subset R^\#,$$

with the operations and relations carrying over from one system to the next. In all these systems, note the following properties:

1. The associative laws hold for $+$ and $\cdot$.
2. The commutative laws hold for $+$ and $\cdot$.
3. The distributive law holds.
4. The cancellation laws hold for $+$ and $\cdot$.
5. There is a multiplicative identity element 1.
6. The trichotomy law holds for $<$.
7. The relation $<$ is compatible with $+$ and $\cdot$.

The systems I, R, and $R^\#$ have the following additional properties in common:

8. There is an additive identity element 0.
9. Each element has an additive inverse.

In the systems R and $R^\#$, the additional properties listed below hold:

10. Each nonzero element has a multiplicative inverse.
11. Denseness holds relative to $<$.

Finally, $R^\#$ has one additional property as follows:

12. Completeness holds relative to $<$.

The reader might wonder why we stop with the real number system. Why not extend this to a larger system with more properties? The reason is that the real number system is the last possible step in this extension process in the sense that there is no larger number system containing $R^\#$ and having the twelve properties listed above. In a later chapter, the system of real numbers will be extended to the system of complex numbers C. While all the properties above concerning the operations $+$ and $\cdot$ carry over to C, it is not possible to introduce an order relation "less than" agreeing with the one on $R^\#$.

2-63 EXERCISES

1. If A is a positive real number, define the D-cut $\sqrt{A}$.
2. Supply the rest of the proof of 2-60.
3. Define a D-cut in Q analogous to the D-cut in R_p. Show that the set S of all D-cuts in Q is essentially the same as Q, that is, if the operations $+$ and $\cdot$ are introduced in S as usual, then S is isomorphic to Q.

CHAPTER III

Integral Domains and Fields

In the previous chapter, the specific algebraic systems of natural numbers, integers, rational numbers, and real numbers were developed. We could go on indefinitely introducing such concrete algebraic systems and analyzing their particular properties. However, in so doing, we would essentially repeat ourselves many times, and we might lose sight in a mass of details of the common characteristics of all these systems. It is the purpose of this chapter to define general algebraic systems of which the integers, rational numbers, and real numbers are but instances, and to develop some of the properties of such general systems. Then many more examples of such systems will be exhibited.

8. Integral domains

If $\times$ is any operation on the set S, and T is a subset of S, then T is said to be *closed* relative to the operation $\times$ if for every pair (a,b) of elements of T, $a \times b$ is again in T. For example, if T is made up of the *odd integers* ± 1, ± 3, ± 5, . . ., T is a subset of I that is closed relative to the operation $\cdot$ (since the product of two odd integers is odd), but T is not closed relative to the operation $+$ (since the sum of two odd integers is an even integer). If U is the subset of I containing all the *even integers* 0, ± 2, ± 4, ± 6, . . ., then U is closed relative to both operations $+$ and $\cdot$.

3-1 DEFINITION. An algebraic system $\{S; +, \cdot\}$ made up of a set S and two operations on S is called an *integral domain* provided that:
   (i) both operations are *associative*: for each $a,b,c \in S$,

$$a + (b + c) = (a + b) + c, \qquad a \cdot (b \cdot c) = (a \cdot b) \cdot c;$$

   (ii) both operations are *commutative*: for each $a,b \in S$,

$$a + b = b + a, \qquad a \cdot b = b \cdot a;$$

(iii) the operation · is *distributive* relative to the operation +: for each $a,b,c \in S$,

$$a \cdot (b + c) = a \cdot b + a \cdot c, \qquad (b + c) \cdot a = b \cdot a + c \cdot a;$$

(iv) there exist *identity elements* 0 and 1 in S relative to the operations + and · respectively: for each $a \in S$,

$$a + 0 = 0 + a = a, \qquad a \cdot 1 = 1 \cdot a = a;$$

(v) each element $a \in S$ has an *inverse* $-a \in S$ relative to the operation +:

$$a + (-a) = (-a) + a = 0;$$

(vi) the *cancellation* law holds relative to the operation ·: for each $a,b,c \in S$,

$$\text{if} \quad a \cdot c = b \cdot c \quad \text{and} \quad c \neq 0, \quad \text{then} \quad a = b.$$

We shall call the operation + "addition" and the operation · "multiplication" as we did in the previous chapter.

It is evident from 2-18 that the system $\{I; +, \cdot\}$ of integers is an example of an integral domain, since the six properties listed in 3-1 hold in $\{I; +, \cdot\}$. As a matter of fact, the system we had in mind when we defined the integral domain was the system of integers. Naturally, the systems of rational numbers and real numbers also are examples of integral domains.

The reader should keep these examples of integral domains in mind in the general discussion that follows. However, while it is true that the system of integers is an integral domain, it is not true that an integral domain necessarily has all the properties of the system of integers. For example, the order relation "less than," which plays such an important role in the system of integers, plays no part at all in a general integral domain. Thus the division process, the well-ordering theorem, the fundamental theorem of arithmetic, and so on, will not enter into our discussion of general integral domains. As we shall see presently, there exist examples of integral domains which are considerably different from $\{I; +, \cdot\}$. For example, there is an integral domain having precisely two elements!

In the following pages, when we refer to "the integral domain S," we are always referring to an algebraic system $\{S; +, \cdot\}$ for which the six properties listed in 3-1 hold. We shall always use the symbols "+" and "·" for the operations of the integral domain; for this reason, it is not always necessary to point out what the operations are. Our primary concern in this section is to find properties in common to all integral domains.

Before deriving these common properties, we should like to point out that properties (i), (ii), and (iv) of 3-1 are symmetric in $+$ and $\cdot$, while the others are not. Thus, for example, if we replace $+$ by $\cdot$ and 0 by 1 in the equation

$$a + 0 = 0 + a = a,$$

we obtain the equation

$$a \cdot 1 = 1 \cdot a = a$$

which also holds; and if we replace $+$ by $\cdot$ in the equation $a + (b + c) = (a + b) + c$, we obtain $a \cdot (b \cdot c) = (a \cdot b) \cdot c$ which is valid also; and so on. Property (iii) would be symmetric in $+$ and $\cdot$, for example, if we included

$$a + (b \cdot c) = (a + b) \cdot (a + c); \qquad (b \cdot c) + a = (b + a) \cdot (c + a)$$

along with what was given. The above are not valid in the system of integers, and therefore cannot hold in an integral domain in general.

It is immediate from definition that an identity element relative to an operation is unique; thus 0 and 1 are unique elements of S. Other properties of any integral domain S are listed below.

3-2. The cancellation law relative to $+$ holds in S.

To prove this, let us assume that $a + c = b + c$ for some $a, b, c \in S$. Then

$$(a + c) + (-c) = (b + c) + (-c),$$

so that by 3-1, (i), we have

$$a + (c + (-c)) = b + (c + (-c)).$$

Hence $a + 0 = b + 0$ by 3-1, (v), and $a = b$ according to 3-1, (iv).

A corollary of 3-2 is that the inverse element $-a$ of any a in S is unique. For if we had

$$a + (-a) = 0 \quad \text{and} \quad a + b = 0,$$

then we would have $a + (-a) = a + b$ and $-a = b$ in view of 3-2. Thus, for example, since a is an inverse of $-a$, a must be the inverse of $-a$, that is,

$$a = -(-a).$$

3-3. For each $a \in S$, $\quad a \cdot 0 = 0$.

To prove 3-3, note that the distributive law implies that

$$a \cdot 0 + a \cdot 0 = a \cdot (0 + 0).$$

Now $0 + 0 = 0$ and $a \cdot 0 + 0 = a \cdot 0$, and therefore

$$a \cdot 0 + a \cdot 0 = a \cdot 0 + 0.$$

The cancellation law 3-2 yields $a \cdot 0 = 0$ as desired.

3-4. For each $a,b \in S$, $a \cdot b = 0$ if and only if $a = 0$ or $b = 0$.

In case either $a = 0$ or $b = 0$, $a \cdot b = 0$ by 3-3. To prove the converse, assume that $a \cdot b = 0$. Then, if $a \neq 0$, we can cancel out a in the equation

$$a \cdot b = a \cdot 0$$

by 3-1, (vi). This gives $b = 0$ as desired.

3-5 EXERCISES

1. Which of the following subsystems of the real number system are integral domains? The set of all real numbers of the form:

    (i) $a \cdot \sqrt{2}$, $\quad a \in R$;
    (ii) $a + b \cdot \sqrt{2}$, $\quad a,b \in I$;
    (iii) $a + b \cdot \sqrt{6}$, $\quad a,b \in R$;
    (iv) $a + (b/\sqrt{2})$, $\quad a,b \in I$;
    (v) $a + b \cdot \sqrt{2} + c \cdot \sqrt{3}$, $\quad a,b,c \in I$;
    (vi) $a + b \cdot \sqrt[3]{2} + c \cdot \sqrt[3]{4}$, $\quad a,b,c \in I$.

2. If S is an integral domain and T is a subset of S closed relative to the operations of S, is T necessarily an integral domain? Justify your answer.

3. Does the system of even integers form an integral domain? What are all possible integral domains that are subsystems of I?

4. Does the system of all rational numbers of the form a/b, $a,b \in I$ with b a power of 2 (that is, b is in the set $\{1,2,4,8, \ldots\}$) form an integral domain? What are all possible integral domains that are contained in R, the rational number system?

5. If S is an integral domain, prove that for each $a,b \in S$, (i) $-(a + b) = (-a) + (-b)$; (ii) $(-a) \cdot b = -(a \cdot b)$; (iii) $(-a) \cdot (-b) = a \cdot b$.

6. In an integral domain S, define the binary operation "$-$" by: $a - b = a + (-b)$. List and prove the expected properties of this "minus" operation.

7. Prove that 3-1, (vi), can be deduced from 3-1, (i) to (v), and
3-4. This proves that 3-1, (vi), can be replaced by 3-4 in the definition
of an integral domain.

8. Let the set S consist of the two elements a and b. Prove that S
is an integral domain if the operations $+$ and $\cdot$ are defined on S as
follows: $a + a = b + b = b, a + b = b + a = a; b \cdot b = a \cdot b = b \cdot a =
b, a \cdot a = a.$

9. Let S be an integral domain and T be a subset of S closed rela-
tive to $+$ and $\cdot$ such that: (i) $0 \not\subset T$; (ii) for each $a \in S$, $a \neq 0$,
either $a \in T$ or $-a \in T$. Define the relation $<$ on S as follows: for
each $a, b \in S$,

$$a < b \quad \text{if and only if} \quad b = a + c \quad \text{for some} \quad c \in T.$$

Derive properties of $<$ analogous to the properties of the relation $<$
on I. Such an S is called an *ordered integral domain*.

Let S be an integral domain. For any three elements $a_1, a_2, a_3 \in S$,
define

$$a_1 + a_2 + a_3 = (a_1 + a_2) + a_3,$$

and, whenever $a_1 + a_2 + \ldots + a_n$ is defined, define

$$a_1 + a_2 + \ldots + a_n + a_{n+1} = (a_1 + a_2 + \ldots + a_n) + a_{n+1}.$$

Such a recursive definition allows us to define the sum of any k elements of S, k a positive integer. Evidently a similar definition may
be given for the product of any k elements of S. The reader should
realize that the necessity of defining such sums and products stems
from the fact that $+$ and $\cdot$ are binary operations, while the operations,
for example, that associate with the three elements $a_1, a_2, a_3 \in S$ the
elements $a_1 + a_2 + a_3$ and $a_1 \cdot a_2 \cdot a_3$ are ternary operations.

General associative, commutative, and distributive laws hold relative to these finite sum and product operations in any integral domain
S. A possible form that these laws might take is as follows.

3-6 THEOREM. Let n be an integer greater than 1 and $a_1, a_2, \ldots, a_n, b$
be any $n + 1$ elements of S. Then

(i) the GENERAL ASSOCIATIVE LAWS hold: that is, for each i,
$1 \leq i < n$,

$$(a_1 + \ldots + a_i) + (a_{i+1} + \ldots + a_n) = a_1 + a_2 + \ldots + a_n,$$

$$(a_1 \cdot \ldots \cdot a_i) \cdot (a_{i+1} \cdot \ldots \cdot a_n) = a_1 \cdot a_2 \cdot \ldots \cdot a_n;$$

(ii) the GENERAL COMMUTATIVE LAWS hold: that is, if $1', 2', \ldots, n'$ are the first n positive integers in any order (for example, if $n = 3$, one might have $1' = 3, 2' = 1, 3' = 2$), then

$$a_1 + a_2 + \ldots + a_n = a_{1'} + a_{2'} + \ldots + a_{n'},$$

$$a_1 \cdot a_2 \cdot \ldots \cdot a_n = a_{1'} \cdot a_{2'} \cdot \ldots \cdot a_{n'};$$

(iii) the GENERAL DISTRIBUTIVE LAW holds:

$$(a_1 + a_2 + \ldots + a_n) \cdot b = a_1 \cdot b + a_2 \cdot b + \ldots + a_n \cdot b.$$

This theorem is proved by mathematical induction. We will prove part of (i), and leave the rest of the proof as an exercise for the reader.

Let E_n be the statement "$(a_1 + \ldots + a_i) + (a_{i+1} + \ldots + a_n) = a_1 + a_2 + \ldots + a_n$ for each integer i, $1 \leq i < n$." If $n = 2, i = 1$ and E_2 states that "$a_1 + a_2 = a_1 + a_2$." If $n = 3, i = 1$ or $i = 2$, and E_3 states that

$$a_1 + (a_2 + a_3) = a_1 + a_2 + a_3, \qquad \text{if } i = 1,$$

$$(a_1 + a_2) + a_3 = a_1 + a_2 + a_3, \qquad \text{if } i = 2.$$

That E_3 is true follows from the definition of $a_1 + a_2 + a_3$ and the associative law 3-1, (i). Let us assume that E_k is true, and try to prove that E_{k+1} is also true. The proof proceeds as follows: if $1 \leq i < k + 1$, then

$$(a_1 + \ldots + a_i) + (a_{i+1} + \ldots + a_k + a_{k+1})$$

$$= (a_1 + \ldots + a_i) + ((a_{i+1} + \ldots + a_k) + a_{k+1}),$$

by definition, and in turn this equals

$$((a_1 + \ldots + a_i) + (a_{i+1} + \ldots + a_k)) + a_{k+1} \qquad \text{(associative law)},$$

$$(a_1 + \ldots + a_k) + a_{k+1} \qquad \text{(since } E_k \text{ is true)},$$

$$a_1 + \ldots + a_k + a_{k+1} \qquad \text{(by definition)}.$$

Hence E_{k+1} is true, and the desired result follows by mathematical induction.

The familiar notation for such sums (*multiples*) as $a + a, a + a + a$, and so on, and such products (*powers*) as $a \cdot a, a \cdot a \cdot a$, and so on, will be introduced now in an integral domain $\{S; +, \cdot\}$. Thus we will let $a + a = 2a, a + a + a = 3a, a \cdot a = a^2, a \cdot a \cdot a = a^3$, and so on. More precisely, for each positive integer n and each $a \in S$, define na and a^n

recursively as follows. Define

$$1a = a \quad \text{and} \quad a^1 = a,$$

and whenever ka and a^k are defined, define $(k + 1)a$ and a^{k+1} by (see 2-6)

$$(k + 1)a = ka + a: \quad a^{k+1} = a^k \cdot a.$$

The reason for defining multiples and powers simultaneously is that they are identical concepts, one relative to the operation $+$ and the other relative to the operation $\cdot$. It must be borne in mind that na does not mean n times a; for n is an integer while a is an element of S, and since S need not contain the integers as a subset, multiplication of n by a is undefined in general.

3-7 Theorem. The following properties of multiples and powers hold for any $a,b \in S$, and any positive integers m and n.

(i) $na + ma = (n + m)a: \quad a^n \cdot a^m = a^{n+m}$.

(ii) $na + nb = n(a + b): \quad a^n \cdot b^n = (a \cdot b)^n$.

(iii) $m(na) = (m \cdot n)a: \quad (a^n)^m = a^{n \cdot m}$.

We note that in (i) the $+$ in $na + ma$ is an operation on S, while the $+$ in $(n + m)a$ is an operation on I, the set of integers; likewise, the operation $\cdot$ occurring in (i) and (ii) is on S, while that in (iii) is on I. Since the proofs of (i) to (iii) use only the associative and commutative laws of S, and these hold relative to both operations, the proofs of the equations involving powers will be identical (interchanging the operations $+$ and $\cdot$ of S, and replacing na by a^n) with the proofs of the corresponding equations involving multiples. For this reason, we shall limit our proofs to the equations involving multiples.

The proofs are by mathematical induction. For each positive integer n, $na + 1a = (n + 1)a$ by definition. Assume that for the positive integer k (and any n)

$$na + ka = (n + k)a.$$

Then $na + (k + 1)a = na + (ka + a) = (na + ka) + a = (n + k)a + a = (n + k + 1)a$, that is

$$na + (k + 1)a = (n + (k + 1))a.$$

Thus (i) is proved by mathematical induction.

To prove (ii), note that $1a + 1b = 1(a + b)$ by definition. Assume that for the positive integer k,

$$ka + kb = k(a + b).$$

Then $(k + 1)a + (k + 1)b = (ka + a) + (kb + b) = (ka + kb) + (a + b) = k(a + b) + (a + b) = (k + 1)(a + b)$, and (ii) follows by mathematical induction.

Finally, to prove (iii), we note that $1(na) = na = (1 \cdot n)a$ for each positive integer n. Assume that for the positive integer k (and any n),

$$k(na) = (k \cdot n)a.$$

Then, using (i),

$$(k + 1)(na) = k(na) + na = (k \cdot n)a + na = (k \cdot n + n)a.$$

Hence, using the distributive law in I,

$$(k + 1)(na) = ((k + 1) \cdot n)a,$$

and (iii) is proved by mathematical induction.

If n is any positive integer, we can define

$$(-n)a = -(na).$$

If we also define $0a = 0$, then na is defined for every integer n, whether it be positive, negative, or zero. The properties of multiples in 3-7 may be shown to hold for any integers m and n. No similar properties are possible for powers, since no inverse relative to multiplication is assumed to exist. However, when we get to fields, it will be possible to define negative powers of elements. Then 3-7 will hold for all integers.

3-8 EXERCISES

1. Prove that for any $m,n \in I$, and any $a,b \in S$,
   (i) $(na) \cdot b = a \cdot (nb) = n(a \cdot b)$;
   (ii) $(ma) \cdot (nb) = (m \cdot n)(a \cdot b)$.
Do corresponding formulas for powers hold?
2. Prove 3-6, (ii) and (iii).
3. Prove the power equations in 3-7.

9. The integers modulo k

We have had as yet no examples of integral domains other than those contained in the real number system (except for 3-5, Exercise 8). Some examples of a radically different nature will be introduced at this time.

Let k be any fixed positive integer. Then any two integers a and b are congruent modulo k if $k \mid (a - b)$, that is if $a - b = k \cdot n$ for some integer n. For example, 7 and 19 are congruent modulo 3 since $3 \mid (7 - 19)$; 91 and 35 are congruent modulo 8 since $8 \mid 56$; 153 and -47 are congruent modulo 25 since $25 \mid 200$. On the other hand, 12 and 7 are not congruent modulo 2, since $2 \nmid (12 - 7)$.

3-9 DEFINITION. For any positive integer k, the relation *congruent modulo k* ($\equiv_k$) is defined on I, the set of integers, as follows: for each $a,b \in I$,

$$a \equiv_k b \quad \text{if and only if} \quad k \mid (a - b).$$

Certainly, for each $a \in I$, $a \equiv_k a$; thus $\equiv_k$ is a reflexive relation. If $a \equiv_k b$, then $a - b = k \cdot n$ for some $n \in I$. Since $b - a = k \cdot (-n)$, evidently $b \equiv_k a$ also. Hence the relation $\equiv_k$ is symmetric. Finally, if $a \equiv_k b$ and $b \equiv_k c$, so that $a - b = k \cdot n$ and $b - c = k \cdot m$ for some $m,n \in I$, then $a - c = k \cdot (n + m)$ and $a \equiv_k c$. Thus $\equiv_k$ is transitive. This proves that $\equiv_k$ is an equivalence relation.

Since $\equiv_k$ is an equivalence relation, it partitions I into equivalence sets. As usual, we designate by "$[a]$" the equivalence set containing a:

$$[a] = \{b; b \in I, b \equiv_k a\}.$$

The elements congruent to 0 modulo k are just the multiples of k, and therefore $[0]$ is made up of the elements 0, $\pm k$, $\pm 2k$, $\pm 3k$, ... For example, the equivalence sets related to $\equiv_3$ are as follows:

$$[0] = \{\ldots, -12,-9,-6,-3,0,3,6,9,12, \ldots\},$$
$$[1] = \{\ldots, -11,-8,-5,-2,1,4,7,10,13, \ldots\},$$
$$[2] = \{\ldots, -10,-7,-4,-1,2,5,8,11,14, \ldots\}.$$

These are the only equivalence sets related to $\equiv_3$, since every integer appears in some one of these three sets.

Every integer is a multiple of 1, and therefore I is the only equivalence set related to $\equiv_1$. This uninteresting case will be omitted henceforth. For any given k ($k > 1$), the equivalence sets related to $\equiv_k$ are indicated below.

$$[0] = \{\ldots, -2k,-k,0,k,2k, \ldots\},$$
$$[1] = \{\ldots, -2k + 1,-k + 1,1,k + 1,2k + 1, \ldots\},$$
$$[2] = \{\ldots, -2k + 2,-k + 2,2,k + 2,2k + 2, \ldots\},$$

$$\cdot \quad \cdot \quad \cdot \quad \cdot \quad \cdot \quad \cdot \quad \cdot \quad \cdot \quad \cdot \quad \cdot \quad \cdot \quad \cdot \quad \cdot \quad \cdot \quad \cdot$$

$$\cdot \quad \cdot \quad \cdot \quad \cdot \quad \cdot \quad \cdot \quad \cdot \quad \cdot \quad \cdot \quad \cdot \quad \cdot \quad \cdot \quad \cdot \quad \cdot \quad \cdot$$

$$[k - 1] = \{\ldots, -k - 1,-1,k - 1,2k - 1,3k - 1, \ldots\}.$$

The sets listed above, k in number, are distinct simply because two non-negative integers a and b cannot be congruent modulo k and both be less than k (since $|a - b| < k$). These sets are the only equivalence sets related to $\equiv_k$. For if a is any integer, there exist (by 2-29) $q, r \in I$ such that

$$a = k \cdot q + r, \qquad 0 \leq r < k.$$

But then $a - r = k \cdot q$ and $a \equiv_k r$, that is, $a \in [r]$ and $[a] = [r]$. Since $r \leq k - 1$, $[r]$ is one of the sets listed above. Thus for any integer a there exists an integer r, $0 \leq r \leq k - 1$, such that $[a] = [r]$. For example, if $k = 3$, $[6] = [0]$, $[-8] = [1]$, $[11] = [2]$, $[-1] = [2]$, $[-54] = [0]$, and so on.

3-10 DEFINITION. The equivalence sets of I related to $\equiv_k$ are called *integers modulo k*. The set of all integers modulo k is designated by "$I/(k)$."

The integers modulo 3, for example, are the three sets $[0]$, $[1]$, $[2]$ listed above. The set $I/(k)$ has precisely k elements, namely, the elements $[0]$, $[1]$, $[2]$, . . ., $[k - 1]$.

Operations, depending on those on I, can be introduced on $I/(k)$ in the obvious way.

3-11 DEFINITION. The operations $+$ and $\cdot$ are defined on $I/(k)$ as follows: for each $[a], [b] \in I/(k)$,

$$[a] + [b] = [a + b],$$

$$[a] \cdot [b] = [a \cdot b].$$

The operations appearing on the right side of these equations are those on I. Are the operations on $I/(k)$ well-defined by 3-11? This question arises because the product $[a] \cdot [b]$ of sets is defined in terms of elements of these sets, and so on. We must show that if $[a] = [a']$ and $[b] = [b']$, then

$$[a \cdot b] = [a' \cdot b'].$$

Now $[a] = [a']$ and $[b] = [b']$ imply that for some $m, n \in I$,

$$a = a' + k \cdot n \quad \text{and} \quad b = b' + k \cdot m.$$

On multiplying these equations, left side by left side and right side by right side, we obtain

$$a \cdot b = a' \cdot b' + k \cdot (a' \cdot m + b' \cdot n + k \cdot m \cdot n).$$

Hence $a \cdot b \equiv_k a' \cdot b'$ and $[a \cdot b] = [a' \cdot b']$ as desired. The other operation is shown to be well-defined similarly.

There is a natural way to map I onto $I/(k)$, namely by letting $a \in I$ be mapped into $[a] \in I/(k)$. Designating this mapping by "α," we have

3-12 $$\alpha: \quad a\alpha = [a], \quad a \in I.$$

If $k = 3$, for example, then

$$0\alpha = [0], \quad 3\alpha = [0], \quad -3\alpha = [0], \quad 6\alpha = [0], \quad \dots,$$

$$1\alpha = [1], \quad 4\alpha = [1], \quad -2\alpha = [1], \quad 7\alpha = [1], \quad \dots,$$

$$2\alpha = [2], \quad 5\alpha = [2], \quad -1\alpha = [2], \quad 8\alpha = [2], \quad \dots..$$

Since I is an infinite set while $I/(k)$ is finite, α is never a 1–1 mapping.

It is possible to rewrite the equations of 3-11 in terms of α simply by replacing every $[c]$ by $c\alpha$. Thus $[a] = a\alpha$, $[b] = b\alpha$, $[a + b] = (a + b)\alpha$, $[a \cdot b] = (a \cdot b)\alpha$, and, therefore, by 3-11,

3-13 $$(a + b)\alpha = a\alpha + b\alpha, \qquad a,b \in I,$$
$$(a \cdot b)\alpha = (a\alpha) \cdot (b\alpha).$$

These equations show that the mapping α of I onto $I/(k)$ preserves the operations of I and $I/(k)$. The mapping α is an example of a *homomorphism*. Generally, if $\{S; +, \cdot, \dots\}$ and $\{T; +, \cdot, \dots\}$ are algebraic systems with corresponding operations, and if α is a mapping of S onto T, then α is a *homomorphism* of the first algebraic system onto the second provided that corresponding operations are preserved by α. If the mapping α is also a 1–1 mapping of S onto T, then α is an *isomorphism*.

Once we have established that α is a homomorphism of I onto $I/(k)$, it is an easy matter to show that most of the properties of an integral domain hold for $I/(k)$. Thus the associative, commutative, and distributive laws, 3-1, (i) to (iii), hold in $I/(k)$ simply because they hold in I. For example, $a \cdot b = b \cdot a$ for each $a,b \in I$. Therefore, since $(a \cdot b)\alpha = (a\alpha) \cdot (b\alpha)$, and so on, by 3-13, we have

$$(a\alpha) \cdot (b\alpha) = (b\alpha) \cdot (a\alpha)$$

for each $a\alpha, b\alpha \in I/(k)$. This proves the commutative law of multiplication for $I/(k)$. Since 0 and 1 are the identity elements of I relative to $+$ and $\cdot$, 0α and 1α are the identity elements of $I/(k)$ relative to $+$ and $\cdot$. Also, it is easily seen that $-(a\alpha)$ is the additive inverse of $a\alpha$ in $I/(k)$. The only one of the six defining properties of an integral domain not established for $I/(k)$ is the cancellation law, 3-1, (vi). Examples to be given below will show that this cancellation law holds in $I/(k)$ for some values of k, and does not hold for others. It is the conditional nature of 3-1, (vi), (that is, if something holds, then something else holds) that makes its validity in $I/(k)$ questionable.

Since $I/(k)$ has a finite number of elements, it is possible to write down explicitly (if k is not too large!) the effects of the operations $+$ and $\cdot$ on $I/(k)$. These will take the form of tables, as illustrated below.

For convenience, we shall leave off the brackets from the elements in the tables. Thus, in place of [0] we shall use 0; in place of [1] we shall use 1; and so on. The elements of $I/(k)$ are $0, 1, 2, \ldots, k-1$ under this convention.

$$I/(3)$$

$+$	0	1	2
0	0	1	2
1	1	2	0
2	2	0	1

$\cdot$	0	1	2
0	0	0	0
1	0	1	2
2	0	2	1

For each $a, b \in I/(3)$, $a+b$ is given by the first table above and $a \cdot b$ is given by the second table. To determine $a+b$ from the table, look for a in the column below the plus sign and b in the row to the right of the plus sign. The intersection of the row to the right of a and of the column below b is $a+b$. The other table is read similarly.

The fact that both $+$ and $\cdot$ are commutative accounts for the symmetry of these tables about the main diagonal line drawn from the upper left to the lower right corner of each table. An inspection of the $\cdot$ table shows that 3-1, (vi), holds for $I/(3)$. For if $c \in I/(3)$, $c \neq 0$, then $a \cdot c = b \cdot c$ only if $a = b$, since the elements of the column under 2 are all distinct (and similarly for 1). If this property is to fail, some column of the multiplication table other than the 0 column must have two elements the same. Thus $I/(3)$ is an example of an integral domain.

Next, let us construct tables for $I/(6)$.

$$I/(6)$$

+	0	1	2	3	4	5		·	0	1	2	3	4	5
0	0	1	2	3	4	5		0	0	0	0	0	0	0
1	1	2	3	4	5	0		1	0	1	2	3	4	5
2	2	3	4	5	0	1		2	0	2	4	0	2	4
3	3	4	5	0	1	2		3	0	3	0	3	0	3
4	4	5	0	1	2	3		4	0	4	2	0	4	2
5	5	0	1	2	3	4		5	0	5	4	3	2	1

We read these tables in the same way as the previous ones. Again, the tables are symmetric about the main diagonal due to the commutative laws. The $+$ table is nice and regular, with every element of $I/(6)$ appearing once in each row and each column of the table. However, the $\cdot$ table is quite irregular; the 3 column, for example, has only the elements 0 and 3 in it. Thus $1 \cdot 3 = 3 \cdot 3$ even though $1 \neq 3$. This proves that the multiplicative cancellation law does not hold for $I/(6)$, and therefore that $I/(6)$ is not an integral domain (an algebraic system such as this is an example of a ring, discussed in Chapter X). The reason the cancellation law fails here is that 6 is not a prime number.

3-14 EXERCISES

1. Construct $+$ and $\cdot$ tables for $I/(2)$; $I/(4)$; $I/(5)$; $I/(7)$. Which are integral domains?

2. Show that $I/(2)$ is isomorphic to the algebraic system of 3-5, Exercise 8.

3. Prove that $I/(k)$ is an integral domain if and only if k is a prime number. (Hint: use 3-5, Exercise 7.)

4. Let $<$ be an order relation on $I/(k)$ such that (i) $<$ is transitive, and (ii) the trichotomy law holds relative to $<$. (For example, we might have $[n] < [n + 1]$ for every $n, 0 \leq n < k - 1$.) Prove that there must exist elements $a, b, c \in I/(k)$ such that

$$a < b, \qquad a + c > b + c.$$

5. Under the same assumptions as in Exercise 4, prove that for any

$k > 2$, there must exist elements $a,b,c \in I/(k)$ such that

$$a < b, \qquad a \cdot c > b \cdot c.$$

(Hint: $[k - 1]^2 = [1]$.)

10. The characteristic

In I, the set of integers, the concepts of multiplication and multiple coincide. That is, if a is any integer and n is a positive integer, na (the sum of n a's) and $n \cdot a$ are equal. Consequently, since I is an integral domain, $na = 0$ if and only if $a = 0$. We shall see that this need not be the case in other integral domains.

Let S be an integral domain and a be any nonzero element of S. It might happen that some multiple of a, say na equals 0, n a positive integer. For example, in $I/(3)$ one easily verifies that $3[1] = [1] + [1] + [1] = [0]$ and $3[2] = [2] + [2] + [2] = [0]$. If for the nonzero element a of S there is a positive integer n such that $na = 0$, then, since the positive integers are well-ordered, there exists a least positive integer k such that $ka = 0$. Certainly $k > 1$, for $1a = a \neq 0$ by assumption.

3-15 Definition. Let S be an integral domain. The *characteristic* of the element a of S is the least positive integer k, if such exists, for which

$$ka = 0.$$

If $ka \neq 0$ for each positive integer k, the *characteristic* of a is defined to be 0. Similarly, the *characteristic* of S itself is the least positive integer k, if such exists, for which $ka = 0$ for all $a \in S$. The characteristic of S is 0 if no such k exists.

The characteristic of the element 0 in S is 1. If $a \in I$, $a \neq 0$, then $na \neq 0$ for each positive integer n. Thus a has characteristic 0, and I also has characteristic 0. Both [1] and [2] in $I/(3)$ have characteristic 3. Thus $I/(3)$ itself has characteristic 3. The nonzero elements of $I/(6)$ have the following characteristics (the concept of characteristic applies to an algebraic system satisfying 3-1, (i) to (v), such as $I/(6)$, as well as to an integral domain): [1] has characteristic 6; [2] has characteristic 3; [3] has characteristic 2; [4] has characteristic 3; [5] has characteristic 6. Thus the characteristic of $I/(6)$ is 6.

Analogous to the concept of characteristic relative to multiples is that of order relative to powers. The *order* of the element $a \in S$ is the least positive integer k, if such exists, for which

$$a^k = 1.$$

If no such k exists, we shall say that a has no order. For example, the order of $[2] \in I/(3)$ is two, since $[2]^2 = [1]$. Trivially, $[1]$ has order 1.

3-16 THEOREM. If some nonzero element of the integral domain S has characteristic k different from 0, then k is a prime number and all the nonzero elements of S have characteristic k.

Let a be a nonzero element of S having characteristic $k \neq 0$. To prove that k is a prime number, suppose that $k = m \cdot n$, where m and n are positive integers with $m > 1$. Then $n < k$ and $m \leq k$. Now, by 3-8, Exercise 1, (ii),

$$(ma) \cdot (na) = (m \cdot n)a^2 = ka^2 = (ka) \cdot a,$$

and since $ka = 0$ we conclude that $(ma) \cdot (na) = 0$. By 3-4 we must have $ma = 0$ or $na = 0$. However, $na \neq 0$ because $n < k$ and k is the characteristic of a. Thus $ma = 0$, and since $m \leq k$, the characteristic of a, necessarily $m = k$. This proves that k has no factorization other than $k \cdot 1$, and hence that k is a prime number.

If b is any nonzero element of S, then

$$(kb) \cdot a = b \cdot (ka) = 0,$$

and since $a \neq 0$, necessarily $kb = 0$. To prove that k is the characteristic of b, we must prove that $nb = 0$, $1 < n \leq k$, implies that $n = k$. However, if $nb = 0$, then

$$(na) \cdot b = a \cdot (nb) = 0,$$

and therefore $na = 0$. Since k is the characteristic of a, $n = k$. This completes the proof of 3-16.

In view of this theorem, either all the nonzero elements of an integral domain S have prime characteristic p, or all the nonzero elements of S have characteristic 0. In the former case, S itself is of characteristic p, while in the latter case S is of characteristic 0.

Let S be an integral domain and T be a subset of S. If T is closed relative to the operations of S, if 0 and 1 are in T, and if for each $a \in T$, $-a \in T$ also, then T itself is an integral domain: T is called a *subdomain* of S. Many examples of subdomains come to our mind. Thus I is a subdomain of R, while R is a subdomain of R^*. The set T

of all rational numbers of the form m/n, $m,n \in I$ with n an odd integer, is easily verified to be a subdomain of R. I is a *minimal* integral domain in the sense that it has no subdomains.

The set P of all multiples $n1$, $n \in I$, of the multiplicative identity element 1 of the integral domain S is a subdomain of S. Certainly 1 and 0 ($= 01$) are in P, and whenever $m1$ and $n1$ are in P, also $-(m1)$, $m1 + n1$, and $(m1) \cdot (n1)$ are in P, since:

$$-(m1) = (-m)1; \quad m1 + n1 = (m + n)1; \quad (m1) \cdot (n1) = (m \cdot n)1.$$

Any subdomain T of S must contain the identity element 1, and since T is closed relative to $+$, T must contain all multiples of 1 also. Thus $P \subset T$, and P is the *least* subdomain of S. It is immediate that the mapping θ,

$$\theta: \quad n\theta = n1, \qquad n \in I,$$

is a homomorphism of I onto P.

In case S has characteristic 0, θ is a 1–1 mapping of I onto P; for if $n1 = m1$, $n \geq m$, then $(n - m)1 = 0$ and $n - m = 0$ since 1 has characteristic 0; thus $n = m$ and the mapping is 1–1. It follows that I is isomorphic to P, and identifying I with P, that I is a subdomain of S. Having identified I with P, na and $n \cdot a$ are identical.

If S has characteristic a positive prime p, then P is isomorphic to $I/(p)$. In order to prove this, we first prove that if $k1 = 0$, $k \neq 0$, then $p \mid k$ (that is, $k = p \cdot q$, $q \in I$). The highest common factor, (k,p), of k and p, is either 1 or p. It can be written in the form (2-32)

$$(k,p) = k \cdot u + p \cdot v.$$

Now

$$(k,p)1 = (k \cdot u)1 + (p \cdot v)1 = u(k1) + v(p1) = 0,$$

and since $1 \neq 0$, necessarily $(k,p) = p$; thus $p \mid k$. Next, let us show that the mapping α,

$$\alpha: \quad [n]\alpha = n1, \quad n \in I, \quad [n] \in I/(p),$$

is well-defined and 1–1. To prove that α is well-defined, we must show that if $[m] = [n]$ then $m1 = n1$. However, $[m] = [n]$ implies that $n - m = p \cdot q$ for some $q \in I$, and therefore that $(n - m)1 = (p \cdot q)1 = q(p1) = 0$; thus $n1 = m1$. To prove that α is 1–1, we need to show that if $m1 = n1$, then $[m] = [n]$. Since $m1 = n1$ implies that $(m - n)1 = 0$, we know from previous remarks that $m - n = p \cdot q$ for some $q \in I$. But then $[m] = [n]$ as desired. From 3-11 we deduce that the operations are preserved under this correspondence. For example, $[m] + [n] = [m + n]$, $[m + n]\alpha = (m + n)1$, and $(m + n)1 = m1 + n1$. Thus $([m] + [n])\alpha = m1 + n1$, and we conclude that the operation $+$ is preserved under the mapping α of $I/(p)$ onto P. Similar arguments hold for the other operation. This completes the proof that α is an isomorphism of $I/(p)$ onto P. Upon identifying P and $I/(p)$, we conclude that $I/(p)$ is a subdomain of each integral domain of characteristic p. Then na and $[n] \cdot a$ are identical in such a domain. We have proved the following result.

3-17 Theorem. If S is an integral domain, the set P of all multiples of the element 1 of S is the least subdomain of S. If S has characteristic 0, P is (isomorphic to) the system of integers, while P is (isomorphic to) the system of integers modulo p in case S has characteristic p.

3-18 Exercises

1. Find the characteristic and order (if it exists) of each element of: $I/(4)$; $I/(5)$; $I/(6)$; $I/(12)$.

2. If $a \in I/(8)$, show that either $a^2 = [1]$ or $a^3 = [0]$. For what values of k is it true that some power of each element of $I/(k)$ is either $[0]$ or $[1]$?

3. If the element $a(\neq 1)$ of $I/(k)$ has characteristic k, prove that $a \cdot b \neq [0]$ for all nonzero b of $I/(k)$. Then prove that a has order. (Hint: can the elements a, a^2, a^3, . . ., a^k all be different?)

4. Let $S = \{[0], [3]\}$ and $T = \{[0], [2], [4]\}$ be subsets of $I/(6)$. Prove that S and T are integral domains (using the operations of $I/(6)$, naturally). Show that S is isomorphic to $I/(2)$ and T is isomorphic to $I/(3)$.

5. If S and T are defined as in Exercise 4, prove that every element a of $I/(6)$ can be expressed uniquely in the form

$$a = s + t, \qquad s \in S, \qquad t \in T.$$

Prove that if $a,b \in I/(6)$ with $a = s_1 + t_1$ and $b = s_2 + t_2$, where $s_1, s_2 \in S$ and $t_1, t_2 \in T$, then

$$a + b = (s_1 + s_2) + (t_1 + t_2), \qquad a \cdot b = s_1 \cdot s_2 + t_1 \cdot t_2.$$

11. Fields

The final type of an algebraic system to be discussed in this chapter is the field. The integral domain was modelled after the system of integers; the prototype of a field is the rational number system, as we see by the following definition.

3-19 DEFINITION. An algebraic system $\{F; +, \cdot\}$ composed of a set F and two operations on F is called a *field* provided that:

(i) $\{F; +, \cdot\}$ is an integral domain; and

(ii) each nonzero $a \in F$ has an *inverse* $a^{-1} \in F$ relative to the operation $\cdot$;

$$a \cdot a^{-1} = a^{-1} \cdot a = 1.$$

The system of rational numbers and that of real numbers are examples of fields. From the multiplication table of $I/(3)$ we see that $[1] \cdot [1] = [1]$ and $[2] \cdot [2] = [1]$, that is, that $[1]^{-1} = [1]$ and $[2]^{-1} = [2]$. Thus $I/(3)$ also is an example of a field. Since a field is an integral domain, it follows from 3-16 that the characteristic of a field is either 0 or a prime number p.

The following theorem tells us precisely which ones of the algebraic systems $I/(k)$ are fields.

3-20 THEOREM. The algebraic system $I/(k)$ is a field if and only if k is a prime number.

First we will prove that if k is not a prime then $I/(k)$ is not a field. To this end, let $k = m \cdot n$ with both m and n positive integers less than k. Since $[k] = [0]$, $[m] \cdot [n] = [0]$ although both $[m]$, $[n] \neq [0]$. That $I/(k)$ is not an integral domain, and hence not a field, follows from 3-4.

Conversely, let us prove that if k is a prime then $I/(k)$ is a field. The first five parts of 3-1 are already known to be satisfied by $I/(k)$. On the assumption that k is a prime, let us prove that the cancellation law for multiplication holds in $I/(k)$, and hence that $I/(k)$ is an integral domain. If $[a] \cdot [c] = [b] \cdot [c]$ for some $[a], [b], [c] \in I/(k)$ with $[c] \neq [0]$ (so that $k \nmid c$), then $a \cdot c \equiv_k b \cdot c$ and therefore $k \mid (a \cdot c - b \cdot c)$. Now k is a prime, $k \mid (a - b) \cdot c$, and $k \nmid c$. Hence, by 2-33, $k \mid (a - b)$. It follows that $[a] = [b]$, that the cancellation law holds, and hence that $I/(k)$ is an integral domain. It remains to prove (ii) of 3-19 for $I/(k)$. Select any nonzero element $[c]$ of $I/(k)$. The k elements

$$[0] \cdot [c], \quad [1] \cdot [c], \quad [2] \cdot [c], \quad \cdots, \quad [k-1] \cdot [c]$$

are **all** distinct; for if $[i] \cdot [c] = [j] \cdot [c]$, then by the cancellation law, $[i] = [j]$ and $i = j$ (since i and j both are less than k). But $I/(k)$ has only k elements, so that the above-displayed elements must be all the elements of $I/(k)$. Therefore $[i] \cdot [c] = [1]$ for some i, and we see that

3-19, (ii), is satisfied with $[i] = [c]^{-1}$. Thus $I/(k)$ is a field, and the proof of 3-20 is completed.

As a consequence of this theorem, we know that the systems $I/(2)$, $I/(3)$, $I/(5)$, $I/(7)$, $I/(11)$, and so on, are fields, while the systems $I/(4)$, $I/(6)$, $I/(8)$, and so on, are not even integral domains.

If F is a field and S is a subset of F, S is a *subfield* of F provided that S is closed relative to the operations of F, that $0,1 \in S$, and that if $a \in S, a \neq 0$, then also $-a, a^{-1} \in S$. Thus S is a subfield of F if S is a field with the same operations (and therefore the same identity elements) as F. The rational number field, for example, is a subfield of the real number field.

Consider a field F of characteristic 0. Since F is also an integral domain, 3-17 may be applied to show that I, the set of integers, is the least subdomain of F. Now F is a field, and therefore every element $n \in I$, $n \neq 0$, must have an inverse $n^{-1} \in F$. It follows that F contains all "rational numbers" $m \cdot n^{-1}$; thus it is evident that R is a subfield of F. Since I is the least subdomain of F, R is the least subfield of F. This least subfield is called the *prime subfield* of F.

On the other hand, if F is a field of characteristic p, $I/(p)$ is the least subdomain of F by 3-17. In view of 3-20, $I/(p)$ is also the least subfield of F. Again, $I/(p)$ is called the *prime subfield* of F.

We have proved the following theorem.

3-21 THEOREM. Contained in any field F is a least subfield P called the prime subfield of F. If F has characteristic 0, P is the rational field R, while if F has characteristic p, P is the field $I/(p)$ of integers modulo p.

3-22 EXERCISES

1. Which of the following are subfields of $R^{\#}$? The set of all real numbers of the form:

    (i) $a + b \cdot \sqrt{2}$, $a,b \in R$;

    (ii) $a + b \cdot \sqrt[3]{2}$, $a,b \in R$;

    (iii) $a - b \cdot \sqrt{5}$, $a,b \in R$;

    (iv) $a + b \cdot \sqrt{2} + c \cdot \sqrt{3} + d \cdot \sqrt{6}$, $a,b,c,d \in R$.

2. Prove that the only field with p elements, p a prime, is $I/(p)$.

3. Prove that any integral domain with only a finite number of elements is a field. (Hint: look at the proof of 3-20.)

4. If F is a field and $a \in F$, $a \neq 0$, define $a^0 = 1$, and $a^{-n} = (a^{-1})^n$ for each positive integer n. Show that the power formulas contained

in 3-7 hold for any integers m and n and any nonzero elements $a, b \in F$.

5. Prove that an algebraic system satisfying 3-1, (i) to (v), and 3-19, (ii), is a field.

6. Construct addition and multiplication tables for a field with four elements. (Hint: its characteristic is 2.)

7. If p is a prime number, prove that in $I/(p)$, $[(p - 2)!] = [1]$. (This is known as Wilson's theorem. Hint: the set $\{[2],[3], \ldots,[p - 2]\}$ can be partitioned into two-element subsets of the form $\{a, a^{-1}\}$.)

8. For each $a, b \in I/(p)$, prove that $(a + b)^p = a^p + b^p$. Illustrate this result for $p = 2$, 3, and 5.

12. The quotient field of an integral domain

Just as the system of integers can be extended to the system of rational numbers, so can any integral domain be imbedded in a field of quotients. Since the proofs of the various steps of this imbedding are precisely as given in Section 6, many of the details will be omitted this time.

Let the given integral domain consist of the set S with operations $+$ and $\cdot$. Designate by "T" the set of all pairs a/b of elements of S, the second element b of each pair always being different from 0. Introduce in T the relation $\cap$ defined by: $a/b \cap c/d$ if and only if $a \cdot d = b \cdot c$. The relation $\cap$ is easily shown to be an equivalence relation. As such, $\cap$ partitions T into equivalence sets. As usual, the equivalence sets are labelled by "$[a/b]$," $[a/b] = \{c/d; c/d \in T, c/d \cap a/b\}$. The set of all $[a/b]$ is designated by "F."

The operations $+$ and $\cdot$ are defined on F as follows:

$$[a/b] + [c/d] = [(a \cdot d + b \cdot c)/b \cdot d],$$

$$[a/b] \cdot [c/d] = [a \cdot c/b \cdot d].$$

The associative, commutative, and distributive laws for these operations in F follow easily because of the corresponding laws in S. The element $[0/1]$ is the additive identity while $[1/1]$ is the multiplicative identity in F. The element $-[a/b]$ is the additive inverse of $[a/b]$, while the element $[b/a]$ is the multiplicative inverse of $[a/b]$ in case $a \neq 0$. Thus F is a field.

The field F so derived from the integral domain S is the *quotient field* of S. If we identify the element $[a/1]$ of F with the element $a \in S$, we see that S is a subdomain of F. Since $[a/b] = [a/1] \cdot [b/1]^{-1}$, it follows that every element of F has the form $a \cdot b^{-1}$, a and b in the subdomain S of F.

CHAPTER IV

Polynomial Domains

Expressions of the form $3x^2 + 2x - 1$, $x^4 - 1$, $x^3 - 5x^2 + 4x - 2$, and so on, play a prominent part in elementary mathematics. Such expressions are called "polynomials in x." The "x" in these polynomials is usually understood to be a real variable so that $3x^2 + 2x - 1$, $x^4 - 1$, and so on, are functions of x ranging over the real numbers. A different viewpoint of polynomials will be taken in this chapter; a viewpoint, however, that eventually will be reconciled with that of elementary mathematics.

13. The polynomial domain of an integral domain

Let us begin with a given integral domain S (having the usual operations $+$ and $\cdot$, and identity elements 0 and 1), and a given symbol "x." When we say that "x" is a symbol, we imply that no property of x other than that of being a letter of the alphabet will be used. The letter "x" does not designate an element of S, for example.

We now compose "words" of the form

$$ax^n,$$

where $a \in S$ and n is a non-negative integer. Such a word will be called a *monomial*. Remember, "ax^n" does not mean "a times x to the nth power," since such operations have not been defined. In case S is the system of integers I, $3x^5$, $(-2)x^7$, $9x^0$, $153x^{17}$, and $(-16)x^1$ are examples of monomials. In the monomial ax^n, a is called the *coefficient* and n is called the *degree* of the monomial.

Having settled on the words, we define the "sentences" of our new language as those combinations of the words of the following type:

$$a_0x^0 + a_1x^1 + a_2x^2 + \ldots + a_nx^n.$$

77

This expression is only formally a sum of monomials, since addition of monomials has not been defined. We could just as well write this sentence in the form

$$a_0x^0, \ a_1x^1, \ a_2x^2, \ \ldots, \ a_nx^n.$$

However, the form chosen fits in with our plan eventually to replace x by an element of S and to add the resulting elements of S.

4-1 DEFINITION. An expression of the form

$$a_0x^0 + a_1x^1 + a_2x^2 + \ldots + a_nx^n,$$

where $a_0, a_1, a_2, \ldots, a_n \in S$, is called a *polynomial* in x over S. The set of all polynomials in x over S is designated by

$$S[x].$$

Note that the successive degrees of the monomials, or *terms*, of the polynomial displayed in 4-1 are 0, 1, 2, ..., n. Evidently this polynomial has $n + 1$ terms where n is an integer greater than or equal to zero. Examples of polynomials in $I[x]$ are: $2x^0 + (-1)x^1$; $3x^0 + 4x^1 + (-7)x^2$; $0x^0 + 0x^1 + (-5)x^2 + 0x^3$; $(-12)x^0 + 2x^1 + (-6)x^2 + 0x^3 + (-1)x^4$; $3x^0$; $0x^0$.

It will be convenient to designate elements of $S[x]$ by "$a(x)$," "$b(x)$," "$c(x)$," and so on, with the understanding that the coefficients of the terms of $a(x)$ will be $a_0, a_1, \ldots, a_n$, and so on, as indicated below:

$$a(x) = a_0x^0 + a_1x^1 + \ldots + a_nx^n,$$

4-2
$$b(x) = b_0x^0 + b_1x^1 + \ldots + b_mx^m,$$

$$c(x) = c_0x^0 + c_1x^1 + \ldots + c_rx^r.$$

4-3 DEFINITION. The *degree* of the polynomial $a(x)$, abbreviated deg $a(x)$, is the largest integer k, if such exists, such that $a_k \neq 0$. If all the terms of $a(x)$ have zero coefficients, $a(x)$ is said to have *no degree*.

For the elements of $I[x]$ listed above, we have: deg $(2x^0 + (-1)x^1)$ = 1; deg $(3x^0 + 4x^1 + (-7)x^2)$ = 2; deg $(0x^0 + 0x^1 + (-5)x^2 + 0x^3)$ = 2; deg $(0x^0)$ does not exist (that is, $0x^0$ has no degree); deg $(3x^0)$ = 0.

It is convenient to think of the polynomials $a(x)$ and $b(x)$ (of the form 4-2) as being identical if they have the same degree k and $a_i = b_i$

for each i, $0 \leq i \leq k$, or if both $a(x)$ and $b(x)$ have no degree*. In $I[x]$, for example,

$$3x^0 + (-2)x^1 + 1x^2 = 3x^0 + (-2)x^1 + 1x^2 + 0x^3,$$

$$0x^0 + 1x^1 + 0x^2 = 0x^0 + 1x^1 + 0x^2 + 0x^3 + 0x^4,$$

$$0x^0 = 0x^0 + 0x^1.$$

With this convention, a polynomial $a(x)$ of degree k might as well be written in the form

$$a(x) = a_0 x^0 + a_1 x^1 + \ldots + a_k x^k,$$

where the last coefficient $a_k \neq 0$. Then $0x^0$ is essentially the only polynomial with no degree.

4-4 DEFINITION. The operations $+$ and $\cdot$ are defined on $S[x]$ as follows: for each $a(x), b(x) \in S[x]$ (see 4-2),

$$a(x) + b(x) = (a_0 + b_0)x^0 + (a_1 + b_1)x^1 + \ldots + (a_k + b_k)x^k,$$

$$a(x) \cdot b(x) = (a_0 \cdot b_0)x^0 + (a_0 \cdot b_1 + a_1 \cdot b_0)x^1$$
$$+ (a_0 \cdot b_2 + a_1 \cdot b_1 + a_2 \cdot b_0)x^2 + \ldots + (a_n \cdot b_m)x^{n+m},$$

where k is the larger of m and n, and a_i or b_j is taken to be 0 whenever $i > n$ or $j > m$.

Thus, for example, if $a(x), b(x) \in I[x]$ are given by

$$a(x) = 3x^0 + 2x^1, \qquad b(x) = 0x^0 + (-2)x^1 + 4x^2,$$

then

$$a(x) + b(x) = (3 + 0)x^0 + (2 - 2)x^1 + (0 + 4)x^2,$$
$$= 3x^0 + 0x^1 + 4x^2.$$

$$a(x) \cdot b(x) = (3 \cdot 0)x^0 + (3 \cdot -2 + 2 \cdot 0)x^1 + (3 \cdot 4 + 2 \cdot -2)x^2 + (2 \cdot 4)x^3,$$
$$= 0x^0 + (-6)x^1 + 8x^2 + 8x^3.$$

In the product $a(x) \cdot b(x)$, the coefficient of the term containing x^k is

$$a_0 \cdot b_k + a_1 \cdot b_{k-1} + a_2 \cdot b_{k-2} + \ldots + a_k \cdot b_0.$$

*More precisely, define the relation $\equiv$ on $S[x]$ by: $a(x) \equiv b(x)$ if $\deg a(x) = \deg b(x)$ and $a_i = b_i$ for all $i \leq \deg a(x)$. The relation $\equiv$ is easily seen to be an equivalence relation, and as such it partitions $S[x]$ into equivalence sets. Then, in what is to follow, we will deal with these equivalence sets rather than with the elements of $S[x]$ themselves.

Note that this expression is the sum of all products $a_i \cdot b_j$ for which $i + j = k$, again with the convention that a_i or $b_j = 0$ if $i > n$ or $j > m$.

It is evident that deg $(a(x) + b(x))$ does not exceed the larger of deg $a(x)$ and deg $b(x)$. If deg $a(x) = n$ and deg $b(x) = m$, then deg $a(x) \cdot b(x) = m + n$ since $a_n \neq 0$, $b_m \neq 0$ imply $a_n \cdot b_m \neq 0$. These results are contained in the following theorem.

4-5 THEOREM. If $a(x), b(x) \in S[x]$, with deg $a(x) \leq$ deg $b(x)$, then

$$\text{deg } (a(x) + b(x)) \leq \text{deg } b(x) \quad \text{if} \quad a(x) + b(x) \neq 0x^0,$$

$$\text{deg } a(x) \cdot b(x) = \text{deg } a(x) + \text{deg } b(x).$$

If $a(x)$ has no degree, then $a(x) \cdot b(x)$ has no degree. If $a(x)$ and $b(x)$ both have no degree, then $a(x) + b(x)$ has no degree.

4-6 EXERCISES

1. Let $a(x), b(x), c(x) \in I[x]$ be as follows: $a(x) = 3x^0 + 2x^1$; $b(x) = 0x^0 + 0x^1 + (-2)x^2$; $c(x) = 1x^0 + 4x^1 + 2x^2$. Find $a(x) + b(x)$; $b(x) + c(x)$; $a(x) \cdot b(x)$; $b(x) \cdot c(x)$; $(a(x) \cdot b(x)) \cdot c(x)$; $a(x) \cdot (b(x) \cdot c(x))$.

2. Illustrate 4-5 using the elements of Example 1.

3. Prove the associative and commutative laws of addition in $S[x]$.

4. Prove that $0x^0$ and $1x^0$ are the identity elements of $S[x]$ relative to $+$ and $\cdot$ respectively.

Let us now prove that $\{S[x]; +, \cdot\}$ is an integral domain. The proofs of the associative and commutative laws of addition were left as exercises for the reader, as were the proofs that $0x^0$ and $1x^0$ are the identity elements relative to $+$ and $\cdot$ respectively (4-6). For each $a(x) \in S[x]$, say

$$a(x) = a_0 x^0 + a_1 x^1 + \ldots + a_n x^n,$$

let us define

$$-a(x) = (-a_0)x^0 + (-a_1)x^1 + \ldots + (-a_n)x^n.$$

Clearly

$$a(x) + (-a(x)) = 0x^0 + 0x^1 + \ldots + 0x^n = 0x^0,$$

and hence $-a(x)$ is the additive inverse of $a(x)$.

In order to prove the associative law of multiplication, let

$a(x), b(x), c(x) \in S[x]$ have the form 4-2. Then

$$a(x) \cdot b(x) = d_0 x^0 + d_1 x^1 + \ldots + d_{n+m} x^{n+m},$$

where for each i, $0 \leq i \leq n + m$,

$$d_i = a_0 \cdot b_i + a_1 \cdot b_{i-1} + a_2 \cdot b_{i-2} + \ldots + a_i \cdot b_0.$$

The coefficient of x^k in $(a(x) \cdot b(x)) \cdot c(x)$ is

$$d_0 \cdot c_k + d_1 \cdot c_{k-1} + d_2 \cdot c_{k-2} + \ldots + d_k \cdot c_0,$$

or

$$(a_0 \cdot b_0) \cdot c_k + (a_0 \cdot b_1 + a_1 \cdot b_0) \cdot c_{k-1} + (a_0 \cdot b_2 + a_1 \cdot b_1 + a_2 \cdot b_0) \cdot c_{k-2}$$

$$+ \ldots + (a_0 \cdot b_k + a_1 \cdot b_{k-1} + a_2 \cdot b_{k-2} + \ldots + a_k \cdot b_0) \cdot c_0.$$

Using 3-6, this may be written in the form

$$a_0 \cdot (b_0 \cdot c_k + b_1 \cdot c_{k-1} + b_2 \cdot c_{k-2} + \ldots + b_k \cdot c_0)$$

$$+ a_1 \cdot (b_0 \cdot c_{k-1} + b_1 \cdot c_{k-2} + \ldots + b_{k-1} \cdot c_0) \tag{1}$$

$$+ a_2 \cdot (b_0 \cdot c_{k-2} + \ldots + b_{k-2} \cdot c_0) + \ldots + a_k \cdot (b_0 \cdot c_0).$$

On the other hand, if

$$b(x) \cdot c(x) = e_0 x^0 + e_1 x^1 + \ldots + e_{m+r} x^{m+r},$$

then for each i, $0 \leq i \leq m + r$,

$$e_i = b_0 \cdot c_i + b_1 \cdot c_{i-1} + b_2 \cdot c_{i-2} + \ldots + b_i \cdot c_0.$$

The coefficient of x^k in $a(x) \cdot (b(x) \cdot c(x))$ is

$$a_0 \cdot e_k + a_1 \cdot e_{k-1} + a_2 \cdot e_{k-2} + \ldots + a_k \cdot e_0. \tag{2}$$

On comparison, (1) and (2) are seen to be the same. We conclude that the operation $\cdot$ is associative on $S[x]$.

The proof that $\cdot$ is commutative is simple, and therefore is omitted. We omit the proof of the distributive law for the same reason.

If $a(x)$ and $b(x)$ are both different from zero (that is, $0x^0$), then both have degree, and $a(x) \cdot b(x)$ also has degree in view of 4-5. Thus $a(x) \cdot b(x)$ is different from zero, and property 3-4 holds for $S[x]$. This result implies that the multiplicative cancellation law holds in $S[x]$ (by 3-5, Exercise 7), and hence completes the proof of the following theorem.

4-7 Theorem. If S is an integral domain, then $S[x]$ with operations defined in 4-4 is also an integral domain.

We see from this theorem how to construct new integral domains. Thus $I[x]$, $R[x]$, $R^{\#}[x]$, $I/(p)[x]$ (p prime) all are integral domains. If "y" designates a symbol different from "x," then $S[y]$ also is an integral domain, where $S = I[x]$; $S[y]$ is the set of all polynomials in x and y over the domain of integers.

The subset T of $S[x]$ consisting of all polynomials of the form cx^0 is a subdomain of $S[x]$. For if $ax^0, bx^0 \in T$, then

4-8 $ax^0 + bx^0 = (a + b)x^0; \qquad ax^0 \cdot bx^0 = (a \cdot b)x^0.$

Consequently, we conclude that T is closed relative to the operations of $S[x]$. Also, the identity elements $0x^0$ and $1x^0$ of $S[x]$ are in T, and for each $ax^0 \in T$, $-(ax^0) = (-a)x^0$ is in T. Thus T itself is an integral domain. The mapping α,

$$\alpha: \quad a\alpha = ax^0, \qquad a \in S,$$

of S onto T is obviously a 1–1 mapping. Actually, in view of 4-8, α is an isomorphism of S onto T. If we identify the isomorphic domains S and T, replacing each element ax^0 of $S[x]$ by the element a of S, then S is a subdomain of $S[x]$ and the elements of $S[x]$ take on the form

$$a_0 + a_1x^1 + a_2x^2 + \ldots + a_nx^n.$$

The identity elements of $S[x]$ are just 0 and 1, the identity elements of S.

Further conventions to be employed henceforth will be to replace x^1 by x, to replace $1x^k$ by x^k, to omit terms with zero coefficients, and to replace $(-a)x^k$ by $-ax^k$. Thus, for example, the polynomial

$$3x^0 + (-2)x^1 + (-4)x^2 + 0x^3 + 1x^4$$

of $I[x]$ will be written in the form

$$3 - 2x - 4x^2 + x^4.$$

With these conventions, not only is $S \subset S[x]$, but also $x \in S[x]$; and ax^k actually may be interpreted as a times x to the kth power!

If the polynomial $a(x)$ is of degree k and the coefficient of x^k is 1, then $a(x)$ is called a *monic* polynomial. For example, $7 - 2x + x^2$, $3 + 7x^2 + x^3$, 1, $5 + x$, $7 + x^5$ are monic polynomials in $I[x]$.

It is possible to order the elements of $S[x]$ according to their degrees, although the resulting ordering will not have many of the properties of "less than" in I.

4-9 DEFINITION. If S is an integral domain, the relation "less than" ($<$) is defined on $S[x]$ as follows: for each $a(x)$, $b(x) \in S[x]$, $a(x) < b(x)$ if and only if either (i) deg $a(x) <$ deg $b(x)$ or (ii) $a(x) = 0$ and $b(x) \neq 0$.

In $I[x]$, for example, we have $2 - x^2 < x^3$, $3 + x < 1 - x - x^2$, $0 < -3$, $1 - 12x^4 < x^3 + 3x^5$, $0 < 1 + x$, and so on.

It is apparent that $<$ is transitive, and is neither reflexive nor symmetric. Equally apparent is the fact that the trichotomy law does not hold for this relation. Thus if two distinct polynomials $a(x)$ and $b(x)$ have the same degree, no one of the following is true: $a(x) = b(x)$; $a(x) < b(x)$; $a(x) > b(x)$. The element 0 is the least element of $S[x]$ relative to this ordering by 4-9, (ii).

4-10 EXERCISES

1. Prove the commutative law of multiplication for $S[x]$.
2. Prove the distributive law for $S[x]$.
3. How many elements of $I/(2)[x]$ have degree smaller than the positive integer n? List all the elements of this integral domain of degree less than 4.
4. What are the subdomains of $I[x]$? Of $I/(2)[x]$?
5. Introduce the relation $\curvearrowright$ on $S[x]$ as follows: $a(x) \curvearrowright b(x)$ if and only if $a(x) \not< b(x)$ and $b(x) \not< a(x)$. Prove that $\curvearrowright$ is an equivalence relation. What essentially is the partition of $S[x]$ induced by this relation?
6. If $a(x) < b(x)$ and $c(x) < d(x)$ in $S[x]$, is it necessarily true that $a(x) + c(x) < b(x) + d(x)$? That $a(x) \cdot c(x) < b(x) \cdot d(x)$?

An interesting feature of the integral domain $S[x]$ is that it has many of the factorization properties of the domain of integers. As was the case in the domain of integers (2-29), we start off the discussion of factorization properties of $S[x]$ with the "division process."

4-11 THEOREM. Let S be an integral domain, and $a(x), b(x) \in S[x]$ with $b(x)$ monic. Then there exist unique elements $q(x), r(x) \in S[x]$ such that

$$a(x) = b(x) \cdot q(x) + r(x), \qquad 0 \leq r(x) < b(x).$$

The element $q(x)$ is called the *quotient* and the element $r(x)$ is called the *remainder* of $a(x)$ divided by $b(x)$.

We shall first prove the existence of $q(x)$ and $r(x)$, and later prove their uniqueness. If $a(x) < b(x)$, then

$$a(x) = b(x) \cdot 0 + a(x), \qquad 0 \leq a(x) < b(x),$$

and the theorem is proved. If $b(x) = 1$, then

$$a(x) = b(x) \cdot a(x) + 0,$$

and, again, the theorem is proved. Now let us assume that either $b(x) < a(x)$ or deg $a(x) = $ deg $b(x)$, and that deg $b(x) \geq 1$. If

$$a(x) = a_0 + a_1 x + \ldots + a_{n-1} x^{n-1} + a_n x^n, \qquad a_n \neq 0,$$

$$b(x) = b_0 + b_1 x + \ldots + b_{m-1} x^{m-1} + x^m,$$

then $n \geq m \geq 1$ by these assumptions.

The proof is by mathematical induction on the degree of $a(x)$. Think of $b(x)$ as a fixed monic polynomial of degree $m \geq 1$. The theorem is true for each polynomial $a(x)$ of degree less than m by the preceding remarks. Assume that the theorem is true for each polynomial $a(x)$ of degree $k < n$. From this assumption, we shall prove that the theorem is true for each polynomial of degree n. That the theorem is valid for each $a(x) \in S[x]$ will then follow by mathematical induction (2-34, Exercise 3).

If $a(x)$ is a polynomial of degree n and if

$$a'(x) = a(x) - b(x) \cdot a_n x^{n-m}, \tag{1}$$

then $a'(x)$ has degree $k < n$, since the term of highest degree in $b(x) \cdot a_n x^{n-m}$ is $a_n x^n$, and this cancels $a_n x^n$ in $a(x)$. By our induction assumption,

$$a'(x) = b(x) \cdot q'(x) + r(x), \qquad 0 \leq r(x) < b(x), \tag{2}$$

for some $q'(x), r(x) \in S[x]$. Substituting (2) in (1) and rearranging terms, we obtain

$$a(x) = b(x) \cdot (q'(x) + a_n x^{n-m}) + r(x), \qquad 0 \leq r(x) < b(x).$$

Hence the desired result holds for $a(x)$.

To prove the uniqueness of $q(x)$ and $r(x)$ in 4-11, assume that

$$a(x) = b(x) \cdot q(x) + r(x), \qquad 0 \leq r(x) < b(x),$$

$$a(x) = b(x) \cdot q'(x) + r'(x), \qquad 0 \leq r'(x) < b(x).$$

Then, on subtracting these equations, we obtain

$$b(x) \cdot (q'(x) - q(x)) = r(x) - r'(x). \tag{3}$$

If $r(x) - r'(x) \neq 0$, then $b(x) \cdot (q'(x) - q(x)) = c(x) \neq 0$. That this is impossible follows immediately, since deg $c(x) \geq$ deg $b(x)$, while deg $(r(x) - r'(x)) <$ deg $b(x)$. The only way that (3) can be valid is for $r(x) - r'(x) = 0$, in which case $r(x) = r'(x)$ and $q(x) = q'(x)$. This proves the uniqueness of $q(x)$ and $r(x)$, and completes the proof of 4-11.

The proof of this theorem uses in step (1) the "long division" process familiar to all of us. An example in $I[x]$ is now given to illustrate this process. The terms of the polynomials are arranged in descending powers of x to conform with the usual practice of division.

$$
\begin{array}{lrr}
& \underline{2x - 1} & = q(x) \\
b(x) = \qquad x^2 - 3x + 1 \,\big|\, & 2x^3 - 7x^2 + 4x + 1 & = a(x) \\[4pt]
b(x) \cdot 2x = & \underline{2x^3 - 6x^2 + 2x} & \\
a(x) - b(x) \cdot 2x = & -\ x^2 + 2x + 1 & \\[4pt]
b(x) \cdot (-1) = & \underline{-\ x^2 + 3x - 1} & \\
a(x) - b(x) \cdot 2x - b(x) \cdot (-1) = & -x + 2 & = r(x)
\end{array}
$$

Thus

$$2x^3 - 7x^2 + 4x + 1 = (x^2 - 3x + 1) \cdot (2x - 1) + (-x + 2).$$

Each polynomial $a(x) \in S[x]$ defines a mapping (or function) of S into S in the following way. If

$$a(x) = a_0 + a_1 x + a_2 x^2 + \ldots + a_n x^n,$$

then for each $c \in S$, define

$$a(c) = a_0 + a_1 \cdot c + a_2 \cdot c^2 + \ldots + a_n \cdot c^n.$$

Since the terms a_0, $a_1 \cdot c$, $a_2 \cdot c^2$, and so on, are just elements of S, $a(c)$ itself is an element of S. Thus the substitution of c for x yields the mapping α,

$$\alpha: \quad c\alpha = a(c), \qquad c \in S,$$

of S into S. An element c of S is called a *root* of the polynomial $a(x)$ if

$$a(c) = 0.$$

As an example, consider the polynomial

$$a(x) = x^3 + 5x^2 + 2x - 8$$

in $I[x]$. Then $a(0) = -8$, $a(1) = 0$, $a(2) = 24$, $a(-1) = -6$, $a(-2) = 0$, and so on. Note that 1 and -2 are roots of $a(x)$.

The very way that the operations were defined on $S[x]$ insures that the following properties hold for the substitution defined above. For each $a(x), b(x) \in S[x]$, $c \in S$,

4-12

(i) if $d(x) = a(x) + b(x)$, then $d(c) = a(c) + b(c)$,

(ii) if $d(x) = a(x) \cdot b(x)$, then $d(c) = a(c) \cdot b(c)$.

4-13 REMAINDER THEOREM. For each $a(x) \in S[x]$, $c \in S$, the remainder of $a(x)$ divided by $x - c$ is $a(c)$, that is,

$$a(x) = (x - c) \cdot q(x) + a(c).$$

To prove this theorem, we note by 4-11 that there exist unique elements $q(x), r(x) \in S[x]$ such that

$$a(x) = (x - c) \cdot q(x) + r(x), \qquad 0 \leq r(x) < x - c.$$

Clearly either $r(x) = 0$ or $\deg r(x) = 0$: in either case, $r(x) = r_0 \in S$. Using 4-12, $a(c) = (c - c) \cdot q(c) + r_0$, and hence $r_0 = a(c)$ as desired.

The long division process may be considerably shortened in case $a(x)$ is divided by a polynomial of the form $x - c$. This short division process is called *synthetic division*. Two examples of this process are given below.

Let $a(x) = x^3 + 5x^2 + 2x - 8 \in I[x]$. To divide $a(x)$ by $x - 2$, first put down the coefficients of $a(x)$ in order of descending powers of x (putting down 0's for the missing terms), and then place the 2 from $x - 2$ to the right of these. This 2 is the multiplier. First, 2 is multiplied by the leading coefficient 1, and the result, 2, is placed under the second coefficient 5. Then 2 is multiplied by 7, the sum of 5 and 2, and placed under the third coefficient 2, and so on as indicated below.

$$
\begin{array}{rrrr|r}
1 & 5 & 2 & -8 & \underline{2} \\
  & 2 & 14 & 32 & \\
\hline
1 & 7 & 16 & 24 &
\end{array}
$$

Then

$$x^3 + 5x^2 + 2x - 8 = (x - 2) \cdot (x^2 + 7x + 16) + 24.$$

Note that the remainder 24 is just $a(2)$.

Let $a(x) = -4x^5 + 3x^3 + 2x - 4$ be divided by $x + 2$. We proceed as follows.

$$
\begin{array}{rrrrrr|r}
-4 & 0 & 3 & 0 & 2 & -4 & \underline{-2} \\
   & 8 & -16 & 26 & -52 & 100 & \\
\hline
-4 & 8 & -13 & 26 & -50 & 96 &
\end{array}
$$

Hence

$$-4x^5 + 3x^3 + 2x - 4$$
$$= (x + 2) \cdot (-4x^4 + 8x^3 - 13x^2 + 26x - 50) + 96.$$

Note that $a(-2) = 96$.

4-14 EXERCISES

1. Find the quotient and remainder in $I[x]$ of:
   (i) $3x^3 - 2x + 1$ divided by $x^2 - x - 1$;
   (ii) $x^5 - 1$ divided by $x - 1$;
   (iii) $4x^4 + 2x^2 - 2$ divided by $x^3 + 3$;
   (iv) $x^4 + 3x^2 + 4$ divided by $x^2 - x + 2$.

2. If $a(x) = 3x^4 - 2x^3 - 2x + 1 \in I[x]$, find: $a(0)$; $a(1)$; $a(-1)$; $a(2)$; $a(-2)$; $a(3)$.

3. Show how the process of synthetic division follows from that of long division.

4. Prove 4-12.

The concept of "factor" introduced in I carries over to the integral domain $S[x]$. The polynomial $b(x)$ is a *factor* of the polynomial $a(x)$ if

$$a(x) = b(x) \cdot q(x)$$

for some $q(x) \in S[x]$. As in the case of the integers, we write

$$b(x) \mid a(x)$$

in case $b(x)$ is a factor of $a(x)$. The relation "$\mid$" on $S[x]$ is reflexive and transitive, but not symmetric. If $a(x) \neq 0$ and $b(x) \mid a(x)$, then either $b(x) < a(x)$ or $b(x)$ and $a(x)$ have the same degree. In the latter case,

$$a(x) = q_0 \cdot b(x), \qquad q_0 \in S.$$

It is evident that $b(x) \mid a(x)$ if and only if the remainder of $a(x)$ divided by $b(x)$ is 0. For if $b(x) \mid a(x)$, then

$$a(x) = b(x) \cdot q(x) + 0,$$

and since $r(x)$ in 4-11 is unique, $r(x) = 0$ (to be precise, we must assume that $b(x)$ is monic before using 4-11). In particular, we obtain from 4-13 the following theorem.

4-15 FACTOR THEOREM. For each $a(x) \in S[x]$, $c \in S$, $x - c$ is a factor of $a(x)$ if and only if c is a root of $a(x)$.

The factor theorem leads to the following relationship between the number of roots of a polynomial and its degree.

4-16 THEOREM. *If* $a(x) \in S[x]$ *and* deg $a(x) = n$, *then* $a(x)$ *has at most* n *distinct roots in* S.

Certainly if deg $a(x) = 0$, $a(x)$ has no roots. If deg $a(x) = 1$, say $a(x) = a_0 + a_1 x$, $a_1 \neq 0$, then $a(x)$ might have no roots. For example, if $a(x) = 2 + 3x \in I[x]$, then clearly $a(x)$ has no roots in I. If $a(x)$ has a root c, then

$$a(x) = (x - c) \cdot q(x)$$

by the factor theorem. Evidently $q(x) = a_1$. If $d \in S$, $d \neq c$, then

$$a(d) = (d - c) \cdot a_1 \neq 0,$$

that is, d is not a root of $a(x)$. We conclude that a polynomial of degree 1 has at most one root.

The proof of 4-16 is by mathematical induction. Every polynomial of degree 1 has at most 1 root. Assume that every polynomial of degree $n - 1$, $n > 1$, has at most $n - 1$ distinct roots. Let $a(x)$ be any polynomial of degree n. If $a(x)$ has no roots, the theorem is valid for $a(x)$. If c is a root of $a(x)$, then by 4-15,

$$a(x) = (x - c) \cdot q(x).$$

Since deg $q(x) = n - 1$, $q(x)$ has at most $n - 1$ distinct roots. Any root d of $a(x)$ distinct from c is a root of $q(x)$, since

$$a(d) = (d - c) \cdot q(d) = 0$$

implies $q(d) = 0$. Thus $a(x)$ has at most n distinct roots, since its only roots are c and the roots of $q(x)$. This proves 4-16.

If $c_1, c_2, \ldots, c_n$ are any n distinct elements of S, then $a(x)$ defined by

$$a(x) = (x - c_1) \cdot (x - c_2) \cdot \ldots \cdot (x - c_n)$$

is a polynomial of degree n with the n given elements as roots. Naturally, if S is a finite integral domain, say with k elements, then no polynomial of degree $n > k$ can have n distinct roots.

We saw above that every $a(x) \in S[x]$ defines a mapping $\alpha \colon c\alpha = a(c)$ of S into itself. The question to be considered now is whether distinct elements of $S[x]$ necessarily define distinct mappings of S into itself. Thus, if $a(x), b(x) \in S[x]$ with $a(x) \neq b(x)$, are the mappings $\alpha \colon c\alpha = a(c)$ and $\beta \colon c\beta = b(c)$ necessarily distinct, that is, is $a(c) \neq b(c)$ for some $c \in S$?

A simple example shows that the answer is in the negative. Let $a(x), b(x) \in I/(2)[x]$ be defined as follows:

$$a(x) = 1 + x, \qquad b(x) = 1 + x^2.$$

Certainly $a(x) \neq b(x)$. However,

$$a(0) = b(0) = 1, \qquad a(1) = b(1) = 0,$$

and hence the mappings $\alpha: c\alpha = a(c)$ and $\beta: c\beta = b(c)$ are the same.

With a little reflection, we see that if S is any finite integral domain, say with elements $c_1, c_2, \ldots, c_k$, then it is possible to find distinct polynomials defining the same mapping of S into S. We can choose

$$a(x) = (x - c_1) \cdot (x - c_2) \cdot \ldots \cdot (x - c_k),$$

$$b(x) = a(x) \cdot q(x),$$

where $q(x)$ is any element of $S[x]$ different from 1. Then

$$a(c_i) = b(c_i) = 0, \qquad 1 \leq i \leq k,$$

and $\alpha: c\alpha = a(c)$, $\beta: c\beta = b(c)$ are identical mappings of S into S.

In case the integral domain has an infinite number of elements, examples of the type above cannot be found as the following theorem shows.

4-17 THEOREM. If the integral domain S has an infinite number of elements, then distinct elements of $S[x]$ define distinct mappings of S into S.

To prove this theorem, let $a(x), b(x) \in S[x]$ with $a(x) \neq b(x)$. Then if $d(x) = a(x) - b(x)$, necessarily $d(x) \neq 0$ and $\deg d(x) = n \geq 0$. Since $d(x)$ has at most n distinct roots, and S has more than n elements, we can find some $e \in S$ such that $d(e) \neq 0$. But then $a(e) \neq b(e)$ and the mappings of S into S defined by $a(x)$ and $b(x)$ are different. This proves 4-17.

4-18 EXERCISES

1. The following polynomials are in $I[x]$. Find all their roots in I. (i) $x^2 - x - 6$. (ii) $3x - 5$. (iii) $2x^2 + x - 1$. (iv) $x^3 - x^2 - x - 2$. (v) $x^7 + 1$.

2. The following polynomials are in $I/(3)[x]$. Find all their roots in $I/(3)$. (i) $x^2 + x + 1$. (ii) $2x + 2$. (iii) $x^3 + x^2 + 2$. (iv) $x^5 + 2x$. (v) $x^6 + x^4 + x + 1$.

3. Let $a(x) = a_0 + a_1 x + \ldots + a_n x^n \in I[x]$. Prove that if $c \in I$ is a root of $a(x)$, then $c \mid a_0$.

4. List all the factors of the following elements of $I[x]$:
  (i) $6x^2 - 4x - 2$;   (ii) $6x^3 - 3x^2 + 6x - 3$.

5. If $kx - 1$ is a factor of $a_0 + a_1 x + \ldots + a_n x^n \in I[x]$, prove that k is a root of $a_n + a_{n-1} x + \ldots + a_0 x^n$, and conversely.

6. If $c(x) \mid a(x)$ and $c(x) \mid b(x)$ in the integral domain $S[x]$, prove that $c(x) \mid (a(x) \cdot s(x) + b(x) \cdot t(x))$ for each $s(x), t(x) \in S[x]$.

14. The polynomial domain of a field

In the remainder of this chapter, we shall restrict the coefficients of our polynomials to a field. Let F be the field under consideration, and $F[x]$ be the corresponding polynomial domain. Naturally, all the theorems of the previous section are valid in $F[x]$, since a field is an integral domain.

An element $a(x) \in F[x]$ is called a *unit* of $F[x]$ if there exists an element $b(x) \in F[x]$ such that $a(x) \cdot b(x) = 1$. By 4-5, deg $[a(x) \cdot b(x)]$ = deg $a(x)$ + deg $b(x)$ = deg 1 = 0; thus deg $a(x)$ = 0 and deg $b(x)$ = 0, and $a(x)$ and $b(x)$ are in F. Since for each $c \in F$, $c \cdot c^{-1} = 1$, we conclude that the units of $F[x]$ are the nonzero elements of F.

If $a(x) \in F[x]$, say

$$a(x) = a_0 + a_1 x + \ldots + a_n x^n, \qquad a_n \neq 0,$$

then also

$$a(x) = a_n \cdot (a_n^{-1} \cdot a_0 + a_n^{-1} \cdot a_1 x + \ldots + x^n).$$

That is, each nonzero polynomial in $F[x]$ is the product of a unit and a monic polynomial. For example, in $R[x]$,

$$3 + \tfrac{1}{2}x + \tfrac{2}{3}x^2 = \tfrac{2}{3}(\tfrac{9}{2} + \tfrac{3}{4}x + x^2).$$

The division process 4-11 may be applied to any two elements $a(x), b(x) \in F[x]$ as long as $b(x) \neq 0$. No longer is it necessary to assume that $b(x)$ is monic. To see this, note that even if $b(x)$ is not monic, there exists $k \in F$ such that $b(x) = k \cdot b'(x)$, where $b'(x)$ is monic. Hence (4-11)

$$a(x) = b'(x) \cdot q'(x) + r(x), \qquad 0 \leq r(x) < b'(x),$$

and if we let $q(x) = k^{-1} \cdot q'(x)$, then

$$a(x) = b(x) \cdot q(x) + r(x), \qquad 0 \leq r(x) < b(x)$$

as desired. As in 4-11, $q(x)$ and $r(x)$ are still unique.

A polynomial $a(x)$ in $F[x]$ is called a *prime polynomial* if $\deg a(x) \geq 1$ and if in each factorization of $a(x)$, say

$$a(x) = b(x) \cdot c(x),$$

either $b(x)$ or $c(x)$ is a unit of $F[x]$. It is evident that each polynomial of degree 1 is prime. For some fields F (the complex number field studied in the next chapter, for example), these polynomials are the only ones that are prime. However, for the fields studied so far, there are prime polynomials of degree higher than one. For example, $x^2 + 2$ is prime in $R^*[x]$, since $x^2 + 2$ has no roots in R^*; $x^2 + x + 1$ is prime in $I/(2)[x]$, since it has no roots, and hence no linear factors; $x^3 - 4$ is prime in $R[x]$, for if it were factorable, one factor would have to be linear, and therefore $x^3 - 4$ would have a root in R, which it does not.

The polynomial $c(x)$ is called the *highest common factor* (HCF) of the polynomials $a(x)$ and $b(x)$ if and only if:

4-19

     (i) $c(x)$ is monic;

     (ii) $c(x) \mid a(x)$ and $c(x) \mid b(x)$;

     (iii) if $d(x) \mid a(x)$ and $d(x) \mid b(x)$, then $d(x) \mid c(x)$.

We see quickly that if $c(x)$ exists, it is unique. For if $c(x)$ and $c'(x)$ satisfy (i) to (iii), then by (iii), $c(x) \mid c'(x)$ and $c'(x) \mid c(x)$. Hence $c'(x) = k \cdot c(x)$, $k \in F$, and since both $c(x)$ and $c'(x)$ are monic, $k = 1$. The same notation for the HCF of $a(x)$ and $b(x)$ will be used as was used in the case of the integers. Thus

$$(a(x), b(x))$$

designates the HCF of $a(x)$ and $b(x)$.

4-20 **Theorem.** Any two nonzero polynomials $a(x)$ and $b(x)$ of $F[x]$ have a HCF. Furthermore, there exist polynomials $u(x)$ and $v(x)$ such that

$$(a(x), b(x)) = a(x) \cdot u(x) + b(x) \cdot v(x).$$

To prove this, let T be the set of all nonzero polynomials of the form

$$a(x) \cdot s(x) + b(x) \cdot t(x), \qquad s(x), t(x) \in F[x]. \tag{1}$$

Since $a(x) = a(x) \cdot 1 + b(x) \cdot 0$, $a(x) \in T$, and, similarly, $b(x) \in T$. If $d(x)$ has the form (1), then for each $e(x) \in F[x]$, $e(x) \neq 0$,

$$e(x) \cdot d(x) = a(x) \cdot (e(x) \cdot s(x)) + b(x) \cdot (e(x) \cdot t(x)),$$

and evidently $e(x) \cdot d(x) \in T$.

Every element of T has degree; by the well-ordering theorem for the integers, there must exist an element $c(x)$ of least degree. This element can be chosen to be monic, since if it were not monic we could multiply it by a unit to make it so. Thus $c(x)$ is the monic polynomial of least degree of the form

$$c(x) = a(x) \cdot u(x) + b(x) \cdot v(x). \tag{2}$$

We shall show now that $c(x)$ is the HCF of $a(x)$ and $b(x)$.

By 4-11, there exist elements $q(x), r(x) \in F[x]$ such that

$$a(x) = c(x) \cdot q(x) + r(x), \qquad 0 \leq r(x) < c(x). \tag{3}$$

Substituting (2) in (3) and simplifying, we obtain

$$r(x) = a(x) \cdot (1 - u(x) \cdot q(x)) + b(x) \cdot (-v(x) \cdot q(x)).$$

Since $r(x)$ is of the form (1), we conclude that either $r(x) \in T$ or $r(x) = 0$. However, $r(x) \not\subset T$ since $r(x) < c(x)$ and $c(x)$ is an element of T of least degree. Thus $r(x) = 0$, $a(x) = c(x) \cdot q(x)$, and hence $c(x) \mid a(x)$. In a similar way we prove that $c(x) \mid b(x)$. Finally, if $d(x) \mid a(x)$ and $d(x) \mid b(x)$, then by (2) and 4-18, Exercise 6, we conclude that $d(x) \mid c(x)$. Thus $c(x)$ has the three properties of 4-19 and $c(x) = (a(x), b(x))$ as desired.

The HCF of two polynomials in $F[x]$ can be found by Euclid's algorithm, just as was the HCF of two integers. We remember that this process is a succession of divisions. Thus starting with the nonzero elements $a(x), b(x) \in F[x]$, we have by successive applications of 4-11:

$$a(x) = b(x) \cdot q_1(x) + r_1(x), \qquad 0 \leq r_1(x) < b(x),$$

$$b(x) = r_1(x) \cdot q_2(x) + r_2(x), \qquad 0 \leq r_2(x) < r_1(x),$$

4-21 $\quad r_1(x) = r_2(x) \cdot q_3(x) + r_3(x), \qquad 0 \leq r_3(x) < r_2(x),$

$$\cdot \quad \cdot \quad \cdot \quad \cdot \quad \cdot \quad \cdot \quad \cdot \quad \cdot \quad \cdot \quad \cdot \quad \cdot \quad \cdot \quad \cdot$$

$$\cdot \quad \cdot \quad \cdot \quad \cdot \quad \cdot \quad \cdot \quad \cdot \quad \cdot \quad \cdot \quad \cdot \quad \cdot \quad \cdot \quad \cdot$$

The successive nonzero remainders are ordered as follows:

$$r_1(x) > r_2(x) > r_3(x) > \ldots..$$

There will exist an integer n such that $r_n(x)$ is the remainder of least degree. Hence we will have (if $r_1(x) \neq 0$)

$$r_n(x) \neq 0, \qquad r_{n+1}(x) = 0.$$

The last two divisions of 4-21 will then be as follows:

$$r_{n-2}(x) = r_{n-1}(x) \cdot q_n(x) + r_n(x),$$
$$r_{n-1}(x) = r_n(x) \cdot q_{n+1}(x). \tag{1}$$

If $c(x) = (a(x), b(x))$, then since $c(x) \mid a(x)$ and $c(x) \mid b(x)$, and since $r_1(x) = a(x) - b(x) \cdot q_1(x)$, $c(x) \mid r_1(x)$. Again, since $r_2(x) = b(x) - r_1(x) \cdot q_2(x)$, $c(x) \mid r_2(x)$. Continuing, we see that $c(x)$ is a factor of each of the remainders. Hence

$$c(x) \mid r_n(x). \tag{2}$$

On the other hand, $r_n(x) \mid r_{n-1}(x)$ by (1). Since $r_{n-2}(x) = r_{n-1}(x) \cdot q_n(x) + r_n(x)$, $r_n(x) \mid r_{n-2}(x)$. Continuing, we see that $r_n(x)$ is a factor of each of the remainders and also of $b(x)$ and $a(x)$. Thus

$$r_n(x) \mid c(x). \tag{3}$$

From (2) and (3) we conclude that

$$r_n(x) = k \cdot c(x), \qquad k \in F.$$

Thus the last nonzero remainder of 4-21, when made monic, is just the HCF of $a(x)$ and $b(x)$.

Let us illustrate Euclid's algorithm by an example. Consider the following as elements of $R[x]$:

$$a(x) = x^4 + 2x^3 - x^2 - x + 2, \qquad b(x) = x^4 + 3x^3 + 2x^2 - x - 2.$$

The reader may verify the following steps of 4-21:

$$a(x) = b(x) \cdot 1 + (-x^3 - 3x^2 + 4),$$
$$r_1(x) = -x^3 - 3x^2 + 4 < b(x),$$
$$b(x) = r_1(x) \cdot (-x) + (2x^2 + 3x - 2),$$
$$r_2(x) = 2x^2 + 3x - 2 < r_1(x),$$
$$r_1(x) = r_2(x) \cdot (-\tfrac{1}{2}x - \tfrac{3}{4}) + (\tfrac{5}{4}x + \tfrac{5}{2}),$$
$$r_3(x) = \tfrac{5}{4}x + \tfrac{5}{2} < r_2(x),$$
$$r_2(x) = r_3(x) \cdot (\tfrac{8}{5}x - \tfrac{4}{5}).$$

Since $r_4(x) = 0$, $r_3(x)$, when made monic, is the HCF of $a(x)$ and $b(x)$:

$$(a(x), b(x)) = \tfrac{4}{5} \cdot r_3(x) = x + 2.$$

Euclid's algorithm may be used to express the HCF of $a(x)$ and $b(x)$ in the form 4-20. We shall show how this may be done with the above example. The steps are as follows:

$$r_1(x) = a(x) - b(x),$$
$$r_2(x) = b(x) + r_1(x) \cdot x,$$
$$= a(x) \cdot x + b(x) \cdot (1 - x),$$
$$r_3(x) = r_1(x) + r_2(x) \cdot (\tfrac{1}{2}x + \tfrac{3}{4}),$$
$$= (a(x) - b(x)) + (a(x) \cdot x + b(x) \cdot (1 - x)) \cdot (\tfrac{1}{2}x + \tfrac{3}{4}),$$
$$= a(x) \cdot (1 + \tfrac{3}{4}x + \tfrac{1}{2}x^2) + b(x) \cdot (-\tfrac{1}{4} - \tfrac{1}{4}x - \tfrac{1}{2}x^2).$$

Hence

$$x + 2 = a(x) \cdot (\tfrac{4}{5} + \tfrac{3}{5}x + \tfrac{2}{5}x^2) + b(x) \cdot (-\tfrac{1}{5} - \tfrac{1}{5}x - \tfrac{2}{5}x^2).$$

4-22 EXERCISES

1. Find the HCF of the following pairs of elements of $R[x]$ and express this HCF in the form of 4-20:

(i) $x^4 + x^3 + 4x^2 + x + 3, \qquad 2x^3 + 3x^2 + 7x + 3;$

(ii) $3x^3 - x^2 + x - 1, \qquad 2x^2 + x - 3;$

(iii) $x^5 + 8x^4 + 25x^3 + 38x^2 + 31x + 14,$
$x^4 + 2x^3 - 15x^2 - 56x - 49.$

2. Find the HCF of the following pairs of elements of $I/(3)[x]$ and express this HCF in the form 4-20:

(i) $x^4 + x^3 + 2x^2 + x + 2, \qquad 2x^4 + x^2 + x + 1;$

(ii) $2x^5 + 1, \qquad x^3 + 2.$

3. If $a(x)$ and $b(x)$ in $F[x]$ are *relatively prime*, that is, if $(a(x),b(x)) = 1$, then for some $s(x),t(x) \in F[x]$,

$$1 = a(x) \cdot s(x) + b(x) \cdot t(x). \tag{1}$$

Let $u(x)$ be the remainder on dividing $s(x)$ by $b(x)$,

$$s(x) = b(x) \cdot q(x) + u(x), \qquad 0 \le u(x) < b(x). \tag{2}$$

On substituting (2) in (1), we obtain

$$1 = a(x) \cdot u(x) + b(x) \cdot v(x), \tag{3}$$

where $v(x) = a(x) \cdot q(x) + t(x)$. Show that $v(x) < a(x)$, and that $u(x),v(x)$ are the only elements satisfying an equation of the form of (3) for which $u(x) < b(x)$ and $v(x) < a(x)$.

4. List all the primes of $I/(2)[x]$ of degrees 1, 2, 3, 4, and 5. There exist primes in $I/(2)[x]$ of any degree n. As a matter of fact, each prime

of degree n is a factor of the polynomial $x^k + 1$, where $k = 2^n - 1$. Show that this is so for the primes in your list.

5. The polynomial $x^n + x + 1$ is prime in $I/(2)[x]$ if $n = 2, 3, 4$, but not prime if $n = 5$. Find the smallest $n > 5$ for which this polynomial is not prime, and factor it into a product of primes in this case.

6. Prove the following *Lemma of Gauss*. Let $a(x)$, $b(x)$, and $c(x)$ be monic polynomials in $R[x]$ such that

$$a(x) = b(x) \cdot c(x).$$

If all the coefficients of $a(x)$ are integers, then so are all the coefficients of $b(x)$ and $c(x)$. (Hint. There must exist least positive integers e and f such that $e \cdot b(x)$ and $f \cdot c(x)$ have integers for coefficients. One wishes to prove that $e = f = 1$. If $a(x) = a_0 + a_1 x + \ldots + a_n x^n$, $e \cdot b(x) = b_0 + b_1 x + \ldots + b_r x^r$, $f \cdot c(x) = c_0 + c_1 x + \ldots + c_s x^s$, then $e \cdot f \cdot a(x) = e \cdot b(x) \cdot f \cdot c(x)$, and

$$e \cdot f \cdot a_t = a_0 \cdot b_t + a_1 \cdot b_{t-1} + \ldots + a_t \cdot b_0, \quad 0 \le t \le n. \quad (1)$$

If $e \cdot f \ne 1$, then some prime $p \mid e \cdot f$. However, p cannot be a factor of each b_i, or of each c_i. Let j be the least integer such that $p \nmid b_j$, and let k be the least integer such that $p \nmid c_k$. If $t = j + k$ in (1), then every term of the right side of (1) with one exception has p as a factor. This is not possible, since $p \mid e \cdot f \cdot a_t$.)

7. Prove that $x^n + 2$ is a prime in $R[x]$ for each positive integer n.

Let us now prove the analogue in $F[x]$ of the fundamental theorem of arithmetic in I (2-35). The proof of the following theorem is omitted, since it is the same as that of 2-33.

4-23 Theorem. If $a(x), b(x), p(x) \in F[x]$ with $p(x)$ prime, and if $p(x) \mid a(x) \cdot b(x)$, then $p(x) \mid a(x)$ or $p(x) \mid b(x)$.

If $p(x)$ is prime and $p(x) \mid a_1(x) \cdot a_2(x) \cdot \ldots \cdot a_k(x)$, then by mathematical induction we may prove that $p(x) \mid a_i(x)$ for some i.

If the polynomial $a(x) \in F[x]$ has positive degree n, then any factor $p_1(x)$ of $a(x)$ of least positive degree is evidently a prime polynomial. Thus

$$a(x) = p_1(x) \cdot a_1(x).$$

If $a_1(x)$ is not a unit, it, too, has a prime factor $p_2(x)$, and

$$a(x) = p_1(x) \cdot p_2(x) \cdot a_2(x).$$

In at most n such steps, $a(x)$ can be factored into a product of prime polynomials. This proves part of the following theorem.

4-24 THEOREM. Each polynomial $a(x) \in F[x]$ of positive degree can be factored uniquely (except for order) into a product of monic prime polynomials and a unit of $F[x]$:

$$a(x) = k \cdot p_1(x) \cdot p_2(x) \cdot \ldots \cdot p_m(x), \qquad k \in F.$$

In this factorization of $a(x)$, it is evident that $k = a_n$, the coefficient of the term of highest degree in $a(x)$. If

$$a(x) = k \cdot q_1(x) \cdot q_2(x) \cdot \ldots \cdot q_i(x)$$

is another factorization of $a(x)$ into a product of monic prime polynomials, then

$$p_1(x) \cdot p_2(x) \cdot \ldots \cdot p_m(x) = q_1(x) \cdot q_2(x) \cdot \ldots \cdot q_i(x).$$

Now $q_1(x)$ is a factor of the left side of this equation, and hence $q_1(x)$ is one of the monic primes appearing on the left side, say $q_1(x) = p_1(x)$. By mathematical induction, we conclude that the $q_i(x)$ are just the $p_i(x)$ in some order. In this way, 4-24 is proved.

4-25 EXERCISES

1. Prove that the polynomial $ax^2 + bx + c$, $a \neq 0$, of $R^\#[x]$ is prime if and only if $b^2 - 4ac < 0$.

2. If the cubic polynomial $ax^3 + bx^2 + cx + d$, $a \neq 0$, is not prime, then one of its factors is of degree one; hence the polynomial has a root. Use this fact to factor the following polynomials of $R[x]$ into primes.

    (i) $x^3 + 3x^2 + 8x + 12$.   (ii) $2x^3 + x^2 - 10x + 6$.

    (iii) $4x^3 + 8x + 12$.   (iv) $6x^3 - x^2 - 4x - 1$.

3. If $a(x) = a_0 + a_1 x + \ldots + a_n x^n \in I[x]$, and $r, s \in I$ with $(r,s) = 1$, and if r/s is a root of $a(x)$ in R, then prove that necessarily $r \mid a_0$ and $s \mid a_n$. (Hint: since $a(r/s) = 0$, $a_0 \cdot s^n + a_1 \cdot r \cdot s^{n-1} + \ldots + a_n \cdot r^n = 0$. Thus $a_0 \cdot s^n = r \cdot (\ldots)$ and $r \mid a_0$, and so on.)

4. Use the preceding exercise to help in finding the roots of the following polynomials in $R[x]$. Then write the polynomials in a factored form.

    (i) $x^5 - 1$.   (ii) $8x^4 + 20x^3 + 10x^2 - 5x - 3$.

    (iii) $18x^4 + 27x^3 - 20x^2 - 20x + 16$.

5. The equation $\sin 3\theta = 3 \sin \theta - 4 \sin^3 \theta$ holds for all angles θ. Use this equation to prove that $\sin 10°$ is not a rational number. Actually, this equation may be used to prove that an angle of $30°$ cannot be trisected by ruler and compass.

CHAPTER V

The Complex Number Field

If the field F is a subfield of the field F', then it is evident that the polynomial domain $F[x]$ is a subdomain of $F'[x]$. Thus, for example, $R[x]$ is a subdomain of $R^*[x]$. A polynomial $a(x) \in F[x]$, and hence in $F'[x]$, might well be prime as an element of $F[x]$, but not prime as an element of the larger domain $F'[x]$. For example,

$$x^2 - 2$$

is a prime polynomial in $R[x]$, while, in $R^*[x]$, it is not a prime, since

$$x^2 - 2 = (x + \sqrt{2}) \cdot (x - \sqrt{2}).$$

That such a phenomenon is not unusual is seen in Section 15 below. There it is proved that if $a(x)$ is a prime polynomial of $F[x]$ of degree more than one, then there exists a field F' containing F as a subfield such that $a(x)$ has a root in F', and hence such that $a(x)$ is not prime in $F'[x]$.

The case of this theorem of primary interest to us in this chapter is of the polynomial

$$x^2 + 1$$

in $R^*[x]$. We shall construct a field containing the real field in which $x^2 + 1$ has a root. This field, the so-called complex number field, rates special attention because of its wide use in both pure and applied mathematics.

15. The field of polynomials modulo a given prime

Let F be a given field, and $F[x]$ be the polynomial domain in x over F. For any fixed polynomial $s(x) \in F[x]$ of positive degree, the relation of congruence modulo $s(x)$ is defined on $F[x]$ just as was the relation $\equiv_k$ on I (3-9).

5-1 DEFINITION. The relation of *congruent modulo* $s(x)$ ($\equiv_s$) is defined on $F[x]$ as follows: for each $a(x),b(x) \in F[x]$,

$$a(x) \equiv_s b(x) \quad \text{if and only if} \quad s(x) \mid a(x) - b(x).$$

The proof that $\equiv_s$ is an equivalence relation on $F[x]$ is precisely the same as the proof that $\equiv_k$ is an equivalence relation on I. For example, to show that $\equiv_s$ is transitive, assume that $a(x) \equiv_s b(x)$ and $b(x) \equiv_s c(x)$. Then

$$s(x) \mid a(x) - b(x) \quad \text{and} \quad s(x) \mid b(x) - c(x),$$

$$s(x) \mid (a(x) - b(x)) + (b(x) - c(x)),$$

$$s(x) \mid a(x) - c(x),$$

and $a(x) \equiv_s c(x)$.

The equivalence sets related to $\equiv_s$ are designated by "$[a(x)]$" as usual. Thus

$$[a(x)] = \{b(x); b(x) \in F[x], b(x) \equiv_s a(x)\}.$$

In $[a(x)]$, there is one and only one polynomial $r(x)$ having the property

$$r(x) < s(x).$$

This $r(x)$ is the remainder on dividing $a(x)$ by $s(x)$,

$$a(x) = s(x) \cdot q(x) + r(x), \qquad r(x) < s(x).$$

Since $s(x) \mid a(x) - r(x)$, evidently $r(x) \equiv_s a(x)$ and therefore $r(x) \in [a(x)]$. No other $r'(x) < s(x)$ can be in $[a(x)]$. For if both $r(x)$ and $r'(x)$ were in $[a(x)]$, then we would have $r(x) \equiv_s r'(x)$ and $s(x) \mid r(x) - r'(x)$. Since $r(x) - r'(x) < s(x)$, necessarily $r(x) - r'(x) = 0$ and $r(x) = r'(x)$.

If a is a unit of $F[x]$, that is, if $a \in F$, then $[a]$ consists of all polynomials of the form

$$a + s(x) \cdot t(x), \qquad t(x) \in F[x].$$

According to the preceding paragraph, a is the only unit of $F[x]$ in $[a]$.

The equivalence sets of $F[x]$ related to $\equiv_s$ are called *polynomials modulo* $s(x)$. The set of all polynomials modulo $s(x)$ is designated by

$$F[x]/(s(x)).$$

To illustrate these concepts, consider the polynomial $s(x) = x^2 - 2 \in R[x]$. The equivalence sets related to $\equiv_s$ have the form

$[ax + b]$, $a,b \in R$. For example, we have by the division process that

$$x^3 + 3x - 4 = (x^2 - 2) \cdot x + (5x - 4).$$

Hence $(x^3 + 3x - 4) - (5x - 4) = (x^2 - 2) \cdot x$, $x^3 + 3x - 4 \equiv_s$ $5x - 4$, and $x^3 + 3x - 4 \in [5x - 4]$. The equivalence set $[3]$, for example, consists of all polynomials of the form

$$3 + (x^2 - 2) \cdot a(x), \qquad a(x) \in R[x].$$

To return to the general case, operations can be introduced on $F[x]/(s(x))$ just as they were on $I/(k)$ (3-11). Thus the operations $+$ and $\cdot$ are defined as follows: for each $[a(x)],[b(x)] \in F[x]/(s(x))$,

5-2
$$[a(x)] + [b(x)] = [a(x) + b(x)],$$
$$[a(x)] \cdot [b(x)] = [a(x) \cdot b(x)].$$

These operations can easily be shown to be well-defined.

Again, as in the case of $I/(k)$, there is a natural mapping α of $F[x]$ onto $F[x]/(s(x))$ given by

$$\alpha: \quad a(x)\alpha = [a(x)], \qquad a(x) \in F[x].$$

In terms of α, 5-2 may be written in the following form:

5-3
$$(a(x) + b(x))\alpha = a(x)\alpha + b(x)\alpha,$$
$$(a(x) \cdot b(x))\alpha = a(x)\alpha \cdot b(x)\alpha.$$

These equations show that the mapping α of $F[x]$ onto $F[x]/(s(x))$ preserves the operations of addition and multiplication in these systems; that is, that α is a *homomorphism* of $F[x]$ onto $F[x]/(s(x))$.

Since α is a homomorphism of $F[x]$ onto $F[x]/(s(x))$ and $F[x]$ is an integral domain, $F[x]/(s(x))$ will have all the properties of an integral domain with the possible exception of the multiplicative cancellation law. The identity elements of $F[x]/(s(x))$ are the elements $[0]$ and $[1]$, $[0]$ being the set of all multiples of $s(x)$ and $[1]$ being the set of all elements of the form $1 + s(x) \cdot a(x)$, $a(x) \in F[x]$.

If $s(x)$ is not prime in $F[x]$, say $s(x) = a(x) \cdot b(x)$ where both $a(x)$ and $b(x)$ are of positive degree, then

$$[a(x)] \cdot [b(x)] = [s(x)] = [0].$$

Since $[a(x)] \neq [0]$ and $[b(x)] \neq [0]$, it is evident that $F[x]/(s(x))$ is not an integral domain (see 3-4). This proves part of the following result.

5-4 THEOREM. $F[x]/(s(x))$ is a field if and only if $s(x)$ is a prime polynomial in $F[x]$.

We have already proved that if $s(x)$ is not prime, $F[x]/(s(x))$ is not an integral domain, and hence not a field. Assume now that $s(x)$ is prime. Then, if $[a(x)]$ is any nonzero element of $F[x]/(s(x))$, evidently $(a(x),s(x)) = 1$. Thus there exist polynomials $u(x),v(x) \in F[x]$ such that (4-20)

$$a(x) \cdot u(x) + s(x) \cdot v(x) = 1.$$

Hence

$$[a(x)] \cdot [u(x)] + [s(x)] \cdot [v(x)] = [1],$$

and, since $[s(x)] = [0]$,

$$[a(x)] \cdot [u(x)] = [1].$$

This proves that every nonzero element of $F[x]/(s(x))$ has a multiplicative inverse. Thus $F[x]/(s(x))$ is a field (3-22, Exercise 5), and 5-4 is proved.

The mapping β defined by

$$\beta: \quad \alpha\beta = [a], \qquad a \in F,$$

is an isomorphism of F into $F[x]/(s(x))$, since, for each $a,b \in F$, $[a] = [b]$ if and only if $a = b$. Let us identify a with $[a]$; then F is actually a subfield of $F[x]/(s(x))$.

We know that for each $a(x) \in F[x]$ there exists a unique element $r(x) \in F[x]$ such that

$$[a(x)] = [r(x)], \qquad r(x) = r_0 + r_1 x + \cdots + r_k x^k < s(x).$$

Now

$$[r(x)] = [r_0] + [r_1 x] + \ldots + [r_k x^k],$$

and since we are going to identify $[r_0]$ with r_0, and so on,

$$[r(x)] = r_0 + r_1[x] + \ldots + r_k[x^k].$$

For convenience, let us designate by "i" the element $[x]$ of $F[x]/(s(x))$. Then

$$[r(x)] = r_0 + r_1 i + \ldots + r_k i^k.$$

Remember, every element of $F[x]/(s(x))$ can be expressed uniquely in the form

5-5 $$r_0 + r_1 i + r_2 i^2 + \ldots + r_k i^k, \qquad k < \deg s(x).$$

Suppose that $s(x)$ is a monic polynomial, say

$$s(x) = s_0 + s_1 x + \ldots + s_{n-1} x^{n-1} + x^n.$$

Then, since $[s(x)] = 0$, $s_0 + s_1 i + \ldots + i^n = 0$, that is,

5-6 $\qquad\qquad i^n = -s_0 - s_1 i - \ldots - s_{n-1} i^{n-1}.$

Each element $a_0 + a_1 i + \ldots + a_m i^m$, $m \geq n$, of $F[x]/(s(x))$ not already in the form 5-5 may be put in this form by successive applications of 5-6. For, by 5-6,

$$i^m = -s_0 i^{m-n} - s_1 i^{m-n+1} - \ldots - s_{n-1} i^{m-1},$$

and hence, on replacing i^m by this expression of degree $m - 1$ in i, we obtain

$$a_0 + a_1 i + \ldots + a_m i^m = b_0 + b_1 i + \ldots + b_{m-1} i^{m-1}$$

for some $b_i \in F$. Repeated applications of 5-6 will eventually reduce the given element to the form 5-5.

A simple example will now be given to illustrate the work of this section. Let $F = I/(2)$, a field with two elements 0 and 1, and let

$$s(x) = x^3 + x^2 + 1,$$

a prime polynomial of $F[x]$. Then, by 5-4, $F[x]/(s(x))$ is a field. Since the eight elements $(i = [x])$

$$0, \quad 1, \quad i, \quad i + 1, \quad i^2, \quad i^2 + 1, \quad i^2 + i, \quad i^2 + i + 1$$

are all possible polynomials in i of degree less than 3, the degree of $s(x)$, these are all the elements of $F[x]/(s(x))$ (see 5-5). The characteristic of $F[x]/(s(x))$ is 2; its prime subfield is just $I/(2)$ (this illustrates 3-21). Thus each element of $F[x]/(s(x))$ is its own additive inverse (for example, $i^2 + i^2 = 0$). Since $[s(x)] = i^3 + i^2 + 1 = 0$,

$$i^3 = i^2 + 1.$$

With the aid of this equation, the product of two elements of $F[x]/(s(x))$ may be expressed as a polynomial of degree less than 3 in i. As examples,

$$(i + 1) \cdot (i^2 + i) = i^3 + i = (i^2 + 1) + i = i^2 + i + 1,$$

$$(i^2 + i + 1)^2 = i^4 + i^2 + 1 = i \cdot i^3 + i^2 + 1,$$

$$= i \cdot (i^2 + 1) + i^2 + 1 = i^3 + i^2 + i + 1,$$

$$= (i^2 + 1) + i^2 + i + 1 = i.$$

It is shown in more advanced books on algebra that there exists a unique field with p^n elements for each prime p and each positive integer n. These fields are called *Galois fields* in honor of the famous nineteenth-century French mathematician Galois. The example above is a Galois field with 2^3 elements.

5-7 EXERCISES

1. Let $F = I/(3)$, a field with three elements. Prove that $x^2 + x + 2$ is prime in $F[x]$. Make addition and multiplication tables for the field $F[x]/(x^2 + x + 2)$.

2. If F is a field with prime subfield P, and $s(x)$ is a prime polynomial in $F[x]$, prove that P is the prime subfield of $F[x]/(s(x))$.

3. It can be proved that for each positive prime number p and each positive integer n there exists a prime polynomial $s(x)$ in $I/(p)[x]$ of degree n. Use this result to prove that there exists a field with p^n elements for each positive prime number p and each positive integer n.

4. Find a field with 4 elements; with 27 elements; with 25 elements; with 49 elements; with 32 elements.

5. Describe the field $R[x]/(x^2 - 2)$ as a subfield of $R^\sharp$.

6. Describe the field $R[x]/(x^3 + x + 1)$ as a subfield of $R^\sharp$.

7. Show that $x^4 - 10x^2 + 1$ is prime in $R[x]$. Prove that the field $R[x]/(x^4 - 10x^2 + 1)$ is isomorphic to the field of 3-22, Exercise 1, (iv). (Hint: let $i \to \sqrt{3} + \sqrt{2}$.)

If $s(x)$ is a monic prime polynomial of $F[x]$, let us designate the field $F[x]/(s(x))$ by "F'." In view of our results above, F' consists of all elements of the form

$$r_0 + r_1 i + \ldots + r_{n-1} i^{n-1},$$

where the r_i are in F and $n = \deg s(x)$. If

$$s(x) = s_0 + s_1 x + \ldots + s_{n-1} x^{n-1} \oplus x^n,$$

then the multiplication of elements of F' is carried out by using the usual commutative, associative, and distributive laws, and the equation

$$i^n = -s_0 - s_1 i - \ldots - s_{n-1} i^{n-1}.$$

Let us look now at the polynomial domain $F'[y]$ made up of all polynomials in the symbol y over F'. In particular, let us look at the polynomial

$$s(y) = s_0 \oplus s_1 y \oplus \ldots \oplus s_{n-1} y^{n-1} + y^n.$$

Since

$$s(i) = s_0 + s_1 i + \ldots + s_{n-1} i^{n-1} + i^n = 0,$$

the polynomial $s(y)$ has a root in F', and hence $s(y)$ is not a prime polynomial in $F'[y]$. This proves the following result.

5-8 THEOREM. Let $s(x)$ be a prime polynomial in $F[x]$ and F' be the field $F[x]/(s(x))$. Then the polynomial $s(y) \in F'[y]$ is not prime since it has a root in F'.

In the example before 5-7, where $F = I/(2)$, $s(x) = x^3 + x^2 + 1$, and $F' = F[x]/(s(x))$, the polynomial $s(y) = y^3 + y^2 + 1$ has the root i in F', and hence, by 4-15, $y - i$ $(= y + i)$ is a factor of $s(y)$. The complete factorization of $s(y)$ in $F'[y]$ is as follows:

$$y^3 + y^2 + 1 = (y + i) \cdot (y + i^2) \cdot (y + i^2 + i + 1).$$

16. The complex number field

We turn now to a special instance of the preceding section. The polynomial $x^2 + 1$ is prime in $R^*[x]$, since $r^2 + 1 > 0$ for each $r \in R^*$.

5-9 DEFINITION. The field $R^*[x]/(x^2 + 1)$, labelled hereafter "C," is called the *complex number field*. The elements of C are called *complex numbers*.

In view of the results of Section 15, C consists of all elements of the form

$$a + bi, \qquad a, b \in R^*.$$

The element i $(= [x])$ satisfies the equation $i^2 + 1 = 0$, or

$$i^2 = -1.$$

Note that i is a square root of -1 in C. The field R^* is a subfield of C; if $b = 0$, the complex number $a + bi = a$, a real number.

Using the fact that $i^2 = -1$, it is an easy matter to verify that the operations of C act in the way indicated below:

$$(a + bi) + (c + di) = (a + c) + (b + d)i,$$

$$(a + bi) \cdot (c + di) = (a \cdot c - b \cdot d) + (a \cdot d + b \cdot c)i.$$

It hardly need be pointed out that

$$a + bi = c + di \quad \text{if and only if} \quad a = c \text{ and } b = d.$$

The complex number $a - bi$ is called the *conjugate* of $a + bi$. Evidently

5-10
$$(a + bi) + (a - bi) = 2a,$$
$$(a + bi) \cdot (a - bi) = a^2 + b^2.$$

We note that the sum or the product of a complex number and its conjugate is a real number. A complex number $a + bi$ is its own conjugate (that is, $a + bi = a - bi$) if and only if $a + bi = a$, a real number. If $a + bi \neq 0$, then we obtain from 5-10 that

$$(a + bi) \cdot ((a - bi)/(a^2 + b^2)) = 1,$$

that is, that

$$(a + bi)^{-1} = (a - bi)/(a^2 + b^2).$$

Part of the usefulness of the set C of complex numbers in applied mathematics is due to its geometric representation as the set of all points in a plane. Consider a rectangular coordinate system in a plane. The points on the x- and y-axes are given real number coordinates in the usual way. Then associated with each point P in the plane is a unique ordered pair (a,b) of real numbers, and, conversely, with each ordered pair (c,d) of real numbers is associated a unique point Q in the plane (Figure 7). Since every ordered pair (a,b) of real numbers uniquely defines a complex number $a + bi$, and conversely, we might just as well assign the complex number $a + bi$ as the coordinate of P. *Thus the complex number $a + bi$ is the coordinate of the point P having x-coordinate a and y-coordinate b.* Some examples are given in Figure 8. Note that for each point $(a,0)$ on the x-axis, the complex number associated with this point is $a + 0i$, or just a. Similarly, the complex number associated with the point $(0,b)$ on the y-axis is $0 + bi$, or just bi (sometimes referred to as an *imaginary number*).

If the angle θ is in standard position in the coordinate plane (so that the vertex of θ is the origin and the initial side of θ is the positive x-axis as in Figure 9) and $a + bi$ is a point on the terminal side of θ, r units from the origin, then by the very definitions of the trigonometric functions,

$$\sin \theta = \frac{b}{r}, \qquad \cos \theta = \frac{a}{r}.$$

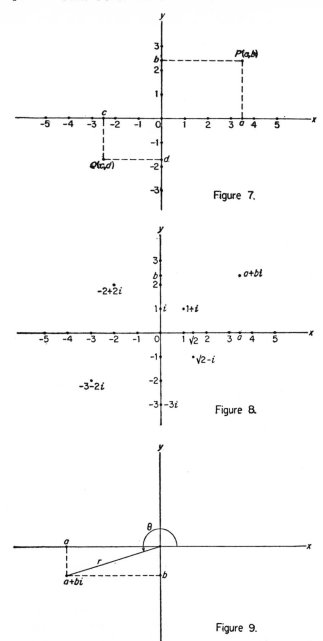

Figure 7.

Figure 8.

Figure 9.

Thus $a = r \cdot \cos \theta$, $b = r \cdot \sin \theta$, and $a + bi = r \cdot \cos \theta + (r \cdot \sin \theta)i$,
or $\qquad\qquad a + bi = r \cdot (\cos \theta + i \sin \theta).$

The *trigonometric form* $r \cdot (\cos \theta + i \sin \theta)$ of a complex number is very useful as we shall see. The trigonometric form of the complex number 0 can be taken as $0 \cdot (\cos \theta + i \sin \theta)$ for any angle θ. The non-negative number r appearing in the trigonometric form of a complex number is called the *absolute value* of the complex number $a + bi$, and is designated by "$| a + bi |$." It is easily proved that

$$| a + bi | = \sqrt{(a^2 + b^2)}.$$

We define $| 0 | = 0$. The angle θ is called the *argument* of the complex number $a + bi$, and is written "arg $(a + bi)$."

For convenience, we shall abbreviate the expression $\cos \theta + i \sin \theta$ to cis θ:

$$\operatorname{cis} \theta = \cos \theta + i \sin \theta.$$

Since $| \operatorname{cis} \theta | = \sqrt{(\cos^2 \theta + \sin^2 \theta)} = 1$, the complex number cis θ is on the circle of radius 1 having its center at the origin (the *unit circle*) as indicated in Figure 10. Thus, for example, cis $0° = 1$,

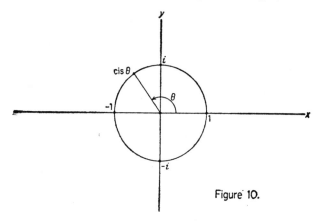

Figure 10.

cis $90° = i$, cis $180° = -1$, and cis $270° = -i$. If a complex number has absolute value r and argument θ, then $r \cdot \operatorname{cis} \theta$ is the trigonometric form of this complex number. Since the trigonometric functions sine and cosine are periodic with period $360°$, cis $(\theta + k \cdot 360°) = \operatorname{cis} \theta$ for any integer k. It is always possible to express a complex number in the form $r \cdot \operatorname{cis} \theta$ where $r \geq 0$ and $0° \leq \theta < 360°$. Such an expression is unique if $r \neq 0$.

The following result, known as *de Moivre's Theorem*, is of fundamental importance in the work to follow.

5-11 THEOREM. For each $u,v \in C$,
  (i) $|u \cdot v| = |u| \cdot |v|$, and, (ii) arg $(u \cdot v) = $ arg $u + $ arg v.

To prove this result, assume that

$$u = r \cdot \text{cis } \theta \quad \text{and} \quad v = s \cdot \text{cis } \phi.$$

Then (using the addition formulas of trigonometry)

$$u \cdot v = (r \cdot (\cos \theta + i \sin \theta)) \cdot (s \cdot (\cos \phi + i \sin \phi)),$$

$$= (r \cdot s) \cdot ((\cos \theta \cdot \cos \phi - \sin \theta \cdot \sin \phi) + i(\cos \theta \cdot \sin \phi$$
$$+ \sin \theta \cdot \cos \phi)),$$

$$= (r \cdot s) \cdot (\cos (\theta + \phi) + i \sin (\theta + \phi)),$$

$$= (r \cdot s) \cdot \text{cis } (\theta + \phi).$$

Hence

$$|u \cdot v| = r \cdot s = |u| \cdot |v|, \qquad \text{arg } (u \cdot v) = \theta + \phi = \text{arg } u + \text{arg } v,$$

and 5-11 is proved.

Another way of writing the results of 5-11 is

$$(r \cdot \text{cis } \theta) \cdot (s \cdot \text{cis } \phi) = (r \cdot s) \cdot \text{cis}(\theta + \phi).$$

For example,

$$(3 \cdot \text{cis } 30°) \cdot (12 \cdot \text{cis } 120°) = 36 \cdot \text{cis } 150°,$$

$$(2 \cdot \text{cis } -70°) \cdot (4 \cdot \text{cis } 160°) = 8 \cdot \text{cis } 90° = 8i,$$

$$(\sqrt{2} \cdot \text{cis } 210°) \cdot (\sqrt{3} \cdot \text{cis } 300°) = \sqrt{6} \cdot \text{cis } 510° = \sqrt{6} \cdot \text{cis } 150°.$$

5-12 EXERCISES

1. Express each of the following complex numbers in trigonometric form.
  (i) 7.
  (ii) $3 + 3i$.
  (iii) $-\sqrt{3} - i$.
  (iv) $-5i$.
  (v) $1 - \sqrt{3} \, i$.
  (vi) -5.
  (vii) $\sqrt[3]{2} \, i$.
  (viii) $-\sqrt{2} + \sqrt{2} \, i$.
  (ix) $\sqrt{3} + 3i$.
  (x) $-2 - 2i$.

2. Express each of the following complex numbers in the form $a + bi$.

(i) $2 \cdot \text{cis } 30°$.
(ii) $4 \cdot \text{cis } 180°$.
(iii) $7 \cdot \text{cis } 315°$.
(iv) $\sqrt{2} \cdot \text{cis } 90°$.
(v) $\sqrt{3} \cdot \text{cis } 120°$.

(vi) $\text{cis } 210°$.
(vii) $(4 \cdot \text{cis } 20°) \cdot (7 \cdot \text{cis } 340°)$.
(viii) $(3 \cdot \text{cis } 15°)^2$.
(ix) $(12 \cdot \text{cis } 100°) \cdot (\text{cis } 200°)$.
(x) $(2 \cdot \text{cis } 0°) \cdot (\sqrt{2} \cdot \text{cis } 60°)$.

3. Prove that the multiplicative inverse of $\text{cis } \theta$ is $\text{cis } (-\theta)$. Hence show that $(r \cdot \text{cis } \theta)/(s \cdot \text{cis } \phi) = (r/s) \cdot \text{cis } (\theta - \phi)$.

4. Prove that for each integer n, $(r \cdot \text{cis } \theta)^n = r^n \cdot \text{cis } n\theta$.

5. Prove that the sum $u + v$ of the complex numbers u and v is the vertex opposite to 0 (the origin) in the parallelogram with 0, u, and v as three vertices.

6. Use the preceding exercise to prove:

(i) $|u + v| \le |u| + |v|$;   (ii) $|u - v| \ge |u| - |v|$.

7. Prove that the distance between the points with coordinates u and v is $|u - v|$. Also prove that $(u + v)/2$ is the coordinate of the midpoint of the segment connecting u and v.

If u and v are two complex numbers such that

$$u^n = v$$

for the positive integer n, then u is called an *nth* *root* of v. The remainder of this section will be used to show that each nonzero complex number v has exactly n distinct nth roots.

First, let us find the nth roots of 1. Trivially, 1 is an nth root of 1. In view of de Moivre's Theorem, the absolute value of an nth root of 1 must be 1. Thus each nth root of 1 must have the form $\text{cis } \theta$, that is, it is a point on the unit circle. Since $(\text{cis } \theta)^n = \text{cis } n\theta$ by 5-12, Exercise 4, $\text{cis } \theta$ is an nth root of 1 if and only if

$$\text{cis } n\theta = 1.$$

Now the only angles ϕ such that $\text{cis } \phi = 1$ are the angles $k \cdot 360°$, k an integer, and therefore $\text{cis } \theta$ is an nth root of 1 if and only if

$$n\theta = k \cdot 360°, \qquad k \text{ an integer.}$$

By giving k the successive values $1, 2, \ldots, n - 1$, it follows that the n complex numbers

$$1, \quad \text{cis } (360°/n), \quad \text{cis } (720°/n), \quad \cdots, \quad \text{cis } ((n - 1) \cdot 360°/n)$$

are nth roots of 1. Since the angles $360°/n, 720°/n, \ldots, (n-1)\cdot 360°/n$ are all distinct and less than $360°$, the n nth roots of 1 listed above are all different. In case $k \geq n$, cis $(k\cdot 360°/n)$ is one of the nth roots of 1 listed above (why?). We conclude that there are precisely n nth roots of 1 for each positive integer n.

For example, the two square roots of 1 are 1 and cis $360°/2 = -1$. The three cube roots of 1 are 1, cis $360°/3$, and cis $720°/3$. Since cis $120° = \cos 120° + i \sin 120° = -1/2 + (\sqrt{3}/2)i$, and so on, the cube roots of 1 are

$$1, \quad -1/2 + (\sqrt{3}/2)i, \quad -1/2 - (\sqrt{3}/2)i.$$

Geometrically, the nth roots of 1 are n equispaced points on the unit circle, one of the points being 1. For example, the three cube roots of 1 are as indicated in Figure 11.

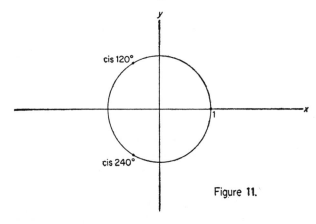

Figure 11.

Let us designate by "w" the nth root of 1 with least positive argument;

$$w = \text{cis} \, (360°/n).$$

Then, since $w^2 = \text{cis} \, (720°/n)$, $w^3 = \text{cis} \, (1080°/n)$, and so on, it is clear that

$$1, \quad w, \quad w^2, \quad \ldots, \quad w^{n-1}$$

are the n nth roots of 1. Note that $w^n = 1$.

The problem of finding the nth roots of any complex number v is now easily solved. If $v = r\cdot\text{cis} \, \theta$ and $\sqrt[n]{r}$ is the unique positive real nth root of r, then u given by

$$u = \sqrt[n]{r}\cdot \text{cis} \, (\theta/n)$$

is obviously an nth root of v (5-12, Exercise 4). The n distinct complex numbers

$$u, \quad w \cdot u, \quad w^2 \cdot u, \quad \ldots, \quad w^{n-1} \cdot u$$

are all nth roots of v, since $(w^k \cdot u)^n = 1 \cdot u^n = v$. The proof that these are the only nth roots of v is left as an exercise for the reader. We have proved the following result.

5-13 Theorem. If $r \cdot \text{cis } \theta$ is any nonzero complex number, and if

$$u = \sqrt[n]{r} \cdot \text{cis } (\theta/n), \qquad w = \text{cis } (360°/n),$$

then the n distinct numbers

$$u, \quad w \cdot u, \quad w^2 \cdot u, \quad \ldots, \quad w^{n-1} \cdot u$$

are all the nth roots of $r \cdot \text{cis } \theta$.

For example, let us find the cube roots of $1 + i$. First, we find the trigonometric form of $1 + i$ to be $\sqrt{2} \cdot \text{cis } 45°$. Hence $u = \sqrt[6]{2} \cdot \text{cis } 15°$ and $w = \text{cis } 120°$, and

$$\sqrt[6]{2} \cdot \text{cis } 15°, \quad \sqrt[6]{2} \cdot \text{cis } 135°, \quad \sqrt[6]{2} \cdot \text{cis } 255°$$

are the three cube roots of $1 + i$.

5-14 Exercises

1. Find the 4th roots of 1; the 5th roots of 1; the 6th roots of 1. Represent the answers geometrically.

2. Find the indicated roots, and represent them geometrically:
    (i) cube roots of $-8 + 8i$;   (v) seventh roots of -128;
    (ii) fifth roots of $-1 - \sqrt{3}i$; (vi) cube roots of $27i$;
    (iii) square roots of i;   (vii) cube roots of $8 \cdot \text{cis } 21°$;
    (iv) fourth roots of -1;   (viii) fourth roots of $-8 + 8 \cdot \sqrt{3}i$.

3. Let G be the set of all complex numbers of the form $a + bi$, a and b integers (G is called the set of *Gaussian integers*). Prove that G is an integral domain, and that $1, -1, i, -i$, are the only elements of G having multiplicative inverses. Also prove that for each $u, v \in G$ with $v \neq 0$, there exist $q, r \in G$ such that $u = v \cdot q + r$, $|r| < |v|$.

4. If u is an nth root of 1, u is called *primitive* if u is not an mth root of 1 for any $m < n$. Find the primitive nth roots of 1 for $n = 2$, 3, 4, 5, 6, 12.

5. If $w = \text{cis } (360°/n)$, prove that w^k is a primitive nth root of 1 if and only if $(k, n) = 1$.

6. Prove that the sum of the n distinct nth roots of 1 is zero.

17. The polynomial domain $C[x]$

We turn now to the consideration of the set $C[x]$ of all polynomials in x with complex number coefficients. In particular, we shall discuss the roots of the polynomials in $C[x]$. Since the roots of

$$a_0 + a_1 x + \ldots + a_n x^n, \qquad a_n \neq 0,$$

are the same as the roots of the monic polynomial

$$\frac{a_0}{a_n} + \left(\frac{a_1}{a_n}\right)x + \ldots + x^n,$$

we shall restrict our attention to monic polynomials for the most part.

First, let us consider the quadratic polynomial

5-15 $$x^2 + bx + c, \qquad b, c \in C.$$

The familiar process of completing the squares yields

$$x^2 + bx + c = \left(x + \frac{b}{2}\right)^2 - \left(\frac{b^2}{4} - c\right).$$

Let d be either one of the square roots of the complex number $b^2/4 - c$. Then

$$x^2 + bx + c = \left(x + \frac{b}{2}\right)^2 - d^2,$$

$$= \left(x + \frac{b}{2} + d\right) \cdot \left(x + \frac{b}{2} - d\right).$$

By 4-15, the two roots of 5-15 are

5-16 $$-\frac{b}{2} - d \quad \text{and} \quad -\frac{b}{2} + d, \quad \text{where} \quad d^2 = \frac{b^2}{4} - c.$$

These are the roots of a quadratic polynomial given by the familiar quadratic formula of elementary algebra. We note that the two roots of the polynomial 5-15 coincide in case $b^2 - 4c = 0$.

We have shown that every quadratic polynomial in $C[x]$ has a root. Thus there are no prime polynomials in $C[x]$ of degree 2. This is a property of the field of complex numbers not possessed by the field of real numbers. The polynomial $x^2 + 1$ in $R^{\#}[x]$, for example, is prime.

To find the roots of the polynomial

$$a(x) = x^2 + 2ix + i - 1,$$

for example, we let $b = 2i$ and $c = i - 1$ in 5-16. Then, since $b^2/4 - c = -i = \operatorname{cis} 270°$, and $d = \operatorname{cis} 135° = -(\sqrt{2}/2) + (\sqrt{2}/2)i$ is a square root of $-i$, the roots of $a(x)$ are

$$\frac{\sqrt{2}}{2} - \left(\frac{\sqrt{2}}{2} + 1\right)i \quad \text{and} \quad -\frac{\sqrt{2}}{2} + \left(\frac{\sqrt{2}}{2} - 1\right)i$$

by 5-16.

Consider now a cubic polynomial

$$a(x) = a_0 + a_1 x + a_2 x^2 + x^3$$

in $C[x]$. Upon replacing x by $x - a_2/3$ in $a(x)$, we obtain

$$a\left(x - \frac{a_2}{3}\right) = a_0 + a_1\left(x - \frac{a_2}{3}\right) + a_2\left(x - \frac{a_2}{3}\right)^2 + \left(x - \frac{a_2}{3}\right)^3,$$

$$= \left(a_0 - a_1 \cdot \frac{a_2}{3} + \frac{2a_2^3}{27}\right) + \left(a_1 - \frac{a_2^2}{3}\right)x + x^3.$$

The resulting polynomial $f(x)$,

$$f(x) = a\left(x - \frac{a_2}{3}\right),$$

has no x^2 term, that is, $f(x)$ has the form

5-17 $$f(x) = x^3 + bx + c, \qquad b,c \in C.$$

Since for each $u \in C$, $f(u) = a(u - a_2/3)$, u is a root of $f(x)$ if and only if $u - a_2/3$ is a root of $a(x)$. Hence, if the roots of $f(x)$ can be found, then so can the roots of $a(x)$. We shall demonstrate at this point how to find the roots of $f(x)$.

If, in the polynomial of 5-17, $c = 0$, then the roots of $f(x)$ are easily seen to be 0, d, and $-d$, where d is a square root of $-b$. We shall assume henceforth that $c \neq 0$. If z is any nonzero complex number, then

$$f\left(z - \frac{b}{3z}\right) = \left(z - \frac{b}{3z}\right)^3 + b\left(z - \frac{b}{3z}\right) + c,$$

$$= z^3 - 3z^2 \cdot \frac{b}{3z} + 3z \cdot \left(\frac{b}{3z}\right)^2 - \left(\frac{b}{3z}\right)^3 + b \cdot z - \frac{b^2}{3z} + c,$$

$$= z^3 - \frac{b^3}{27z^3} + c.$$

Thus $$f\left(z - \frac{b}{3z}\right) = \frac{z^6 + c \cdot z^3 - b^3/27}{z^3}.$$

Could z have been selected so that

$$f\left(z - \frac{b}{3z}\right) = 0?$$

Yes, for we would have only to select z so that

$$z^6 + c \cdot z^3 - \frac{b^3}{27} = 0.$$

This equation, quadratic in z^3, can be solved for z^3 by 5-16:

5-18 $\qquad z^3 = -\frac{c}{2} - d, \quad \text{where} \quad d^2 = \frac{c^2}{4} + \frac{b^3}{27}.$

We may select $z^3 = -c$ in case $b = 0$. Thus we need only select z as a cube root of $-c/2 - d$ according to 5-18.

The choice of z as a cube root of $-c/2 - d$ makes

$$f\left(z - \frac{b}{3z}\right) = 0.$$

Therefore the complex number u given by

5-19 $\qquad\qquad\qquad u = z - \frac{b}{3z}$

is a root of $f(x)$. By synthetic division, $f(x)$ can be factored as follows:

$$f(x) = (x - u) \cdot (x^2 + ux + u^2 + b).$$

The other roots of $f(x)$ are thus the roots of the quadratic polynomial

$$x^2 + ux + u^2 + b.$$

Note that when the values of z and d obtained from 5-18 are substituted in 5-19, the roots of $f(x)$ are expressed in terms of powers and roots of b and c, the coefficients of $f(x)$.

For example, let us find the roots of

$$f(x) = x^3 - 9x - 12.$$

While $f(x)$ actually is in $R[x]$, one easily verifies that $f(x)$ has no rational roots. The complex roots of $f(x)$ can be found by letting $c = -12$ and $b = -9$ in 5-18 and 5-19. Since $c^2/4 + b^3/27 = 9$, we may take $d = 3$ and $z = \sqrt[3]{3}$, in which case

$$u = \sqrt[3]{3} + \sqrt[3]{9}.$$

This is a real root of $f(x)$. The other roots of $f(x)$ are the roots of

$x^2 + ux + u^2 + b$, namely, (see 5-20, Exercise 4)

$$w \cdot \sqrt[3]{3} + w^2 \cdot \sqrt[3]{9}, \quad w^2 \cdot \sqrt[3]{3} + w \cdot \sqrt[3]{9},$$

where $w = \text{cis } 120°$.

By a similar kind of algebraic manipulation, one can show that every quartic polynomial (one of degree 4) in $C[x]$ has a root. The roots of such a polynomial can be exhibited in terms of powers and roots of the coefficients of the polynomial just as were the roots of quadratic and cubic polynomials.

The quadratic formula of elementary algebra was known, in a restricted form, to the Babylonians of 1800 B.C. It is interesting to note that the formula for the roots of a general cubic polynomial was not discovered until the beginning of the sixteenth century A.D., when it was found by a group of Italian mathematicians, notably by Tartaglia. The same group of Italian mathematicians also discovered the formula for the roots of a quartic polynomial.

Many mathematicians of the seventeenth and eighteenth centuries tried unsuccessfully to find analogous formulas for the roots of a general quintic polynomial (one of degree 5). Finally, about 1820, the great Norwegian mathematician Abel proved that the roots of a general quintic polynomial can not be expressed in terms of powers and roots of its coefficients. Thus there can exist no formula such as those for polynomials of degree less than five giving the roots of a general quintic polynomial. Shortly after and independently of Abel's discovery, the youthful French mathematician Galois proved that it is impossible to express the roots of any general polynomial of degree higher than four in terms of powers and roots of its coefficients. Out of Galois' brilliant work was to come the concept of group to be introduced in the next chapter.

5-20 EXERCISES

1. Find the roots of the following quadratic polynomials of $C[x]$:
   (i) $x^2 + 3x + 5$;
   (ii) $x^2 - 4x - 7$;
   (iii) $x^2 + 2x + 1 + 2i$;
   (iv) $x^2 + 4ix + 2i - 4$;
   (v) $x^2 + (1 + i)x - i$;
   (vi) $x^2 - 3ix + 3$;
   (vii) $3x^2 - ix + i + 3$;
   (viii) $x^2 - 2(i - 1)x - 2i$.

2. Find the roots of the following cubic polynomials of $C[x]$:
   (i) $x^3 + 9x + 12$;
   (ii) $x^3 + 12x - 30$;
   (iii) $x^3 - 18x - 42$;
   (iv) $x^3 + x + 2$;
   (v) $x^3 - 9x^2 - 9x - 15$;
   (vi) $x^3 + 3x + 2i$;
   (vii) $x^3 + ix + i - 1$;
   (viii) $x^3 - 6x - 6$.

3. If v is an nth root of 1, $v \neq 1$, and $m = k \cdot n$ where $k \geq 1$, prove that $v^{m-1} + v^{m-2} + \ldots + v = -1$.

4. Show that the roots of the polynomial $x^2 + ux + u^2 + b$, u as given in 5-19, are

$$w \cdot z - w^2 \cdot (b/3z), \qquad w^2 \cdot z - w \cdot (b/3z).$$

5. Under what conditions on b and c are: (i) two of the roots of 5-17 equal?; (ii) all three roots of 5-17 equal? What are the roots in each case?

6. The *discriminant*, D, of the quadratic polynomial $f(x)$ (5-15) is defined as follows: $D = b^2 - 4c$. Prove that if $f(x) \in R^{\#}[x]$, then: (i) $f(x)$ has two distinct real roots if D is positive; (ii) $f(x)$ has two conjugate complex roots if D is negative; (iii) $f(x)$ has two equal roots if $D = 0$.

7. The *discriminant*, D, of the cubic polynomial $f(x)$ (5-17) is defined by: $D = -27c^2 - 4b^3$. Prove that if $f(x) \in R^{\#}[x]$, then: (i) $f(x)$ has three distinct real roots if D is positive; (ii) $f(x)$ has precisely one real root if D is negative; (iii) $f(x)$ has at least two equal real roots if $D = 0$.

We have shown so far in this section that every polynomial in $C[x]$ of degree less than four has a root. Previously, we had shown that every polynomial in $C[x]$ of the form $x^n - a$ has a root, namely an nth root of a. These are but special cases of a far-reaching theorem of algebra called the *Fundamental Theorem of Algebra*. It is as follows.

5-21 THEOREM. Every polynomial in $C[x]$ of positive degree has a root in C.

This theorem was first proved rigorously by the German mathematician Gauss about 1800, although the Swiss mathematician Euler was probably aware of the theorem some time before. Today, many different proofs of the Fundamental Theorem of Algebra are known. No one of these proofs is algebraic in nature, and, indeed, the very nature of the theorem is such that no purely algebraic proof may be expected. Since some knowledge of the theory of functions is necessary for the understanding of the proof of this theorem, we shall omit its proof in this book. However, we shall assume the validity of the theorem and use it whenever the need arises.

A consequence of the Fundamental Theorem of Algebra is the following factorization theorem.

5-22 THEOREM. If $f(x)$ is a monic polynomial in $C[x]$ of degree n, there exist n complex numbers $u_1, u_2, \ldots, u_n$ such that

$$f(x) = (x - u_1) \cdot (x - u_2) \cdot \ldots \cdot (x - u_n).$$

If $n > 0$, then by 5-21 there exists $u_1 \in C$ such that $f(u_1) = \mathbf{0}$. This implies that

$$f(x) = (x - u_1) \cdot g(x)$$

for some $g(x) \in C[x]$ (4-15). If $n - 1 > 0$, then $g(x)$ has a root, and thus has a factor $(x - u_2)$. The desired result follows by mathematical induction relative to the degree of $f(x)$.

5-23 COROLLARY. The only prime polynomials in $C[x]$ are those of degree one.

For each complex number $u = a + bi$, let us designate the conjugate of u by "u^*," that is, $u^* = a - bi$. If $u = a + bi$ and $v = c + di$, then it is clear that $(u + v)^* = u^* + v^*$. Also $(u \cdot v)^* = (a \cdot c - b \cdot d) - (a \cdot d + b \cdot c)i$, while

$$u^* \cdot v^* = (a - bi) \cdot (c - di) = (a \cdot c - b \cdot d) - (a \cdot d + b \cdot c)i,$$

so that $(u \cdot v)^* = u^* \cdot v^*$. It is evident that $(u^*)^* = u$, and that $u^* = u$ if and only if u is a real number. We have verified the following equations.

5-24 $(u + v)^* = u^* + v^*;$ $(u \cdot v)^* = u^* \cdot v^*;$

$(u^*)^* = u;$ $u^* = u$ if and only if $u \in R^*.$

A natural mapping of C onto itself is suggested by the conjugate, namely the mapping γ defined by

5-25 $\gamma: \ u\gamma = u^*, \quad u \in C.$

This mapping is obviously a 1–1 mapping of C onto C. For each $u, v \in C$, $(u + v)\gamma = (u + v)^* = u^* + v^*$ and $(u \cdot v)\gamma = (u \cdot v)^* = u^* \cdot v^*$ by 5-24. Thus

$$(u + v)\gamma = u\gamma + v\gamma \quad \text{and} \quad (u \cdot v)\gamma = u\gamma \cdot v\gamma$$

for each $u, v \in C$. These equations show that the operations of C are preserved by the mapping γ, and hence that γ is an isomorphism of C onto C. The mapping γ^2 defined by (see 1-5)

$$\gamma^2: \ u\gamma^2 = (u\gamma)\gamma = (u^*)\gamma = u, \quad u \in C,$$

is the identity mapping that maps each element of C into itself. An isomorphism such as γ for which γ^2 is the identity mapping is called an *involution*. By 5-24, $u\gamma = u$ if and only if u is a real number. We have proved the following result.

5-26 THEOREM. The mapping γ defined by 5-25 is an involution of C. Under the mapping γ, each real number corresponds to itself.

Geometrically, the involution γ is just a reflection of the coordinate plane in the x-axis, as indicated in Figure 12.

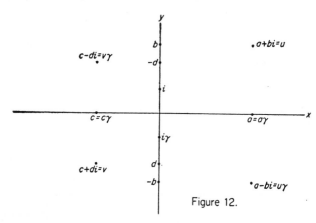

Figure 12.

5-27 EXERCISES

1. For each $u \in C$, $u \neq 0$, and each integer n, prove that
$$(nu)^* = nu^*, \qquad (u^n)^* = (u^*)^n.$$

2. For each $f(x) \in C[x]$, say
$$f(x) = a_0 + a_1x + \ldots + a_nx^n,$$
define the *conjugate* of $f(x)$ as follows:
$$f^*(x) = a_0^* + a_1^*x + \ldots + a_n^*x^n.$$
Prove that u is a root of $f(x)$ if and only if u^* is a root of $f^*(x)$ by showing that $(f(u))^* = f^*(u^*)$.

3. What can be said about the mapping $\alpha: f(x) \rightarrow f^*(x)$ of $C[x]$ onto itself?

4. Prove that if α is an isomorphism of C onto C such that $u\alpha = u$ for all real numbers u, then either $\alpha = \gamma$ (5-25) or α is the identity mapping. (Hint: prove that $i\alpha$ must equal i or $-i$.)

Consider now a monic polynomial $f(x) \in R^{\#}[x]$, say

5-28 $f(x) = a_0 + a_1 x + \ldots + a_{n-1} x^{n-1} + x^n$, $a_i \in R^{\#}$.

Then $f(x)$ is also in $C[x]$, and for each $u \in C$, (see 5-27, Exercise 2)

$$[f(u)]^* = f(u^*).$$

It follows that if u is a root of $f(x)$, then $0 = 0^* = f(u^*)$, and therefore u^* is also a root of $f(x)$. Thus the complex roots of a real polynomial come in conjugate pairs. A simple example of this fact is that the roots of the real polynomial $x^2 + 1$ are i and $-i$.

Let $u = a + bi$ be a complex root ($b \neq 0$) of 5-28. Then $u^* = a - bi$ also is a root of $f(x)$ and $(x - u) \cdot (x - u^*)$ is a factor of $f(x)$. By 5-10,

$$(x - u) \cdot (x - u^*) = x^2 - 2ax + a^2 + b^2.$$

Since $x^2 - 2ax + a^2 + b^2 \in R^{\#}[x]$ and is a factor of $f(x)$,

$$f(x) = (x^2 - 2ax + a^2 + b^2) \cdot g(x)$$

for some polynomial $g(x) \in R^{\#}[x]$. Evidently $x^2 - 2ax + a^2 + b^2$ is a prime polynomial in $R^{\#}[x]$, for it can have no roots in C other than u and u^*, and hence it can have no roots in $R^{\#}$.

5-29 THEOREM. If $f(x)$ is a monic polynomial in $R^{\#}[x]$ of positive degree, then there exist prime monic polynomials $p_1(x), p_2(x), \ldots, p_k(x)$ in $R^{\#}[x]$ with each $p_i(x)$ of degree one or two such that

$$f(x) = p_1(x) \cdot p_2(x) \cdot \ldots \cdot p_k(x).$$

The $p_i(x)$ of degree two are of the form

$$p_i(x) = (x - u_i) \cdot (x - u_i^*),   u_i \in C, u_i \not\subset R^{\#}.$$

The proof of this theorem is by mathematical induction. Assume that $f(x)$ is given by 5-28, and that the theorem is true for all polynomials of degree less than n. If some one of the roots, say u, of $f(x)$ is real, then $f(x) = (x - u) \cdot g(x)$, $g(x) \in R^{\#}[x]$. Since the theorem is true for $g(x)$, it also is true for $(x - u) \cdot g(x)$, that is, for $f(x)$. If $f(x)$ has no real root, then for any complex root u of $f(x)$, $f(x) = (x - u) \cdot (x - u^*) \cdot g(x)$ for some $g(x) \in R^{\#}[x]$, and $(x - u) \cdot (x - u^*)$ is prime in $R^{\#}[x]$. Again the theorem holds for $g(x)$, and hence for $f(x)$. This proves 5-29.

5-30 COROLLARY. If $f(x)$ is a polynomial in $R^*[x]$ of odd degree, then $f(x)$ has at least one real root.

This is evident, since at least one of the $p_i(x)$ of 5-29 must be of degree one.

If $u = a + bi$ is not real, then $p(x) = x^2 - 2ax + a^2 + b^2 = (x - a)^2 + b^2$ is prime in $R^*[x]$. Since $p(c) = (c - a)^2 + b^2$, evidently $p(c) > 0$ for all c in R^*. Thus, if the monic polynomial $f(x)$ has no real roots, $f(c) > 0$ for all real numbers c.

Suppose now that the monic polynomial $f(x) \in R^*[x]$ has been factored as in 5-29. Assume further that for the real numbers r and s, $f(r) < 0$ while $f(s) > 0$. It is evident then that $p_m(r)$ and $p_m(s)$ must have different signs (that is, $p_m(r) \cdot p_m(s) < 0$) for some integer m, and that such a $p_m(x)$ must be of degree one. If $p_m(x) = (x - u)$, $u \in R^*$, then $r - u < 0$ and $s - u > 0$, or vice versa. Thus $r < u < s$, or $s < u < r$. This proves the following theorem.

5-31 THEOREM. If $f(x)$ is an element of $R^*[x]$ and $f(r) < 0$, $f(s) > 0$ for the real numbers r and s, then $f(x)$ has a real root between r and s.

Let us find the complete factorization of the polynomial

$$f(x) = x^4 - \tfrac{3}{2} x^3 - 3x^2 - 4x - \tfrac{3}{2}.$$

By synthetic division, we verify that 3 and $-\tfrac{1}{2}$ are roots of $f(x)$, and that

$$f(x) = (x - 3) \cdot (x + \tfrac{1}{2}) \cdot (x^2 + x + 1).$$

Since the roots of $x^2 + x + 1$ are complex, $f(x)$ has been factored into primes in $R^*[x]$.

The real roots of a polynomial in $R^*[x]$ can be approximated by 5-31. For example, let us approximate the real root u of $f(x)$:

$$f(x) = x^3 + 3x - 1.$$

Now $f(0) = -1$ while $f(1) = 3$; thus $0 < u < 1$. Since $f(.3) = -.073$, and $f(.4) = .264$, evidently $.3 < u < .4$. Again, $f(.32) < 0$ while $f(.33) > 0$, and therefore $.32 < u < .33$. Thus the root u is approximately $.32$. It is evident that this process can be carried on indefinitely to give any desired degree of accuracy to the approximation of u. (u is the only real root of $f(x)$ by 5-20, Exercise 7.)

5-32 EXERCISES

1. Factor the following polynomials of $R^\#[x]$ into products of prime polynomials of $R^\#[x]$:

(i) $x^4 + 1$;   (iv) $x^4 + 3x^2 + 1$;

(ii) $x^4 + 3x^3 - 5x^2 - 13x + 6$;   (v) $x^6 + 1$;

(iii) $x^5 + 1$;   (vi) $x^4 + x^3 + 2x^2 + x + 1$.

2. Approximate the real roots of the following polynomials of $R^\#[x]$:

(i) $x^3 - 2x + 3$;   (ii) $x^4 + x - 1$;   (iii) $x^3 - 5x + 1$.

3. Expand $(\cos \theta + i \sin \theta)^n$, n any positive integer, by the binomial theorem, and thus obtain formulas for $\cos n\theta$ and $\sin n\theta$ in terms of $\cos \theta$ and $\sin \theta$. What does this yield in case $n = 3$? $n = 4$? $n = 5$?

4. Prove that any two of the roots of $x^3 - 3x^2 + 3x - 2$ satisfy an equation of the form $(\sqrt{3} - i) \cdot u + (\sqrt{3} + i) \cdot v - 2 \cdot \sqrt{3} = 0$.

5. If u is one of the roots of the polynomial $x^3 - 21x + 35$, prove that $u^2 + 2u - 14$ is another root of the given polynomial.

6. Describe geometrically the set of all points u in the plane (the complex numbers are the points in this plane) for which $f(u)$ is a real number in case: (i) $f(x) = a + bx + x^2$, $f(x) \in R^\#[x]$; (ii) $f(x) = a + bx + x^3$, $f(x) \in R^\#[x]$.

CHAPTER VI

Groups

An algebraic system of much importance in present day mathematics is the group. The theory of groups was conceived about one hundred years ago to aid in solving for the roots of a polynomial. To be more precise, the problem of determining if the roots of a given polynomial can be expressed in terms of powers and roots of the coefficients of the polynomial was reduced to a problem in group theory. In the century since then, group theory has become widely used in geometry, analysis, and even in mathematical physics. The present introduction to group theory emphasizes the groups of mappings of a set onto itself, the so-called permutation groups.

18. Permutation groups

Consider any set S with elements designated by such letters as "a," "c," . . .. The notion of a mapping of S into itself or another set was discussed in the first chapter.

6-1 DEFINITION. Any 1–1 mapping of a set S onto itself is called a *permutation* of S. The set consisting of all permutations of S will be designated by "$P(S)$."

As in the first chapter, the permutations of S will be designated by small Greek letters. Thus, if α is a permutation of S, that is, if $\alpha \in P(S)$, then $\alpha: a \to a\alpha$, $a \in S$, is a 1–1 mapping of S onto S.

For example, let the given set be I, the set of integers. Define the mapping α of I into I as follows:

$$\alpha: \quad n\alpha = n + 2, \quad n \in I.$$

Since α maps distinct integers into distinct integers (if $n \neq m$, then $n\alpha \neq m\alpha$), α is a 1–1 mapping. For each integer k, there is some integer, namely $k - 2$, such that $(k - 2)\alpha = k$. Thus α is a mapping of I onto I, and we conclude that α is a permutation of I. In geometric language, α is a *translation* of the integral points on the line two units to the right, as indicated in Figure 13.

$(-7)\alpha$	$(-6)\alpha$	$(-5)\alpha$	$(-4)\alpha$	$(-3)\alpha$	$(-2)\alpha$	$(-1)\alpha$	0α	1α	2α	3α	4α
-5	-4	-3	-2	-1	0	1	2	3	4	5	6

Figure 13.

Of particular importance to us are the permutations of a set with a finite number of elements. If $S = \{a\}$, a set with only one element, then $P(S)$ consists of only one element, namely the permutation α defined by α: $a\alpha = a$. In case $S = \{a,b\}$, a set with two elements, $P(S)$ has the two elements α and β defined as follows:

$$\alpha: \quad a\alpha = a, \quad b\alpha = b; \qquad \beta: \quad a\beta = b, \quad b\beta = a.$$

If $S = \{a,b,c\}$, a set with three elements, then there are precisely 6 permutations of S, $\alpha_1, \alpha_2, \ldots, \alpha_6$, as defined below:

$$\alpha_1: \quad a\alpha_1 = a, \quad b\alpha_1 = b, \quad c\alpha_1 = c$$

$$\alpha_2: \quad a\alpha_2 = a, \quad b\alpha_2 = c, \quad c\alpha_2 = b$$

6-2

$$\alpha_3: \quad a\alpha_3 = c, \quad b\alpha_3 = b, \quad c\alpha_3 = a$$

$$\alpha_4: \quad a\alpha_4 = b, \quad b\alpha_4 = a, \quad c\alpha_4 = c$$

$$\alpha_5: \quad a\alpha_5 = b, \quad b\alpha_5 = c, \quad c\alpha_5 = a$$

$$\alpha_6: \quad a\alpha_6 = c, \quad b\alpha_6 = a, \quad c\alpha_6 = b$$

If we think of (a,b,c) as an ordered set of elements, then a permutation can be thought of as a reordering of this set. Thus the permutation α_4 rearranges (a,b,c) into (b,a,c); the permutation α_6 rearranges (a,b,c) into (c,a,b); and so on. That $P(S)$ has six elements is a consequence of the fact that there are six possible ways of ordering three elements.

If S is a finite set with n elements, say $a_1, a_2, \ldots, a_n$, then $P(S)$ has $n!$ elements $(n! = n \cdot (n - 1) \cdot \ldots \cdot 2 \cdot 1)$. This represents the number of different orderings of the set $(a_1, a_2, \ldots, a_n)$. To see that this is so, think of $(b_1, b_2, \ldots, b_n)$ as any rearrangement of the given ordered set $(a_1, a_2, \ldots, a_n)$. What could b_1 be? Evidently any one of the n a_i's. If b_1 is known, what could b_2 be? Certainly b_2 could not be b_1, but it could be any one of the $n-1$ remaining a_i's. Having fixed b_1 and b_2, there are n–2 a_i's that b_3 could be, and so on. Then $n\cdot(n-1)\cdot(n-2)\cdot\ldots\cdot2\cdot1$ gives the total number of rearrangements, or permutations, of the given ordered set.

The set $P(S)$ of all permutations of the set S essentially does not depend on what the elements of the set S are, but only on the number of elements in S. Thus, for example, the permutations of the set $\{a,b,c\}$ are essentially the same as the permutations of the set $\{1,2,3\}$. For this reason, if S is a finite set with n elements, the set of all permutations of S will be designated by "P_n" rather than "$P(S)$." The elements of P_3, for example, are the six elements defined in 6-2.

6-3 EXERCISES

1. List the elements of P_4.

2. Which of the following mappings α of I into itself are permutations?

    (i) α: $n\alpha = 2n - 3$;   (iv) α: $n\alpha = 1 + 3n$;

    (ii) α: $n\alpha = 5 - n$;   (v) α: $n\alpha = n - 3$;

    (iii) α: $n\alpha = n^2$;   (vi) α: $n\alpha = -n - 1$.

3. For what choices of the integers a,b,c can α defined by

$$\alpha\colon\quad n\alpha = a\cdot n^2 + b\cdot n + c$$

be a permutation of I?

We return now to any set S and its associated set of permutations $P(S)$. Included in $P(S)$ is the *identity* permutation ϵ defined by

$$6\text{-}4 \qquad\qquad \epsilon\colon\quad a\epsilon = a, \qquad a \in S.$$

In 6-2, α_1 is the identity permutation. Every permutation α has an *inverse* α^{-1} defined by (see 1-4)

$$6\text{-}5 \qquad\qquad \alpha^{-1}\colon\quad (a\alpha)\alpha^{-1} = a, \qquad a \in S.$$

In 6-2, we verify that $(a\alpha_5)\alpha_6 = a$, $(b\alpha_5)\alpha_6 = b$, and $(c\alpha_5)\alpha_6 = c$, and hence that $\alpha_6 = \alpha_5^{-1}$. For any two permutations α and β, the *product* $\alpha\cdot\beta$ is defined by (see 1-5)

$$6\text{-}6 \qquad\qquad \alpha\cdot\beta\colon\quad a\alpha\cdot\beta = (a\alpha)\beta, \qquad a \in S.$$

Is $\alpha\cdot\beta$ also a permutation of S? Since both α and β are mappings of S onto S, evidently $\alpha\cdot\beta$ is a mapping of S onto S. If $a \neq b$, then $a\alpha \neq b\alpha$ and $(a\alpha)\beta \neq (b\alpha)\beta$ since both α and β are 1–1 mappings. Thus, if $a \neq b$, $a\alpha\cdot\beta \neq b\alpha\cdot\beta$ and $\alpha\cdot\beta$ is proved to be a 1–1 mapping. It follows that $\alpha\cdot\beta$ is a permutation of S.

Since, for each two elements α and β of $P(S)$, $\alpha \cdot \beta$ is a uniquely defined element of $P(S)$, we conclude that $\cdot$ is an *operation* on $P(S)$. An immediate consequence of 6-4 and 6-6 is that

6-7 $$\alpha \cdot \epsilon = \epsilon \cdot \alpha = \alpha, \qquad \alpha \in P(S).$$

That is, ϵ is the *identity element* relative to the product operation of $P(S)$. The product operation is *associative* (see 1-7, Exercise 2), that is,

6-8 $$\alpha \cdot (\beta \cdot \gamma) = (\alpha \cdot \beta) \cdot \gamma, \qquad \alpha, \beta, \gamma \in P(S).$$

The proof of 6-8 consists of showing that

$$a[\alpha \cdot (\beta \cdot \gamma)] = a[(\alpha \cdot \beta) \cdot \gamma]$$

for each a in S. Since both sides of this equation can be shown to be equal to $[(a\alpha)\beta]\gamma$, 6-8 follows readily. A consequence of 6-5 is that $\alpha \cdot \alpha^{-1} = \epsilon$. Since $(a\alpha)\alpha^{-1} \cdot \alpha = a\alpha$ by 6-8, it follows that $\alpha^{-1} \cdot \alpha = \epsilon$ also. Thus

6-9 $$\alpha \cdot \alpha^{-1} = \alpha^{-1} \cdot \alpha = \epsilon, \qquad \alpha \in P(S).$$

Just as in Section 9, we can construct a multiplication table to show the effect of the product operation on $P(S)$ whenever S is a finite set of elements. For example, let us construct a multiplication table for P_3 (defined in 6-2).

6-10

$\cdot$	α_1	α_2	α_3	α_4	α_5	α_6
α_1	α_1	α_2	α_3	α_4	α_5	α_6
α_2	α_2	α_1	α_6	α_5	α_4	α_3
α_3	α_3	α_5	α_1	α_6	α_2	α_4
α_4	α_4	α_6	α_5	α_1	α_3	α_2
α_5	α_5	α_3	α_4	α_2	α_6	α_1
α_6	α_6	α_4	α_2	α_3	α_1	α_5

To illustrate how to read this table, we note that $\alpha_2 \cdot \alpha_4 = \alpha_5$, $\alpha_4 \cdot \alpha_2 = \alpha_6$, $\alpha_6 \cdot \alpha_5 = \alpha_1$, $\alpha_3 \cdot \alpha_3 = \alpha_1$, $\alpha_5 \cdot \alpha_2 = \alpha_3$, and so on. Note that the operation $\cdot$ is not commutative, since, for example, $\alpha_2 \cdot \alpha_4 \neq \alpha_4 \cdot \alpha_2$.

6-11 DEFINITION. Let S be any set of elements, and $P(S)$ be the set of all permutations of S. A subset G of $P(S)$ is called a *permutation group* provided that: (i) G is closed relative to the product operation; and (ii) ϵ is in G, and for each α in G, α^{-1} also is in G.

It is immediate that $P(S)$ is a permutation group. In case S is a finite set with n elements, $P(S)$ $(= P_n)$ is called the *symmetric group* on n letters. The symmetric group P_n has $n!$ elements as we discovered above.

The symmetric group P_3 on 3 letters has multiplication table 6-10. Let us find the permutation groups, other than P_3, contained in P_3. A trivial permutation group is that containing the one element ϵ. Ignoring this, the permutation groups contained in P_3 can be obtained by inspection of 6-10. We must pick out subsets of P_3 closed under multiplication and inverses. The only such subsets of P_3 are listed below.

$$G_1 = \{\alpha_1, \alpha_2\},$$

$$G_2 = \{\alpha_1, \alpha_3\},$$

$$G_3 = \{\alpha_1, \alpha_4\},$$

$$G_4 = \{\alpha_1, \alpha_5, \alpha_6\}.$$

That $\{\alpha_1, \alpha_2, \alpha_4\}$ is not a permutation group, for example, is a consequence of the fact that $\alpha_2 \cdot \alpha_4$ $(= \alpha_5)$ is not in the set.

An example of a permutation group contained in P_4 is the so-called *octic group*. This group of eight elements can be described geometrically as follows. Think of the four elements a, b, c, d of the underlying set S as the vertices of a square. Then the elements of the octic group are the permutations of S that result from rigid motions (in space) of the square into itself. Let ρ denote a rotation

Figure 14.

of the square through an angle of $90°$ as indicated in Figure 14. Then

$$\rho: \quad a\rho = b, \quad b\rho = c, \quad c\rho = d, \quad d\rho = a.$$

The elements ρ^2, ρ^3, and $\rho^4 (\rho^2 = \rho \cdot \rho, \rho^3 = \rho^2 \cdot \rho,$ and so on) are rotations through angles of $180°$, $270°$, and $360°$ respectively. Evidently $\rho^4 = \epsilon$, the identity permutation. The other possible rigid motions of the square into itself also are rotations, though not in the plane of the square. These rotations are indicated in Figure 15.

Figure 15.

$$\delta: \quad a\delta = a, \quad b\delta = d, \quad c\delta = c, \quad d\delta = b;$$
$$\delta': \quad a\delta' = c, \quad b\delta' = b, \quad c\delta' = a, \quad d\delta' = d;$$
$$\sigma: \quad a\sigma = b, \quad b\sigma = a, \quad c\sigma = d, \quad d\sigma = c;$$
$$\sigma': \quad a\sigma' = d, \quad b\sigma' = c, \quad c\sigma' = b, \quad d\sigma' = a.$$

The octic group G_8 is made up of these eight elements:

$$G_8 = \{\epsilon,\ \rho,\ \rho^2,\ \rho^3,\ \delta,\ \delta',\ \sigma,\ \sigma'\}.$$

That the set G_8 is closed under multiplications and inverses is geometrically obvious, since the successive application of two rigid motions (that is, the product of two elements of G_8) and the inverse of a rigid motion are again rigid motions.

6-12 Exercises

1. Fill in the rest of the accompanying multiplication table of the octic group G_8.

$\cdot$	ϵ	ρ	ρ^2	ρ^3	δ	δ'	σ	σ'
ϵ	ϵ	ρ	ρ^2	ρ^3	δ	δ'	σ	σ'
ρ	ρ	ρ^2	—	—	—	—	—	—
ρ^2	ρ^2	—	ϵ	—	—	—	—	—
ρ^3	ρ^3	—	—	ρ^2	—	—	—	δ
δ	δ	—	—	—	ϵ	—	ρ	—
δ'	δ'	—	—	—	—	ϵ	—	—
σ	σ	—	—	—	ρ^3	—	ϵ	—
σ'	σ'	—	—	δ'	—	—	—	ϵ

2. Find the permutation groups contained in G_8.

3. Describe the group of rigid motions of an equilateral triangle into itself.

4. Describe the group of rigid motions of a regular pentagon into itself.

19. Abstract groups

Let R^* be the set of all nonzero rational numbers. Since the product of two nonzero rational numbers is a nonzero rational number, R^* is closed under multiplication. We proved previously (2-41) that R^* enjoys the following properties relative to multiplication. For each $r,s,t \in R^*$,

$$r \cdot 1 = 1 \cdot r = r \qquad \text{(identity element);}$$

$$r \cdot (s \cdot t) = (r \cdot s) \cdot t \qquad \text{(associative law);}$$

$$r \cdot r^{-1} = r^{-1} \cdot r = 1 \qquad \text{(inverse element).}$$

Note that these are precisely the properties 6-7 to 6-9 satisfied by the elements of a permutation group relative to the product operation! Thus other algebraic systems seemingly quite different from permutation groups have essentially the same properties as the permutation groups. This leads us to define the concept of an abstract group.

6-13 Definition. An algebraic system made up of a set G of elements and an operation $\circ$ on G is called an *abstract group* (or, just *group*) if the following properties hold:

(i) there exists an *identity element* e in G relative to $\circ$:

$$a \circ e = e \circ a = a, \qquad a \in G.$$

(ii) the operation $\circ$ is *associative*:

$$a \circ (b \circ c) = (a \circ b) \circ c, \qquad a,b,c \in G.$$

(iii) every a in G has an *inverse element* a^{-1} relative to $\circ$:

$$a \circ a^{-1} = a^{-1} \circ a = e, \qquad a \in G.$$

It is evident that every permutation group is a group. That every group is not a permutation group follows from the example given at the start of this section. However, we shall see a little later that every group is isomorphic to a permutation group. Let us now give some additional examples of groups.

The set of integers I under the operation $+$ forms a group. Certainly I is closed relative to $+$. By 2-18, for $x,y,z \in I$,

$$x + 0 = 0 + x = x,$$
$$x + (y + z) = (x + y) + z,$$
$$x + (-x) = (-x) + x = 0.$$

This proves that I forms a group under addition.

The set $I/(n)$ of integers modulo n is a group under addition. The desired three properties were verified in Section 9. Since $I/(n)$ has n elements, we conclude that there exists a group with n elements for each natural number n.

Again, let $I^*/(p)$ be the set $I/(p)$ with 0 excluded. If p is a prime, $I^*/(p)$ forms a group relative to multiplication. This group has $p - 1$ elements. These results follow from 3-20.

If U_n is the set of all nth roots of 1, then U_n forms a group relative to multiplication. Certainly U_n is closed relative to multiplication, and 1 is an element of U_n. Since for each u in U_n, $u^n = 1$, $u \cdot u^{n-1} = 1$ and u^{n-1} is the inverse of u. Multiplication of complex numbers is associative, and therefore the three properties 6-13, (i) to (iii), hold in U_n.

6-14 EXERCISES

1. Which of the following algebraic systems are groups?

(i) The set of odd integers, operation multiplication.

(ii) The set of even integers (0 is an even integer), operation addition.

(iii) The set of all real numbers of the form $a + b \cdot \sqrt{2}$, $a,b \in R^*$, operation multiplication.

(iv) The set of all complex numbers u for which $|u| = 1$, operation multiplication.

(v) The set of complex numbers $\{1, -1, i, -i\}$, operation multiplication.

(vi) The set of four elements $\{a,b,c,d\}$, operation $\circ$, multiplication table as follows:

$\circ$	a	b	c	d
a	a	b	c	d
b	b	a	d	c
c	c	d	a	b
d	d	c	b	a

2. If F is a field with operations $+$ and $\cdot$, and F^* is the set of all nonzero elements of F, show that F forms a group under addition, and that F^* forms a group under multiplication.

3. Make out the multiplication table for the group $I^*/(7)$ with operation multiplication.

4. If G is a group under the operation $\circ$, prove that the cancellation laws hold in G (that is, $a \circ c = b \circ c$ implies $a = b$, and $c \circ a = c \circ b$ implies $a = b$). Prove that for each a in G, a^{-1} is unique; hence prove that $(a^{-1})^{-1} = a$.

A group G with operation $\circ$ is called *abelian* (or *commutative*) if

$$a \circ b = b \circ a$$

for each $a,b \in G$. All the examples of groups given in this section have been of abelian groups. Not all groups are abelian; for example, the group P_3 of 6-10 and the octic group are nonabelian groups.

A general associative law holds in a group just as in an integral domain (see 3-6). In an abelian group, a general commutative law also holds. The proofs of these facts are identical with the proofs of the corresponding results in 3-6.

If G is a group with operation $\cdot$, the *power* of an element of G can be defined in the usual way. Thus $a^1 = a$, and, recursively,

$$a^{n+1} = a^n \cdot a$$

for each positive integer n. If we define $a^0 = e$, the identity element of G, and

$$a^{-n} = (a^{-1})^n$$

for each positive integer n, then a^k is defined for all integers k. Certain laws of exponents hold in G. Thus (see 3-7)

6-15　　　　　　$a^n \cdot a^m = a^{n+m}; \qquad (a^n)^m = a^{n \cdot m}$

for each $a \in G$ and each integer m and n. These are proved just as were the corresponding laws in 3-7. In general, $a^n \cdot b^n$ is not equal to $(a \cdot b)^n$ in a group. However, it is true that

$$a^n \cdot b^n = (a \cdot b)^n$$

in an abelian group.

In case the operation of the group G is designated by "$+$," we shall use *multiples* instead of powers in order to be consistent with our previous notation of Chapters II and III. Thus we will have $1a = a, 2a = a + a, 3a = a + a + a$, and in general,

$$(n + 1)a = na + a.$$

Designating the identity element of G by "0" and the inverse of the element a of G by "$-a$," we may define

$$(-n)a = n(-a)$$

for each negative integer $-n$. Hence, if we let $0a = 0$, ka is defined for each integer k.

We will never designate the operation of a group by "$+$" unless the group is abelian. As a consequence, the properties of such a group will be identical with the properties of an integral domain (or a field) relative to the operation of addition. For example, the properties of multiples listed in 3-7,

$$na + ma = (n + m)a; \qquad na + nb = n(a + b); \qquad m(na) = (m \cdot n)a;$$

hold in a group with operation $+$.

6-16 DEFINITION. Let G be a group with operation $\cdot$ and identity element e. The *order* of any element a in G is the least positive integer n, if such exists, for which

$$a^n = e.$$

If $a^n \neq e$ for each positive integer n, then a is said to have *infinite order*. The *order* of the group G itself is the number of elements in the set G.

Groups are quite naturally divided into two classes, namely of finite or of infinite order. The group of integers under addition is an example of a group of infinite order, while P_3 is an example of a group of finite order. On inspection of 6-10, we see that α_1 has order 1; α_2, α_3, and α_4 have order 2; α_5 and α_6 have order 3. The group P_3 has order 6.

Again, if the group G is abelian with operation $+$, the order of the element a is the least positive integer n such that $na = 0$ (this is just the characteristic as defined in 3-15). If $na \neq 0$ for each positive integer n, a has infinite order.

6-17 EXERCISES

1. Determine the order of each element of the octic group.
2. Prove that for any two elements a and b of the group G,

$$(a \cdot b)^{-1} = b^{-1} \cdot a^{-1}.$$

3. Prove that if

$$(a \cdot b)^2 = a^2 \cdot b^2$$

for every a and b in the group G, then G is abelian.

4. Prove that a group of order less than 6 is necessarily abelian. Give multiplication tables for all such groups.

If G is a group with operation $\cdot$ and identity element e, then a subset H of G is called a *subgroup* of G if H also forms a group under the operation $\cdot$. It is evident that H is a subgroup of G if and only if (i) H is closed under $\cdot$, and (ii) for each $a \in H$, $a^{-1} \in H$ also. The identity element of the subgroup H of G is necessarily e, the identity element of G. The subgroups of P_3, for example, were given in Section 18.

In any group G, the set H of all powers of an element a of G, $H = \{a^n; n \in I\}$, is a subgroup of G. The set H is closed under the operation $\cdot$ of G in view of 6-15, while the inverse of the element a^n of H is a^{-n}, which also is in H. We shall call H the subgroup of G *generated* by a. Evidently H is an abelian group.

6-18 DEFINITION. A group G with operation $\cdot$ is called *cyclic* if G is generated by an element a of G, that is, if each element of G has the form a^n for some integer n.

Since a cyclic group is necessarily abelian, P_3 and the octic group G_8 are not cyclic groups. However, the group of integers I under addition is cyclic with generator 1, since each element of I has the form $n1$ (a multiple of 1) for some integer n. In like fashion, the additive group of $I/(k)$ is cyclic for each integer k. That these are essentially the only cyclic groups will be established below.

If G is a cyclic group with generator a, and if a has infinite order, then $a^n \neq a^m$ for any two distinct integers m and n (if $a^n = a^m$ and $n < m$, then $a^{m-n} = e$ so that a has finite order). Hence G has an infinite number of elements,

$$G = \{\ldots, a^{-3}, a^{-2}, a^{-1}, e, a, a^2 \, a^3, \ldots\}.$$

Clearly the mapping $\alpha: n\alpha = a^n$ is a 1–1 mapping of I onto G.

If the generator a of the cyclic group G has finite order n, then G itself has order n. In order to prove this, let $m \in I$; then there exist integers q and r such that (2-29)

$$m = q \cdot n + r, \qquad 0 \leq r < n.$$

Since $a^n = e$, and

$$a^m = a^{q \cdot n + r} = a^{q \cdot n} \cdot a^r = (a^n)^q \cdot a^r = a^r,$$

it follows that for each $m \in I$, a^m is some one of the n elements

$$e, \quad a, \quad a^2, \quad \ldots, \quad a^{n-1}.$$

These n distinct elements must therefore be all the elements of G. We have established the following theorem.

6-19 THEOREM. The order of a cyclic group is equal to the order of any generator of the group.

The concepts of homomorphism and isomorphism, encountered in the previous chapters of this book, obviously may be applied to groups. Thus if the algebraic systems $\{G; \cdot\}$ and $\{H; \circ\}$ are groups, a mapping θ of G onto H is a *homomorphism* of the group G onto the group H provided that

$$(a \cdot b)\theta = (a\theta) \circ (b\theta)$$

for each $a,b \in G$. If, furthermore, θ is a 1–1 mapping of G onto H, then θ is an *isomorphism* of the group G onto the group H. Two groups are *isomorphic* if there exists an isomorphism of one group onto the other.

For example, the mapping α of I onto $I/(k)$,

$$\alpha: \quad n\alpha = [n], \quad n \in I, \quad [n] \in I/(k),$$

was shown in Section 9 to be a homomorphism of the additive group of I onto the additive group of $I/(k)$.

As a further illustration, it is clear that the orders of the additive group $I/(6)$ and the multiplicative group $I^*/(7)$ are equal, and therefore that there exist 1–1 mappings of $I/(6)$ onto $I^*/(7)$. Is any one of these mappings an isomorphism of $I/(6)$ onto $I^*/(7)$? The answer to this question is yes, as we shall now show. Let the 1–1 mapping θ of $I/(6)$ onto $I^*/(7)$ be defined by

$$\theta: 0\theta = 1^*, \quad 1\theta = 3^*, \quad 2\theta = 2^*, \quad 3\theta = 6^*, \quad 4\theta = 4^*, \quad 5\theta = 5^*.$$

For the sake of clarity, we have marked each element of $I^*/(7)$ with an asterisk. We assert that θ is an isomorphism of the additive group $I/(6)$ onto the multiplicative group $I^*/(7)$. One way of verifying this statement is to construct the addition table for $I/(6)$ and the multiplication table for $I^*/(7)$, and then show that corresponding elements appear at the same place in the two tables. The reader may easily check that this is so in the following tables.

$I/(6)$							$I^*/(7)$					
+	0	1	2	3	4	5	**·**	1*	3*	2*	6*	4*	5*
0	0	1	2	3	4	5	**1***	1*	3*	2*	6*	4*	5*
1	1	2	3	4	5	0	**3***	3*	2*	6*	4*	5*	1*
2	2	3	4	5	0	1	**2***	2*	6*	4*	5*	1*	3*
3	3	4	5	0	1	2	**6***	6*	4*	5*	1*	3*	2*
4	4	5	0	1	2	3	**4***	4*	5*	1*	3*	2*	6*
5	5	0	1	2	3	4	**5***	5*	1*	3*	2*	6*	4*

We are now in a position to prove the following theorem.

6-20 THEOREM. The group G with operation $\cdot$ is cyclic if and only if it is isomorphic to the additive group of the integers I in case G is of infinite order, and is isomorphic to the additive group of $I/(n)$ in case G is of order n.

If G is of infinite order with generator a, the mapping α of I onto G defined by

$$\alpha: \quad n\alpha = a^n, \qquad n \in I,$$

is 1–1 by 6-19. Since

$$(m + n)\alpha = a^{m+n} = a^m \cdot a^n = (m\alpha) \cdot (n\alpha),$$

α is an isomorphism of the group G onto the additive group of integers.

In case G is of finite order n, and a is a generator of G, the mapping θ of $I/(n)$ onto G defined by

$$\theta: \quad [k]\theta = a^k, \qquad [k] \in I/(n),$$

is an isomorphism. First off, we observe that the mapping θ is well-defined, for if $[k] = [m]$, then $k = m + n \cdot q$ and $a^k = a^m$. Furthermore, θ is a 1–1 mapping, since $a^k = a^m$ if and only if $a^{m-k} = e$, in which case $n \mid m - k$, by an observation in the proof of 6-19, and $[m] = [k]$. That θ is an isomorphism follows as in the previous paragraph. This completes the proof of 6-20.

The subgroups of a cyclic group are also cyclic. This is established by the following theorem in case the given group is of finite order.

6-21 Theorem. If G is a cyclic group of order n with generator a, then the only subgroups of G are the cyclic subgroups generated by a^k where k is a factor of n.

To prove this theorem, let H be any subgroup of G, and let k be the least positive integer such that $a^k \in H$. If also $a^m \in H$, then $m = q \cdot k + r$ for some $q, r \in I$ with $0 \le r < k$, and

$$a^r = a^{(-q) \cdot k + m} = (a^k)^{-q} \cdot a^m.$$

Now both $a^k, a^m \in H$, so $a^r \in H$ also. Since $r < k$ and k is the least positive integer such that $a^k \in H$, obviously $r = 0$. Thus $m = q \cdot k$ and $a^m = (a^k)^q$. This proves that H is cyclic with generator a^k. Certainly $a^n \in H$, and therefore $k \mid n$. On the other hand, if k is any factor of n, evidently the elements $a^k, a^{2 \cdot k}, \ldots, a^{p \cdot k}$, where $n = p \cdot k$, form a subgroup of G.

6-22 Exercises

1. If G is a group of finite order, prove that the subset H of G is a subgroup of G if and only if H is closed under the operation of G.

2. Are the groups of 6-14, Exercise 1, (v) and (vi), isomorphic?

3. List all the subgroups of $I/(18)$.

4. Prove that the multiplicative group of $I^*/(11)$ is cyclic, and hence that it is isomorphic to the additive group $I/(10)$. Find all isomorphisms between these two groups.

5. Prove that all the subgroups of an infinite cyclic group are cyclic. What are the subgroups of such a group?

6. Give multiplication tables for all abelian groups with six elements.

7. Let G be a group, and a be any element of G. Prove that $H = \{x; x \in G, x \cdot a = a \cdot x\}$ is a subgroup of G.

From the very definition of an abstract group, it is evident that every permutation group is an abstract group. While not every abstract group is a permutation group, it is true that every abstract group is isomorphic to some permutation group. This is proved in the following theorem due to the nineteenth-century English mathematician Cayley.

6-23 Theorem. Any abstract group H is isomorphic to some permutation group.

The proof of this theorem involves a fundamental procedure in algebra, that of using an element (and an operation) of a given algebraic system to induce a mapping of the set of the system. We illustrate what we mean in the case of the group $\{H; \cdot\}$.

For each $a \in H$, let θ_a be the mapping of the set H into itself defined by

$$\theta_a: \quad x\theta_a = x \cdot a, \quad x \in H.$$

Thus θ_a is the mapping that associates with each $x \in H$ the element $x \cdot a \in H$.

A familiar example of such a mapping is a translation such as indicated in Figure 13. The mapping α defined by

$$\alpha: \quad n\alpha = n + 2, \quad n \in I,$$

is a translation of the integral points on a line two units to the right.

Let us first of all prove that θ_a is a permutation of the set H. If $x, y \in H$ with $x \neq y$, then $x \cdot a \neq y \cdot a$; hence $x\theta_a \neq y\theta_a$, and we conclude that θ_a is a 1–1 mapping. Since for each $x \in H$,

$$(x \cdot a^{-1})\theta_a = (x \cdot a^{-1}) \cdot a = x,$$

θ_a is a mapping of H onto H. Therefore, for each $a \in H$, θ_a is a permutation of the set H.

Next, let

$$G = \{\theta_a; a \in H\}.$$

We shall show now that this set G of permutations of H is a permutation group. For each $\theta_a, \theta_b \in G$, the product $\theta_a \cdot \theta_b$ is defined by

$$x(\theta_a \cdot \theta_b) = (x\theta_a)\theta_b, \quad x \in H.$$

However,

$$(x\theta_a)\theta_b = (x \cdot a)\theta_b = (x \cdot a) \cdot b = x \cdot (a \cdot b) = x\theta_{a \cdot b}, \quad x \in H,$$

and therefore $x(\theta_a \cdot \theta_b) = x\theta_{a \cdot b}$ for each $x \in H$. Thus the mappings $\theta_a \cdot \theta_b$ and $\theta_{a \cdot b}$ are equal,

$$\theta_a \cdot \theta_b = \theta_{a \cdot b}. \tag{1}$$

Since $\theta_{a \cdot b} \in G$, we conclude that G is closed relative to the product operation. If e is the identity element of H, then

$$x\theta_e = x \cdot e = x, \quad x \in H,$$

and $\theta_e = \epsilon$, the identity permutation. Since

$$\theta_a \cdot \theta_{a^{-1}} = \theta_{a \cdot a^{-1}} = \epsilon,$$

$\theta_{a^{-1}}$ is the inverse of θ_a. These remarks prove that G is a permutation group.

The final step in the proof of 6-23 is to show that the mapping α,

$$\alpha: \quad a\alpha = \theta_a, \quad a \in H,$$

is an isomorphism of the group H onto the group G. If $a \neq b$, certainly $\theta_a \neq \theta_b$, and therefore α is a 1–1 mapping of H onto G. Now, by (1) above and the definition of α,

$$(a \cdot b)\alpha = \theta_{a \cdot b} = \theta_a \cdot \theta_b = (a\alpha) \cdot (b\alpha),$$

and the operations of H and G are preserved by α. This completes the proof of 6-23.

20. The symmetric group P_n

Let $S = \{1, 2, \ldots, n\}$, the set of the first n positive integers, and P_n be the group of all permutations of S, the so-called *symmetric group* on n letters.

6-24 DEFINITION. An element α of P_n is called a *cycle* if there exists an ordered subset $(k_1, k_2, \ldots, k_m)$ of S such that

$$k_1\alpha = k_2, \quad k_2\alpha = k_3, \quad \ldots, \quad k_{m-1}\alpha = k_m, \quad k_m\alpha = k_1,$$

while $j\alpha = j$ for all other $j \in S$.

Thus a cycle permutes cyclically the elements of some ordered subset of S, while it maps every other element of S into itself. The notation

$$(k_1 \ k_2 \ \ldots \ k_m)$$

is used to designate the cycle α defined in 6-24. For example, the elements (134) and (5241) of P_5 are defined as follows:

$$(134): \quad 1(134) = 3, \quad 3(134) = 4, \quad 4(134) = 1,$$
$$2(134) = 2, \quad 5(134) = 5.$$
$$(5241): \quad 5(5241) = 2, \quad 2(5241) = 4, \quad 4(5241) = 1,$$
$$1(5241) = 5, \quad 3(5241) = 3.$$

If $\alpha = (k_1 \ k_2 \ \ldots \ k_m)$, a cycle in P_n, then evidently

$$k_1\alpha = k_2, \quad k_1\alpha^2 = k_3, \quad \ldots, \quad k_1\alpha^{m-1} = k_m, \quad k_1\alpha^m = k_1.$$

Also, it is evident that $k_1\alpha^{m+1} = k_1\alpha$, and therefore that $k_2\alpha^m = k_2$. In a similar way, we see that

$$k_i\alpha^m = k_i, \quad i = 1, \quad \ldots, \quad m.$$

Since $j\alpha^m = j$ for all other $j \in S$, it follows that $\alpha^m = \epsilon$, the identity element of P_n. Hence the cycle $(k_1\ k_2\ \ldots\ k_m)$ on m numbers is of order m.

The identity element ϵ of P_n is the only cycle of order 1. The cycles of order 2 are of particular importance; these are called *transpositions*. A transposition therefore is a cycle of the form $(i\ j)$ that permutes the two elements i and j of S, and maps every other element of S into itself.

A glance at 6-2 reveals that α_2, α_3, and α_4 are the only transpositions of P_3. Thus $\alpha_2 = (bc)$, $\alpha_3 = (ac)$, and $\alpha_4 = (ab)$. In the octic group defined in Section 18, δ and δ' are the only transpositions. Using the notation of Section 18, $\delta = (bd)$ while $\delta' = (ac)$.

Two cycles $(j_1\ j_2\ \ldots\ j_r)$ and $(k_1\ k_2\ \ldots\ k_s)$ of P_n are called *disjoint* if the subsets $\{j_1, j_2, \ldots, j_r\}$ and $\{k_1, k_2, \ldots, k_s\}$ of S have no elements in common. Similarly, the m cycles $\alpha_1, \alpha_2, \ldots, \alpha_m$ of P_n are called disjoint if they are pairwise disjoint. The cycles (124), (37), and (85) of P_8 are examples of disjoint cycles. On the other hand, the cycles (124) and (2876) are not disjoint, since they have the element 2 in common.

If α and β are disjoint cycles of P_n, then

$$\alpha\cdot\beta = \beta\cdot\alpha.$$

The proof of this is left for the reader to supply. If, for example, $\alpha = (134)$ and $\beta = (25)$, where α and β are elements of P_6, then $1\alpha\cdot\beta = 1\beta\cdot\alpha = 3$, $2\alpha\cdot\beta = 2\beta\cdot\alpha = 5$, and so on.

6-25 Theorem. Each element of P_n is a product of disjoint cycles.

To prove this, let $\alpha \in P_n$, and let m be the least positive integer such that $1\alpha^m = 1$. Then if

$$\beta_1 = (1\ 1\alpha\ \ldots\ 1\alpha^{m-1}),$$

β_1 is a cycle of P_n having the property that $k\beta_1 = k\alpha$ for all k appearing in β_1. If $j\alpha = j$ for all other elements $j \in S$, then $\alpha = \beta_1$ and the theorem is proven. Otherwise, if $j\alpha \neq j$ for some element of S not appearing in β_1, and if r is the least positive integer such that $j\alpha^r = j$, then define

$$\beta_2 = (j\ j\alpha\ \ldots\ j\alpha^{r-1}).$$

The cycles β_1 and β_2 are disjoint, for if $j\alpha^i = 1\alpha^k$, then $j = 1\alpha^{k-i}$ contrary to assumption.

It is evident that $k\beta_1 \cdot \beta_2 = k\alpha$ for all k appearing in β_1 or β_2. If $k\alpha = k$ for all other $k \in S$, then $\alpha = \beta_1 \cdot \beta_2$ and the theorem follows. Otherwise, a new cycle β_3 can be constructed such that β_1, β_2, and β_3 are disjoint, and $k\beta_1 \cdot \beta_2 \cdot \beta_3 = k\alpha$ for all k appearing in β_1, β_2, and β_3. In at most n such steps, the theorem will finally be established.

To illustrate this theorem, let $\alpha \in P_8$ be defined by

$$\alpha: 1\alpha = 3, 2\alpha = 7, 3\alpha = 2, 4\alpha = 6, 5\alpha = 5, 6\alpha = 8, 7\alpha = 1, 8\alpha = 4.$$

Now $1\alpha = 3, 3\alpha = 2, 2\alpha = 7, 7\alpha = 1$, so $1\alpha^4 = 1$, and

$$\beta_1 = (1327).$$

The number 6 does not appear in β_1; evidently $6\alpha = 8$, $8\alpha = 4$, $4\alpha = 6$, so that

$$\beta_2 = (684).$$

Since 5 is the only number not appearing in β_1 or β_2, and $5\alpha = 5$, evidently $\alpha = \beta_1 \cdot \beta_2$, that is,

$$\alpha = (1327) \cdot (684).$$

If $\beta \in P_8$ is given as the following product of cycles,

$$\beta = (1462) \cdot (2547) \cdot (36) \cdot (413578),$$

then β can easily be written as a product of disjoint cycles. We note that 1 is mapped into 4 by the first cycle, 4 into 7 by the second cycle, 7 into 7 by the third cycle, and 7 into 8 by the fourth cycle. Hence 1 is mapped into 8 by β. Next, 8 is mapped into 8 by the first, second, and third cycles, and into 4 by the fourth cycle. Hence 8 is mapped into 4 by β. In this way, we establish that

$$1\beta = 8, \quad 8\beta = 4, \quad 4\beta = 5, \quad 5\beta = 1,$$
$$2\beta = 3, \quad 3\beta = 6, \quad 6\beta = 7, \quad 7\beta = 2,$$

and hence that

$$\beta = (1845) \cdot (2367),$$

a product of disjoint cycles.

6-26 EXERCISES

1. Express the following elements of P_6 as products of disjoint cycles:

(i) α: $1\alpha = 3$, $2\alpha = 4$, $3\alpha = 1$, $4\alpha = 2$, $5\alpha = 6$, $6\alpha = 5$.
(ii) β: $1\beta = 3$, $2\beta = 6$, $3\beta = 5$, $4\beta = 4$, $5\beta = 1$, $6\beta = 2$.
(iii) γ: $1\gamma = 1$, $2\gamma = 6$, $3\gamma = 4$, $4\gamma = 2$, $5\gamma = 3$, $6\gamma = 5$.
(iv) δ: $1\delta = 6$, $2\delta = 2$, $3\delta = 1$, $4\delta = 4$, $5\delta = 5$, $6\delta = 3$.
(v) θ: $1\theta = 3$, $2\theta = 4$, $3\theta = 5$, $4\theta = 6$, $5\theta = 2$, $6\theta = 1$.

2. Express the following elements of P_9 as products of disjoint cycles:

(i) $(13964) \cdot (86352) \cdot (97246) \cdot (83) \cdot (3754682)$.
(ii) $(27684395) \cdot (389457) \cdot (1254763) \cdot (214)$.
(iii) $(21475) \cdot (32586) \cdot (45316) \cdot (47) \cdot (82)$.
(iv) $(12) \cdot (13) \cdot (14) \cdot (15) \cdot (16) \cdot (17) \cdot (18) \cdot (19)$.
(v) $(135) \cdot (246) \cdot (369) \cdot (178) \cdot (456)$.

3. How many cycles of order m are there in P_n?

4. Under what conditions on a cycle are all its powers also cycles?

5. Prove that the order of any element of P_n is the least common multiple of the orders of its disjoint cycles.

It is evident that the resolution of a permutation into a product of disjoint cycles is unique.

6-27 DEFINITION. Let $\alpha \in P_n$ have the resolution

$$\alpha = \alpha_1 \cdot \alpha_2 \cdot \ldots \cdot \alpha_m$$

into a product of disjoint cycles. Then if the cycle α_i has order k_i, the *weight* of α, $w(\alpha)$, is defined as follows:

$$w(\alpha) = (k_1 - 1) + (k_2 - 1) + \ldots + (k_m - 1).$$

Clearly $w(\epsilon) = 0$, while $w(\alpha)$ is a positive integer for each permutation $\alpha \neq \epsilon$. If, for example, $\alpha \in P_8$ is given by $\alpha = (1327) \cdot (684)$, then $w(\alpha) = 3 + 2 = 5$.

We turn now to the problem of factoring any permutation into a product of transpositions. A cycle of order m (and hence of weight $m - 1$) may be expressed as a product of $m - 1$ transpositions as follows:

6-28 $(k_1 \, k_2 \ldots k_m) = (k_1 \, k_2) \cdot (k_1 \, k_3) \cdot \ldots \cdot (k_1 \, k_m)$.

If α is the permutation on the right side of 6-28, then for each $i < m$,

$$k_i\alpha = k_i(k_1\ k_i)\cdot(k_1\ k_{i+1})\cdot\ \ldots\ \cdot(k_1\ k_m),$$

$$= k_1(k_1\ k_{i+1})\cdot\ \ldots\ \cdot(k_1\ k_m) = k_{i+1},$$

while $k_m\alpha = k_1$. This verifies 6-28.

Since each element of P_n is a product of cycles, each $\alpha \neq \epsilon$ of P_n can be expressed as a product of transpositions in view of 6-28. For example, in P_8,

$$(1327)\cdot(684) = (13)\cdot(12)\cdot(17)\cdot(68)\cdot(64).$$

If we use 6-28 to factor the disjoint cycles of α into transpositions, then α itself will be expressed as a product of $w(\alpha)$ transpositions. The representation of α as a product of transpositions, unlike its representation as a product of disjoint cycles, is by no means unique. It is easily verified, for example, that

$$(684) = (68)\cdot(64) = (68)\cdot(84)\cdot(46)\cdot(68).$$

Before proceeding with our discussion of transpositions, it is necessary to establish the following identities.

6-29 Theorem. If $(k_1\ k_2 \ldots k_m)$ is a cycle of P_n and r is any positive integer less than m, then

(i) $(k_1\ k_2 \ldots k_m) = (k_1\ k_2 \ldots k_r)\cdot(k_{r+1} \ldots k_m)\cdot(k_1\ k_{r+1}),$

(ii) $(k_1\ k_2 \ldots k_m)\cdot(k_1\ k_{r+1}) = (k_1\ k_2 \ldots k_r)\cdot(k_{r+1} \ldots k_m).$

To prove (i), let $\alpha = (k_1\ k_2 \ldots k_r)\cdot(k_{r+1} \ldots k_m)\cdot(k_1\ k_{r+1})$. Then it is evident that

$$k_i\alpha = k_{i+1} \quad \text{if} \quad i < r,$$

$$k_r\alpha = k_1(k_1\ k_{r+1}) = k_{r+1},$$

$$k_j\alpha = k_{j+1} \quad \text{if} \quad r < j < m,$$

$$k_m\alpha = k_{r+1}(k_1\ k_{r+1}) = k_1.$$

Hence $\alpha = (k_1\ k_2 \ldots k_m)$, and the first identity is established.

Identity (ii) follows easily from (i) if we remember that

$$(k_1\ k_{r+1})^2 = \epsilon.$$

Thus (ii) is obtained by multiplying both sides of (i) on the right by $(k_1\ k_{r+1})$.

These identities are now used to establish the following important result.

6-30 THEOREM. Let α be any element of P_n and (uv) be any transposition of P_n. Then

$$w(\alpha \cdot (uv)) = w(\alpha) \pm 1.$$

Let $\alpha = \alpha_1 \cdot \alpha_2 \cdot \ldots \cdot \alpha_t$ be the resolution of α into a product of disjoint cycles. If the transposition (uv) is disjoint from all the cycles of α, then clearly $w(\alpha \cdot (uv)) = w(\alpha) + 1$. Next, if u appears in one of the cycles of α, say in α_1 for convenience, but v appears in no cycle of α, and if

$$\alpha_1 = (k_1 \ k_2 \ \ldots \ k_s)$$

where $k_s = u$, then clearly

$$\alpha_1 \cdot (uv) = (k_1 \ k_2 \ \ldots \ k_{s-1} \ v \ k_s).$$

Since $w(\alpha_1 \cdot (uv)) = w(\alpha_1) + 1$, we have $w(\alpha \cdot (uv)) = w(\alpha) + 1$ in this case also.

Finally, suppose that both u and v appear in cycles of α. Two cases naturally present themselves, namely the case in which u and v appear in the same cycle of α, and the case in which u and v appear in different cycles of α. If the first case holds, let us assume u and v both appear in α_1, and $u = k_1$ while $v = k_{r+1}$ for some $r < s$. Then, by 6-29 (ii),

$$\alpha_1 \cdot (uv) = (k_1 \ k_2 \ \ldots \ k_r) \cdot (k_{r+1} \ \ldots \ k_s).$$

Hence

$$w(\alpha_1 \cdot (uv)) = (r - 1) + (s - r - 1) = s - 2 = w(\alpha_1) - 1,$$

and consequently $w(\alpha \cdot (uv)) = w(\alpha) - 1$. If the second case holds, let us assume that u appears in α_1 and v in α_2, where, for simplicity,

$$\alpha_2 = (k_{s+1} \ k_{s+2} \ \ldots \ k_m),$$

and $u = k_1$ while $v = k_{s+1}$. Then, by 6-29, (i),

$$\alpha_1 \cdot \alpha_2 \cdot (uv) = (k_1 \ k_2 \ \ldots \ k_m).$$

Since $w(\alpha_1 \cdot \alpha_2) = (s - 1) + (m - s - 1) = m - 2$, while

$$w(\alpha_1 \cdot \alpha_2 \cdot (uv)) = m - 1 = w(\alpha_1 \cdot \alpha_2) + 1,$$

evidently $w(\alpha \cdot (uv)) = w(\alpha) + 1$ in this case. This proves 6-30.

An immediate consequence of this theorem is that one of the two integers $w(\alpha)$, $w(\alpha \cdot (uv))$ is odd while the other is even for each

$\alpha \in P_n$. More generally, if $w(\alpha)$ is an even integer and γ is a product of an odd number of transpositions, then $w(\alpha \cdot \gamma)$ is an odd integer; while if γ is a product of an even number of transpositions, $w(\alpha \cdot \gamma)$ is an even integer; and so on. The following theorem also is a consequence of the results above.

6-31 Theorem. If one factorization of the permutation α into a product of transpositions has an even (odd) number of factors, then every factorization of α into a product of transpositions has an even (odd) number of factors.

Assume that $w(\alpha)$ is an even integer, so that α has a factorization into an even number (namely $w(\alpha)$) of transpositions by 6-28. If α also has a factorization as a product of m transpositions, say

$$\alpha = (u_1\, v_1) \cdot (u_2\, v_2) \cdot \ \ldots \ \cdot (u_m\, v_m),$$

then α^{-1} has a factorization as a product of m transpositions, namely

$$\alpha^{-1} = (u_m\, v_m) \cdot \ \ldots \ \cdot (u_2\, v_2) \cdot (u_1\, v_1).$$

By remarks following Theorem 6-30, evidently $w(\alpha \cdot \alpha^{-1})$ is even if m is even, and is odd if m is odd. However, $\alpha \cdot \alpha^{-1} = \epsilon$, and hence $w(\alpha \cdot \alpha^{-1}) = 0$, an even integer. Thus we conclude that m is an even integer, and consequently every factorization of α into transpositions has an even number of factors. The proof for the case that $w(\alpha)$ is odd is similar and so is omitted.

This theorem allows us to define an *even (odd) permutation* as one having a factorization into an even (odd) number of transpositions. It is immediate that if α and β are both even or both odd permutations, then $\alpha \cdot \beta$ is even; while if one of α and β is even and the other odd, then $\alpha \cdot \beta$ is odd. The inverse of an even permutation is even, while the inverse of an odd permutation is odd.

6-32 Exercises

1. Prove that the set A_n of even permutations of P_n is a subgroup of P_n. This is called the *alternating subgroup* of P_n.

2. List the elements (as products of disjoint cycles) of A_3 and of A_4.

3. Show that the cycle (12345) can be expressed as a product of 3-cycles (for example, (123) is a 3-cycle). Also show that the cycle (1234) cannot be expressed as a product of 3-cycles.

4. Prove that each even permutation can be expressed as a product

of 3-cycles in P_n, where $n \geq 3$. (Hint: the product of two distinct transpositions is either a 3-cycle or the product of two 3-cycles.)

5. If $\alpha, \beta \in P_n$, with β a transposition, prove that $w(\beta \cdot \alpha \cdot \beta) = w(\alpha)$. (Hint: use 6-29.)

6. Prove that for each $\alpha, \beta \in P_n$, $w(\beta \cdot \alpha \cdot \beta^{-1}) = w(\alpha)$. (Hint: use the preceding Exercise.)

7. Prove that $w(\alpha)$ is the least number of factors appearing in any factorization of α into a product of transpositions.

8. If α and β are cycles of the same order in P_n, prove that there exists a γ in P_n such that $\beta = \gamma \cdot \alpha \cdot \gamma^{-1}$.

9. Prove that if all the cycles appearing in the representation of α as a product of disjoint cycles have the same order, then α itself is a power of a cycle.

10. Prove that the subgroup of P_8 generated by the two elements $(1234) \cdot (5678)$ and $(1638) \cdot (5274)$ is of order 8. Is it isomorphic to the octic group?

21. Cosets of a subgroup in a group

Let G be a group of finite order, and H be any subgroup of G. If a is any element of G, then define the subset Ha of G as follows:

$$Ha = \{x \cdot a; x \in H\}.$$

Thus if H has the m elements $c_1, c_2, \ldots, c_m$, the set Ha is made up of the m elements $c_1 \cdot a, c_2 \cdot a, \ldots, c_m \cdot a$. Note that these m elements of Ha are distinct, for if $c_i \cdot a = c_j \cdot a$ then $c_i = c_j$ by the cancellation law. Since the identity element e of G is in H, evidently $a \in Ha$. The set aH can be defined analogously.

6-33 DEFINITION. If H is a subgroup of G and a is an element of G, then the set Ha is called a *right coset* of H in G. Similarly, the set aH is called a *left coset* of H in G.

We limit our discussion henceforth to right cosets, which we shall call just *cosets*.

If Ha and Hb are two cosets of H in G, and if

$$Ha \cap Hb \quad \text{is not void,}$$

then necessarily

$$Ha = Hb.$$

To prove this, let $u \in Ha \cap Hb$; then

$$u = x \cdot a = y \cdot b$$

for some $x,y \in H$. Hence

$$a = (x^{-1} \cdot y) \cdot b,$$

and since $x^{-1} \cdot y \in H$, we conclude that $a \in Hb$. However, then $z \cdot a = (z \cdot x^{-1} \cdot y) \cdot b$ is also in Hb, which proves that

$$Ha \subset Hb.$$

It is obvious that we may prove

$$Hb \subset Ha$$

merely by interchanging the roles of a and b in the above argument. This proves that $Ha = Hb$ as desired. It follows that for each two cosets Ha and Hb of H in G, either

$$Ha \cap Hb \quad \text{is void, or} \quad Ha = Hb.$$

6-34 THEOREM. If H is a subgroup of the finite group G, then there exist a finite number of disjoint cosets of H in G, say $Ha_1, \ldots, Ha_k$, such that

$$G = Ha_1 \cup Ha_2 \cup \ldots \cup Ha_k.$$

This theorem is an easy corollary of our remarks above. For if the elements of G are $b_1, b_2, \ldots, b_n$, then we have only to select the distinct cosets from the sets $Hb_1, Hb_2, \ldots, Hb_n$ to establish the theorem.

Another way of stating the conclusions of 6-34 is that the set $\{Ha_1, Ha_2, \ldots, Ha_k\}$ is a partition of G.

For example, let $H = \{\alpha_1, \alpha_2\}$, a subgroup of P_3 (6-10). Then $Ha_1 = \{\alpha_1, \alpha_2\}$, $Ha_2 = \{\alpha_1, \alpha_2\}$, $Ha_3 = \{\alpha_3, \alpha_6\}$, $Ha_4 = \{\alpha_4, \alpha_5\}$, $Ha_5 = \{\alpha_5, \alpha_4\}$, $Ha_6 = \{\alpha_6, \alpha_3\}$. The distinct cosets of H in G are $\{\alpha_1, \alpha_2\}$, $\{\alpha_3, \alpha_6\}$, and $\{\alpha_4, \alpha_5\}$, and

$$G = \{\alpha_1, \alpha_2\} \cup \{\alpha_3, \alpha_6\} \cup \{\alpha_4, \alpha_5\}.$$

If the subgroup H of G is of order m, then each coset Ha_i appearing in 6-34 has m elements. So G itself has $k \cdot m$ elements. This proves the following important theorem due to the Italian mathematician Lagrange.

6-35 THEOREM. The order of any subgroup of a finite group is a factor of the order of the group.

The only factors of a prime number p are 1 and p, and therefore a group of prime order has no subgroups other than (e) and the whole group. If a is an element of a finite group G, and if a has order m, then a generates a subgroup of order m. Hence, by 6-35, m is a factor of the order of G. This proves the following corollary of 6-35.

6-36 Corollary. The order of each element of a finite group is a factor of the order of the group.

In the octic group G_8, for example, ρ has order 4, while δ, δ', σ, and σ' each have order 2. Both 4 and 2 are factors of 8.

An interesting special case of 6-36 is afforded by the group $I^*/(p)$ of nonzero elements of $I/(p)$ with operation multiplication. Since this group has $p - 1$ elements, namely $[1], [2], \ldots, [p - 1]$, the order of every element must be a factor of $p - 1$. Hence for each $a \in I^*/(p)$,

$$a^m = [1]$$

for some $m \mid p - 1$. If $p - 1 = m \cdot k$, then $a^{m \cdot k} = [1]^k = [1]$, and we see that $a^{p-1} = [1]$. This proves the following theorem attributed to the French mathematician Fermat.

6-37 Theorem. For each element $a \in I^*/(p)$,

$$a^{p-1} = [1].$$

6-38 Exercises

1. Illustrate Theorem 6-37 by finding the orders of the elements of $I^*/(13)$.
2. Find the cosets of the subgroup $H = \{\alpha_1, \alpha_5, \alpha_6\}$ in P_3. Note that H is the alternating subgroup of P_3.
3. Find the cosets of the subgroup $\{\epsilon, \delta\}$ in the octic group G_8.
4. Find the cosets of the octic group G_8 in P_4.
5. Prove that the alternating subgroup A_n of P_n has order $n!/2$. (Hint: find the cosets of A_n in P_n.)
6. Let H be a subgroup of G, and define the relation $\sim$ on G as follows: for each $a, b \in G$, $a \sim b$ if and only if $b \cdot a^{-1} \in H$. Prove that $\sim$ is an equivalence relation, and that $\sim$ partitions G just as in 6-34.
7. Fermat conjectured in about 1640 that numbers of the form $2^{2^n} + 1$ are necessarily prime. This is now known to be false, since, for example, 641 is a factor of $2^{2^5} + 1$. However, it is true that if $2^m + 1$ is a prime, then necessarily $m = 2^n$ for some integer n. Prove

this. (Hint: if $2^m + 1 = p$, a prime, what then is the order of [2] in $I^*/(p)$? Remember that $[2]^m = [p - 1]$.)

8. Prove that $I^*/(p)$ is a cyclic group for every prime p by showing that some element of $I^*/(p)$ has order $p - 1$.

9. Prove that any abelian group of order $p \cdot q$, where p and q are distinct primes, is necessarily cyclic, and hence isomorphic to the additive group of $I/(p \cdot q)$.

22. Invariant subgroups and quotient groups

We shall restrict ourselves to groups of finite order in this section, although the results are valid for any group. If G is a finite group with operation $\cdot$, and H is a subgroup of G, then it is not generally true that the partition of G into right cosets of H is the same as the partition of G into left cosets of H.

For example, the partition of P_3 (6-10) into right cosets of the subgroup $H = \{\alpha_1, \alpha_2\}$ was shown in Section 21 to be as follows:

$$P_3 = \{\alpha_1, \alpha_2\} \cup \{\alpha_3, \alpha_6\} \cup \{\alpha_4, \alpha_5\}.$$

Since $\alpha_3 H = \{\alpha_3, \alpha_5\}$ and $\alpha_4 H = \{\alpha_4, \alpha_6\}$, the partition of P_3 into left cosets of H is as follows:

$$P_3 = \{\alpha_1, \alpha_2\} \cup \{\alpha_3, \alpha_5\} \cup \{\alpha_4, \alpha_6\}.$$

The partitions of P_3 into right cosets and left cosets of the subgroup $\{\alpha_1, \alpha_2\}$ are clearly different.

Those subgroups H of G for which the partition of G into right cosets of H is the same as the partition of G into left cosets of H are of special significance in group theory. Now for any $a \in G$, the cosets Ha and aH have the element a in common; therefore, if the partitions of G into right and left cosets of H are to be the same, we must have $Ha = aH$. This leads to the following definition.

6-39 DEFINITION. A subgroup H of G is an *invariant* (or *normal*) subgroup of G if

$$Ha = aH$$

for each $a \in G$.

It is evident that each subgroup H of an abelian group G is invariant, since $Ha = aH$ trivially in this case.

The alternating subgroup $A_3 = \{\alpha_1, \alpha_5, \alpha_6\}$ of P_3 (6-10) is an example of an invariant subgroup. The reader may easily check that

$$P_3 = \{\alpha_1, \alpha_5, \alpha_6\} \cup \{\alpha_2, \alpha_3, \alpha_4\}$$

is the partition of P_3 into right cosets and also into left cosets of A_3.

It is clear that if a group G has order $2n$, and if H is a subgroup of order n, then H is an invariant subgroup of G. For in this case G has two cosets relative to H, and these cosets must be H and the set H' of all elements of G not in H. Thus, for example, the alternating subgroup A_n is an invariant subgroup of P_n for each n.

If G is a group, and A and B are any two subsets (not necessarily subgroups) of G, then the *product* of A by B is defined as follows:

6-40 $$A \cdot B = \{a \cdot b; a \in A, b \in B\}.$$

Thus the product of A by B is the subset of G consisting of all elements of the form $a \cdot b$, where $a \in A$ and $b \in B$.

6-41 THEOREM. If H is an invariant subgroup of the group G, then

$$(Ha) \cdot (Hb) = H(a \cdot b)$$

for each $a, b \in G$.

To prove this theorem, we observe that each $z \in (Ha) \cdot (Hb)$ has the form $z = (u \cdot a) \cdot (v \cdot b)$ for some $u, v \in H$. Since $aH = Ha$, $a \cdot v = w \cdot a$ for some $w \in H$. Thus

$$z = (u \cdot w) \cdot (a \cdot b),$$

and since $u \cdot w \in H$, clearly $z \in H(a \cdot b)$. This proves that

$$(Ha) \cdot (Hb) \subset H(a \cdot b).$$

Conversely, if $z \in H(a \cdot b)$, say $z = u \cdot (a \cdot b)$ for $u \in H$, then $u \cdot a = a \cdot v$ for some $v \in H$, and

$$z = a \cdot (v \cdot b) = (e \cdot a) \cdot (v \cdot b),$$

where e is the identity element of G (and H). Thus $z \in (Ha) \cdot (Hb)$, and we have proved that

$$H(a \cdot b) \subset (Ha) \cdot (Hb).$$

This together with the result above proves the theorem.

Let H be an invariant subgroup of the group G, and let G/H be the partition of G into cosets of H,

$$G/H = \{Ha_1, Ha_2, \ldots, Ha_k\}.$$

The product of two cosets is again a coset in view of 6-41, and hence there is a product operation $\cdot$ defined on G/H.

6-42 Theorem. If H is an invariant subgroup of the group G, then the partition G/H of G into cosets of H is also a group under the product operation defined in 6-40.

The identity element of G/H relative to this product operation $\cdot$ is H ($= He$), since

$$(He)\cdot(Ha) = (Ha)\cdot(He) = Ha$$

by 6-41. That the associative law holds relative to $\cdot$ is a consequence of 6-41 and the associative law of G:

$$H(a\cdot b\cdot c) = ((Ha)\cdot(Hb))\cdot(Hc) = (Ha)\cdot((Hb)\cdot(Hc)).$$

Finally, we see that

$$(Ha)\cdot(Ha^{-1}) = (Ha^{-1})\cdot(Ha) = H,$$

and hence that Ha^{-1} is the inverse of Ha in G/H. This establishes 6-42.

The group G/H is commonly referred to as the *quotient group* of G by H.

6-43 Theorem. If the group G has order n, and the invariant subgroup H has order m, then the quotient group G/H has order n/m.

This theorem is evident from the proof of 6-35.

If H is an invariant subgroup of the group G, then for each $a \in G$, Ha is the coset of G/H that contains a. Thus there exists a natural mapping α of G onto G/H defined as follows:

$$\alpha\colon \quad a\alpha = Ha, \qquad a \in G.$$

The mapping α is actually a homomorphism of G onto G/H, for by 6-41,

$$(a\cdot b)\alpha = H(a\cdot b) = (Ha)\cdot(Hb) = (a\alpha)\cdot(b\alpha).$$

This proves the following important theorem.

6-44 Theorem. If H is an invariant subgroup of the group G, then the mapping $\alpha\colon a \to Ha$ is a homomorphism of G onto G/H.

6-45 Exercises

1. Find the invariant subgroups of the octic group.
2. Show that $H = \{(1),(12)\cdot(34),(13)\cdot(24),(14)\cdot(23)\}$ is an invariant subgroup of P_4.

3. Prove that for the group H of Exercise 2, P_4/H is isomorphic to P_3.

4. If H_1 and H_2 are invariant subgroups of G, prove that $H_1 \cap H_2$ and $H_1 \cdot H_2$ also are invariant subgroups of G.

5. If G is a group of order $p \cdot q$, where p and q are primes and $p < q$, then prove that G has a unique subgroup H of order q. Also prove that H is an invariant subgroup of G.

6. Prove that if G is a group of order 15, then G is necessarily abelian (and hence cyclic by 6-38, Exercise 9).

7. If G and G' are groups and $\theta: a \to a'$ is a homomorphism of G onto G', then prove that $H = \{a; a \in G, a' = e'$, the identity element of $G'\}$ is an invariant subgroup of G. Also prove that the mapping $\alpha: aH \to a'$ is an isomorphism of G/H onto G'.

CHAPTER VII

Vector Spaces

If a given plane has imposed upon it a rectangular coordinate system, then every point in the plane is identified by an ordered pair (a,b) of real numbers. Let us define a vector to be any line segment in this plane having one of its endpoints at the origin. Since the endpoints of a vector are $(0,0)$ and (a,b), it is clear that a vector may be identified by an ordered pair (a,b) of real numbers. If "V" designates the set of all vectors in the plane, then V may be thought of as the set $R^\# \times R^\#$ of all ordered pairs of real numbers.

An operation of addition may be introduced on V as follows:

$$(a,b) + (c,d) = (a + c, b + d).$$

This is the parallelogram addition as used in the physical sciences for the addition of such vector quantities as forces and velocities. That is, if (a,b) and (c,d) are considered as two sides of a parallelogram, then $(a,b) + (c,d)$ is the diagonal of this parallelogram (see Figure 16), as may readily be verified by analytic geometry.

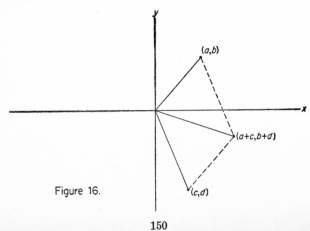

Figure 16.

150

It is evident that the operation of addition introduced on V is both associative and commutative. The vector $(0,0)$, of length zero, is called the zero vector. Since

$$(a,b) + (0,0) = (a,b),$$

the zero vector is the additive identity element of V. The vector $(-a,-b)$ is the additive inverse of (a,b), since

$$(a,b) + (-a,-b) = (0,0).$$

Thus it is clear that V is an abelian group under addition.

For any real number k and any vector (a,b), the operation of scalar multiplication is defined as follows:

$$k(a,b) = (k \cdot a, k \cdot b).$$

It is an operation that associates with the real number k and the vector (a,b) the vector $(k \cdot a, k \cdot b)$; thus it is a mapping of $R^{\#} \times V$ onto V. If (a,b) is any nonzero vector, then the set $\{k(a,b); k \in R^{\#}\}$ of all scalar multiples of (a,b) is the set of all vectors on the line through the origin and the point (a,b) (see Figure 17).

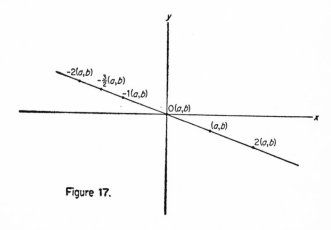

Figure 17.

The set V of all vectors in the plane together with the operations of addition and scalar multiplication is one example of a general type of algebraic system called a vector space. Vector spaces play an important role both in modern mathematics and mathematical physics. We shall present the general properties of vector spaces in this chapter.

23. Definition and elementary properties of a vector space

If F and V are two sets of elements, then a mapping of the product set $F \times V$ into V is called a *scalar multiplication* of V by F. It is convenient to designate the element of V corresponding to the elements $k \in F$ and $x \in V$ by "kx." Thus for each $k \in F$ and $x \in V$, there corresponds a unique element $kx \in V$ according to a given scalar multiplication of V by F.

7-1 DEFINITION. Let $\{F; +, \cdot\}$ be a field and $\{V; +\}$ be an abelian group. Also let there be given a scalar multiplication of V by F that associates with $k \in F$ and $x \in V$ the element $kx \in V$. Then V is a *vector space* over F provided that

  (i) $k(x + y) = kx + ky$,   (ii) $(j + k)x = jx + kx$,

 (iii) $(j \cdot k)x = j(kx)$,   (iv) $1x = x$,

hold for each $j, k \in F$ and each $x, y \in V$.

The element 1 occurring in (iv) is the multiplicative identity element of F. As the reader might notice, we have used the symbol "$+$" in two different ways in this definition, to designate an operation in the field F and also in the group V. In (i) and (ii), $j + k$ is the sum of two elements of F, while $x + y$, $kx + ky$, and $jx + kx$ are sums of elements of V. This should not prove to be too confusing, since it will be perfectly clear in any given situation whether we are adding elements of F or elements of V. In (iii), $j \cdot k$ is the product of two elements of F, while $j(kx)$ is the scalar multiplication of kx by j. (In turn, kx is the scalar multiplication of x by k.)

The notation "$V(F)$" is used to designate the vector space V over F as defined in 7-1. The elements of V are called *vectors* and the elements of F are called *scalars* of this vector space. We shall use the earlier letters of our alphabet such as "a," "k," . . . to designate scalars, and the later letters such as "u," "x," . . . to designate vectors.

We shall use the symbol "0" for the additive identity element of both F and V. Again, the context will dictate whether 0 is in F or V in any given situation. The additive inverse of $k \in F$ is designated by "$-k$" as usual; and the additive inverse of $x \in V$ is also designated by "$-x$." We point out that in scalar multiplication, the scalar will always be on the left and the vector on the right.

We note in passing that 7-1, (i) and (ii), resemble the distributive law that holds in an integral domain, that (iii) resembles the multiplicative associative law, and that (iv) states that 1 is an identity element under scalar multiplication. The fundamental difference between an integral domain S and a vector space $V(F)$ is that S has an operation of multiplication on it while V has no operation of multiplication on it, but only an operation of scalar multiplication by F.

7-2 LEMMA. In a vector space $V(F)$, the following equations hold for each $k \in F$, $x \in V$:

(i) $k0 = 0$;　　　　　　　(ii) $0x = 0$;

(iii) $-(kx) = (-k)x = k(-x)$.

The proof of (i) is based on 7-1, (i). Since $x = x + 0$,

$$kx = k(x + 0) = kx + k0$$

for each $k \in F$, $x \in V$. Hence $k0 = 0$ as desired. The proof of (ii) is analogous, and hence is omitted. To prove (iii), we have

$$0 = 0x = (k + (-k))x = kx + (-k)x$$

for each $k \in F$, $x \in V$, and therefore $(-k)x$ must be the additive inverse of kx, that is, $-(kx) = (-k)x$. The proof of the rest of (iii) is omitted.

We turn now to some examples of vector spaces.

A simple example of a vector space is obtained by letting V be the additive group of a field F, and defining scalar multiplication as ordinary multiplication in F, that is, $kx = k \cdot x$ for each $k \in F$, $x \in V$. Properties 7-1, (i) to (iv), are well-known properties of a field. Thus $F(F)$ is a vector space.

Another example of a similar nature is obtained by taking V to be the additive group of the real number system R^*, and F to be the rational number field R. Again, for each $k \in R$, $x \in R^*$, define scalar multiplication as ordinary multiplication in R^*: $kx = k \cdot x$. Since a rational number multiplied by a real number always yields a real number, it is evident that $R^*(R)$ is a vector space.

As a third example, let F be a field and $V = F[x]$, the polynomial domain in x over F. For each $k \in F$, $f(x) \in V$, define scalar multiplication as ordinary multiplication in $F[x]$: $kf(x) = k \cdot f(x)$. Since $F \subset F[x]$, the distributive and associative laws in 7-1 follow from the corresponding laws in the integral domain $F[x]$. Thus $F[x](F)$ is a vector space.

Another example of a somewhat different nature is afforded by a linear differential equation such as

$$\frac{d^2y}{dx^2} - 3\frac{dy}{dx} + 2y = 0.$$

Let V be the set of all functions f that are solutions of this equation. Thus $f \in V$ if and only if

$$f''(x) - 3f'(x) + 2f(x) = 0,$$

where f' and f'' are the first and second derivatives of f respectively. If $f,g \in V$, then $f + g \in V$, since

$$(f(x) + g(x))'' - 3(f(x) + g(x))' + 2(f(x) + g(x))$$

$$= (f''(x) - 3f'(x) + 2f(x)) + (g''(x) - 3g'(x) + 2g(x)) = 0.$$

Also $0 \in V$, and if $f \in V$, then $-f \in V$. Therefore V is an abelian group. Now for each real number k and each $f \in V$,

$$(kf(x))'' - 3(kf(x))' + 2(kf(x)) = k(f''(x) - 3f'(x) + 2f(x)) = 0,$$

and therefore kf is also in V. It is evident from these remarks that $V(R^\#)$ is a vector space.

The name "vector space" arises from examples such as given in the introduction, in which the elements are vectors in the physical sense. A natural generalization of the example of the introduction will be given now.

An ordered set $(a_1,a_2, \ldots, a_n)$ of n elements from a field F is called an *n-vector* over F. Thus, the elements of the introduction were 2-vectors over $R^\#$. The elements $a_1, a_2, \ldots, a_n$ are respectively the first coordinate, the second coordinate, . . ., the nth coordinate of the n-vector $(a_1,a_2, \ldots, a_n)$. We shall designate by "$V_n(F)$" the set of all n-vectors over F.

The operations of addition and scalar multiplication are introduced on $V_n(F)$ in the natural way. Thus

$$(a_1,a_2, \ldots, a_n) + (b_1,b_2, \ldots, b_n) = (a_1 + b_1, a_2 + b_2, \ldots, a_n + b_n),$$

$$k(a_1,a_2, \ldots, a_n) = (k\cdot a_1, k\cdot a_2, \ldots, k\cdot a_n).$$

Addition is commutative and associative on $V_n(F)$ simply because addition is commutative and associative on F. The n-vector 0 defined by

$$0 = (0,0, \ldots,0)$$

is the additive identity element of $V_n(F)$, while for each

$$x = (a_1, a_2, \ldots, a_n)$$

in $V_n(F)$,

$$-x = (-a_1, -a_2, \ldots, -a_n)$$

is the additive inverse of x. Thus $V_n(F)$ is an abelian group under addition.

We shall prove now that $V_n(F)$ actually is a vector space over F. Let

$$x = (a_1, a_2, \ldots, a_n), \qquad y = (b_1, b_2, \ldots, b_n)$$

be any two elements of $V_n(F)$. Then for each $k \in F$,

$$
\begin{aligned}
k(x + y) &= k(a_1 + b_1, a_2 + b_2, \ldots, a_n + b_n), \\
&= (k \cdot (a_1 + b_1), k \cdot (a_2 + b_2), \ldots, k \cdot (a_n + b_n)), \\
&= (k \cdot a_1 + k \cdot b_1, k \cdot a_2 + k \cdot b_2, \ldots, k \cdot a_n + k \cdot b_n), \\
&= (k \cdot a_1, k \cdot a_2, \ldots, k \cdot a_n) + (k \cdot b_1, k \cdot b_2, \ldots, k \cdot b_n), \\
&= kx + ky,
\end{aligned}
$$

and 7-1, (i), holds. One proves 7-1, (ii), similarly. The proof of 7-1, (iii), is as follows: for each $j, k \in F$,

$$
\begin{aligned}
(j \cdot k)x &= ((j \cdot k) \cdot a_1, (j \cdot k) \cdot a_2, \ldots, (j \cdot k) \cdot a_n), \\
&= (j \cdot (k \cdot a_1), j \cdot (k \cdot a_2), \ldots, j \cdot (k \cdot a_n)), \\
&= j(k \cdot a_1, k \cdot a_2, \ldots, k \cdot a_n), \\
&= j(kx).
\end{aligned}
$$

Since 7-1, (iv), is immediate, its proof is omitted. This proves that $V_n(F)$ is a vector space over F.

7-3 EXERCISES

1. List the elements of the vector space $V_2(I/(2))$. The underlying abelian group has 4 elements. Is it isomorphic to the additive group of $I/(4)$?

2. List the elements of the vector space $V_3(I/(2))$. Is the underlying group in this case isomorphic to $I/(8)$?

3. List the elements of the vector space $V_3(I/(3))$.

4. Give the proof of 7-2, (ii).

5. Prove that $-(kx) = k(-x)$ for each $k \in F$, $x \in V$, (7-2, (iii)).

6. Show how to construct a group of order p^k each element of which (other than the identity) is of order p, where p is a prime and k is any positive integer.

7. Prove that if $kx = 0$ for some $k \in F$ and $x \in V$, then either $k = 0$ or $x = 0$.

24. Linear independence in a vector space

Let $V(F)$ be any vector space.

7-4 DEFINITION. The vectors $x_1, x_2, \ldots, x_n$ of V are *linearly dependent* if and only if there exist elements $k_1, k_2, \ldots, k_n$ of F not all equal to zero such that

$$k_1 x_1 + k_2 x_2 + \ldots + k_n x_n = 0.$$

The vectors $x_1, x_2, \ldots, x_n$ are *linearly independent* if they are not linearly dependent.

An immediate consequence of this definition is that the vectors $x_1, x_2, \ldots, x_n$ are *linearly independent* if and only if

7-5 $\quad k_1 x_1 + k_2 x_2 + \ldots + k_n x_n = 0$ implies each $k_i = \mathbf{0}.$

For example, let us show that the three vectors

$$(1,4,3), \quad (-1,7,4), \quad (5,-13,-6)$$

of $V_3(\boldsymbol{R})$ are linearly dependent. To accomplish this, we must find scalars k_1, k_2 and k_3, not all equal to zero, such that

$$k_1(1,4,3) + k_2(-1,7,4) + k_3(5,-13,-6) = (0,0,0).$$

The left side of this equation can be simplified as follows:

$$k_1(1,4,3) + k_2(-1,7,4) + k_3(5,-13,-6)$$
$$= (k_1, 4 \cdot k_1, 3 \cdot k_1) + (-k_2, 7 \cdot k_2, 4 \cdot k_2) + (5 \cdot k_3, -13 \cdot k_3, -6 \cdot k_3)$$
$$= (k_1 - k_2 + 5 \cdot k_3, \ 4 \cdot k_1 + 7 \cdot k_2 - 13 \cdot k_3, \ 3 \cdot k_1 + 4 \cdot k_2 - 6 \cdot k_3).$$

This vector is the zero vector if and only if the following equations are satisfied:

$$k_1 - k_2 + 5 \cdot k_3 = 0$$
$$4 \cdot k_1 + 7 \cdot k_2 - 13 \cdot k_3 = 0$$
$$3 \cdot k_1 + 4 \cdot k_2 - 6 \cdot k_3 = 0.$$

If we let $k_3 = 1$ (any other nonzero value could be used), then these equations can be solved for k_1 and k_2 to yield $k_1 = -2$ and $k_2 = 3$. Hence

$$-2(1,4,3) + 3(-1,7,4) + 1(5,-13,-6) = (0,0,0),$$

and the given vectors evidently are linearly dependent.

It is easily verified that the functions $f(x) = e^x$ and $g(x) = e^{2x}$ are solutions of the differential equation

$$\frac{d^2y}{dx^2} - 3\frac{dy}{dx} + 2y = 0$$

discussed above. Now

$$k_1 e^x + k_2 e^{2x} = 0$$

holds if and only if

$$k_1 + k_2 e^x = 0.$$

Since e^x is not a constant, this last equation is valid if and only if

$$k_1 = 0 \quad \text{and} \quad k_2 = 0.$$

This proves that the functions e^x and e^{2x} are linearly independent in the vector space $V(R^*)$ of all solutions of the given differential equation.

If some one of the vectors $x_1, x_2, \ldots, x_n$ is the zero vector, say $x_1 = 0$, then these n vectors are necessarily linearly dependent. This is so since the equation

$$1x_1 + 0x_2 + \ldots + 0x_n = 0$$

holds, and the scalar coefficients of the x_i are not all equal to zero.

It is clear that if the vectors $x_1, x_2, \ldots, x_n$ of V are linearly independent, then so are the vectors $x_1, x_2, \ldots, x_m$ for any $m < n$. For if

$$k_1 x_1 + k_2 x_2 + \ldots + k_m x_m = 0,$$

then also

$$k_1 x_1 + k_2 x_2 + \ldots + k_m x_m + 0x_{m+1} + \ldots + 0x_n = 0.$$

This latter equation can hold only if all $k_i = 0$ in view of 7-5. Hence the former equation holds if and only if all $k_i = 0$, which fact implies that the vectors $x_1, x_2, \ldots, x_m$ are linearly independent.

If two nonzero vectors x and y of V are linearly dependent, then necessarily

$$x = ky$$

for some scalar k. This is clear, for if $k_1x + k_2y = 0$, then $x = (-k_1^{-1} \cdot k_2)y$.

7-6 EXERCISES

1. Which of the following sets of vectors are linearly independent?
   (i) $(1,0,2)$, $(2,0,1)$ in $V_3(R)$.
   (ii) $(1,0,2)$, $(2,0,1)$ in $V_3(I/(3))$.
   (iii) $2e^x$, $-3e^{2x}$, $\sqrt{2}e^x$ in the vector space of all solutions of the differential equation

$$\frac{d^2y}{dx^2} - 3\frac{dy}{dx} + 2y = 0.$$

   (iv) $3 + 2x$, $\frac{1}{2} + 4x$, $\frac{1}{2} - \frac{2}{3}x + x^2$ in $R[x](R)$.
   (v) $(1,-1,2)$, $(3,1,-1)$, $(-1,-3,5)$ in $V_3(R)$.

2. Prove that if the vectors $x_1, x_2, \ldots, x_m$ are linearly dependent, then so are the vectors $x_1, x_2, \ldots, x_m, y_1, \ldots, y_n$ for any vectors $y_1, \ldots, y_n$.

3. Show that no three vectors of $V_2(R^\#)$ are linearly independent.

4. Exhibit a set of n linearly independent vectors in $R[x](R)$ for any positive integer n.

If $U(F)$ and $V(F)$ are two vector spaces over the same field F, if $U \subset V$, and if the operations of $U(F)$ are the same as those of $V(F)$, then $U(F)$ is called a *subspace* of $V(F)$. A useful criterion for determining if a subset U of V is a subspace is as follows.

7-7 THEOREM. If $V(F)$ is a vector space, and if U is a subset of V, then $U(F)$ is a subspace of $V(F)$ if and only if U is closed relative to vector addition and scalar multiplication.

If U is closed relative to scalar multiplication, then $0 \in U$, since $0 = 0x$ for any $x \in U$. Also, for each $x \in U$, $(-1)x = -x$ is in U. Since U by assumption is closed relative to addition, evidently U is a *subgroup* of V. Since U also is closed relative to scalar multiplication, it is evident that properties 7-1, (i) to (iv), hold in $U(F)$. Thus $U(F)$ is a subspace of $V(F)$, and 7-7 follows.

The vector x is a *linear combination* of the vectors $x_1, x_2, \ldots, x_n$ if x has the form

$$x = k_1x_1 + k_2x_2 + \ldots + k_nx_n$$

for some scalars $k_1, k_2, \ldots, k_n$. For example, the vector $(2, -4, 3)$ is a linear combination of the three vectors $(1,0,0)$, $(0,1,0)$, $(0,0,1)$ in $V_3(R)$, since

$$(2, -4, 3) = 2(1,0,0) - 4(0,1,0) + 3(0,0,1).$$

Corresponding to any set $\{x_1, x_2, \ldots, x_n\}$ of vectors of V is the set S of all linear combinations of the given vectors. If x and y are in S, say

$$x = k_1 x_1 + k_2 x_2 + \ldots + k_n x_n,$$

$$y = j_1 x_1 + j_2 x_2 + \ldots + j_n x_n,$$

then

$$x + y = (k_1 + j_1)x_1 + (k_2 + j_2)x_2 + \ldots + (k_n + j_n)x_n,$$

$$kx = (k \cdot k_1)x_1 + (k \cdot k_2)x_2 + \ldots + (k \cdot k_n)x_n,$$

and therefore $x + y$ and kx are in S. It follows from 7-7 that $S(F)$ is a subspace of $V(F)$. We call $S(F)$ the subspace of $V(F)$ *generated by* the vectors $x_1, x_2, \ldots, x_n$. Clearly all x_i are in S, and S is the smallest subspace of $V(F)$ containing the vectors $x_1, x_2, \ldots, x_n$.

For example, the subspace S of $V_3(R)$ generated by the two vectors $(1,0,1)$ and $(0,1,1)$ consists of all vectors of $V_3(R)$ of the form $a(1,0,1) + b(0,1,1)$, $a, b \in R$; that is,

$$S = \{(a, b, a + b); a, b \in R\}.$$

From any given set $\{x_1, x_2, \ldots, x_n\}$ of nonzero vectors in the vector space $V(F)$, it is possible to pick subsets of linearly independent vectors. Thus, for example, any subset $\{x_i\}$ made up of one vector is a subset of linearly independent vectors. Among all the subsets of linearly independent vectors are some *maximal subsets*. A subset $\{y_1, y_2, \ldots, y_m\}$ of linearly independent vectors of the given set is maximal provided that every subset $\{y_1, y_2, \ldots, y_m, x_i\}$ formed by adjoining one more vector from the original set is a set of linearly dependent vectors.

As a simple illustration of these ideas, consider the set $\{(1,0), (2,1), (1,1)\}$ of vectors of $V_2(R)$. Since

$$(1,0) - (2,1) + (1,1) = (0,0),$$

the three given vectors are linearly dependent. On the other hand, the subsets $\{(1,0), (2,1)\}$, $\{(1,0), (1,1)\}$, and $\{(2,1), (1,1)\}$ of the given set are all maximal subsets of linearly independent vectors.

We shall now establish the following theorem concerning these maximal subsets of linearly independent vectors.

7-8 THEOREM. If $\{y_1, y_2, \ldots, y_m\}$ is a maximal subset of linearly independent vectors of the set $\{x_1, x_2, \ldots, x_n\}$ of vectors of $V(F)$, then the subspace of $V(F)$ generated by the vectors of the set $\{y_1, y_2, \ldots, y_m\}$ coincides with the subspace generated by the vectors of the set $\{x_1, x_2, \ldots, x_n\}$.

Let $S(F)$ be the subspace generated by the vectors $y_1, y_2, \ldots, y_m$ and $T(F)$ be the subspace generated by the vectors $x_1 x_2, \ldots, x_n$. Since each y_i is some x_j, obviously $S \subset T$. On the other hand, the vectors $x_j, y_1, \ldots, y_m$ are linearly dependent for each vector x_j of the given set, and therefore

$$kx_j + k_1y_1 + \ldots + k_my_m = 0$$

for some $k, k_1, \ldots, k_m$ in F, with not all of these scalars being zero. Now $k \neq 0$ (why?), and hence

$$x_j = -k^{-1}(k_1y_1 + \ldots + k_my_m).$$

This proves that every x_j is in S, and thus that $T \subset S$. Hence $T = S$, and the theorem follows.

7-9 EXERCISES. Find maximal subsets of linearly independent vectors of the following sets of vectors.

1. $\{(1,0,1),(3,0,0),(2,0,1)\}$ in $V_3(R^*)$.
2. $\{(1,0,2),(2,0,1),(1,2,1),(2,1,2)\}$ in $V_3(I/(3))$.
3. $\{1, x, x^2, x^2 - x, 3x^3 + 1, x^3 - x^2 + x, x - 1\}$ in $R[x](R)$.
4. $\{1, \sqrt{2}, \sqrt{2} - \sqrt{3}, \sqrt{6}, 2 + \sqrt{3}, 3\}$ in $R^*(R)$.
5. $\{(2,1,-3),(6,3,-9),(1,1,2),(3,1,-8),(5,2,-11)\}$ in $V_3(R)$.
6. $\{(1,0,1,0),(0,1,1,0),(1,0,0,1),(0,1,0,1)\}$ in $V_4(I/(2))$.

25. Bases of vector spaces

A very important concept in the study of vector spaces is that of a basis defined below.

7-10 DEFINITION. A set $\{x_1, x_2, \ldots, x_n\}$ of vectors from a vector space $V(F)$ is a *basis* of $V(F)$ if
   (i) the vectors $x_1, x_2, \ldots, x_n$ are linearly independent, and
   (ii) the vectors $x_1, x_2, \ldots, x_n$ generate $V(F)$.

Let us turn to the vector space $V_n(F)$ of all n-vectors over a field F for an example of a basis. The *unit vectors* $u_1, u_2, \ldots, u_n$ of $V_n(F)$ are defined as follows:

$$u_1 = (1,0,0, \ldots, 0),$$

$$u_2 = (0,1,0, \ldots, 0),$$

$$\cdot \quad \cdot \quad \cdot \quad \cdot \quad \cdot$$

$$\cdot \quad \cdot \quad \cdot \quad \cdot \quad \cdot$$

$$u_n = (0,0,0, \ldots, 1).$$

Thus the unit vector u_i has 1 as the ith coordinate and zeros elsewhere. It is clear that each vector of $V_n(F)$ is a linear combination of the unit vectors, since

$$k_1 u_1 + k_2 u_2 + \ldots + k_n u_n = (k_1, k_2, \ldots, k_n).$$

Equally evident is the fact that the unit vectors are linearly independent, and therefore they constitute a basis of $V_n(F)$. This is by no means the only basis of $V_n(F)$.

One basis of $V_3(R)$, for example, is the unit basis

$$\{(1,0,0),(0,1,0),(0,0,1)\}.$$

Let us show that the set

$$\{(1,0,1),(1,1,0),(0,1,1)\}$$

also is a basis of $V_3(R)$. First, to prove that these vectors are linearly independent, assume that

$$k_1(1,0,1) + k_2(1,1,0) + k_3(0,1,1) = (0,0,0).$$

Then $$(k_1 + k_2, k_2 + k_3, k_1 + k_3) = (0,0,0),$$

that is,

$$k_1 + k_2 = 0, \qquad k_2 + k_3 = 0, \qquad k_1 + k_3 = 0.$$

The reader may easily verify that $k_1 = 0$, $k_2 = 0$, $k_3 = 0$ is the only solution of this system of equations. Thus the given vectors are linearly independent. Since

$$\tfrac{1}{2}(1,0,1) + \tfrac{1}{2}(1,1,0) - \tfrac{1}{2}(0,1,1) = (1,0,0),$$

clearly $(1,0,0)$ is in the subspace S generated by the given vectors. Similarly, one proves that $(0,1,0),(0,0,1) \in S$. Hence S contains a basis of $V_3(R)$, and therefore $S = V_3(R)$. Thus $\{(1,0,1),(1,1,0),$ $(0,1,1)\}$ is a basis of $V_3(R)$.

7-11 THEOREM. If $\{x_1,x_2, \ldots, x_n\}$ is a basis of the vector space $V(F)$, and if the m vectors $y_1,y_2, \ldots, y_m$ are linearly independent, then necessarily $m \leq n$.

To prove this theorem, note first that the $n + 1$ vectors

$$y_1, x_1, \ldots, x_n$$

are linearly dependent, since y_1 is a linear combination of the basis elements. From this set of $n + 1$ vectors, let us select a maximal subset of linearly independent vectors containing y_1. It is evident that this subset has at most n elements in it, and that the vectors of this subset generate $V(F)$ in view of 7-8. Thus there exists a basis of $V(F)$ containing y_1 and having at most n vectors in it.

Next, let k be any integer such that the vectors $y_1, \ldots, y_k$ are elements of some basis $\{z_1,z_2, \ldots, z_p\}$ of $V(F)$ having at most n vectors in it. In view of the preceding paragraph, a possible choice of k is 1. If $k < m$, then the $p + 1$ vectors $y_{k+1},z_1, \ldots, z_p$ are linearly dependent, and, since the $k + 1$ linearly independent vectors $y_1, \ldots, y_{k+1}$ are among these vectors, there exists a maximal subset of linearly independent vectors of the set $\{y_{k+1},z_1, \ldots, z_p\}$ that contains the vectors $y_1, \ldots, y_{k+1}$. This maximal subset is a basis of $V(F)$ by 7-8, and has at most $p \leq n$ vectors in it. Thus the vectors $y_1, \ldots, y_{k+1}$ are contained in a basis of $V(F)$ having at most n vectors in it. It follows that for each integer $k \leq m$ the vectors $y_1, \ldots, y_k$ are elements of some basis of $V(F)$ having at most n vectors in it. On choosing $k = m$, it follows that $m \leq n$ which proves the theorem.

If $\{x_1,x_2, \ldots, x_n\}$ and $\{y_1,y_2, \ldots, y_m\}$ both are bases of $V(F)$, then, by 7-11, $m \leq n$. However, since $\{y_1,y_2, \ldots, y_m\}$ is a basis of $V(F)$ and the n vectors $x_1,x_2, \ldots, x_n$ are linearly independent, also $n \leq m$ by 7-11. Consequently $n = m$, and we have proved the following important theorem.

7-12 THEOREM. If the vector space $V(F)$ has a basis with n elements in it, then every basis of $V(F)$ has n elements in it.

The number of elements in a basis of a vector space $V(F)$ is called the *dimension* of $V(F)$; the dimension of $V(F)$ will be designated by "$d(V)$."

Since the set of unit vectors $\{u_1,u_2, \ldots, u_n\}$ is a basis of $V_n(F)$, the dimension of $V_n(F)$ is n. The vectors $(a_1, a_2, \ldots, a_n)$ of $V_n(F)$ are frequently called "n-dimensional vectors," a name which is suitable since these vectors are elements of an n-dimensional vector space. A consequence of 7-11 is that any $n + 1$ vectors of $V_n(F)$ are linearly dependent. Thus, for example, the four vectors

$$(1,0,1), \quad (2,-1,3), \quad (0,1,2), \quad (3,-4,0)$$

of $V_3(R)$ are linearly dependent simply because they are four in number.

A vector space such as $R[x](R)$ does not have a basis in the sense of 7-10, and hence does not have dimension. However, it is clear that the infinite set $\{1, x, x^2, \ldots, x^n, \ldots\}$ of vectors of $R[x]$ generates $R[x](R)$ in the sense that each $a(x) \in R[x]$ is a linear combination of a finite number of vectors of this set, that is,

$$a(x) = a_0 \cdot 1 + a_1 x + a_2 x^2 + \ldots + a_m x^m, \qquad a_i \in R.$$

Also, the vectors $1, x, x^2, \ldots, x^n, \ldots$ are linearly independent in the sense that any finite set of these vectors is linearly independent. Thus it is evident that the set $\{1, x, x^2, \ldots, x^n, \ldots\}$ is a basis of $R[x](R)$ if the word basis is redefined in a proper way. Then the vector space $R[x](R)$ would be called an infinite dimensional vector space. We leave the details of the infinite dimensional vector spaces for more advanced texts, and concentrate here on finite dimensional vector spaces.

The concept of isomorphism (or homomorphism) carries over to vector spaces as expected. However, since a vector space involves two sets, namely V and F, it might not be clear how to define an isomorphism in this case. We give this definition below.

7-13 DEFINITION. Let $U(F)$ and $V(F)$ be vector spaces over the same field F, and let γ be a 1–1 mapping of U onto V. Then γ is an *isomorphism* between $U(F)$ and $V(F)$ provided that

(i) $(x + y)\gamma = x\gamma + y\gamma$, and (ii) $(kx)\gamma = k(x\gamma)$

for each $x, y \in U$, $k \in F$.

If $U(F)$ and $V(F)$ are isomorphic under the mapping γ of U onto V, and if $\{x_1, x_2, \ldots, x_n\}$ is a basis of $U(F)$, then $\{x_1\gamma, x_2\gamma, \ldots, x_n\gamma\}$ is a basis of $V(F)$. To see this, let x be any element of U; then

$$x = k_1 x_1 + k_2 x_2 + \ldots + k_n x_n$$

for some $k_i \in F$. Now the corresponding element $x\gamma \in V$ has the representation

$$x\gamma = (k_1 x_1 + k_2 x_2 + \ldots + k_n x_n)\gamma,$$

$$= (k_1 x_1)\gamma + (k_2 x_2)\gamma + \ldots + (k_n x_n)\gamma \quad \text{(by 7-13, (i))},$$

$$= k_1(x_1\gamma) + k_2(x_2\gamma) + \ldots + k_n(x_n\gamma) \quad \text{(by 7-13, (ii))}.$$

Thus $x\gamma$ is a linear combination of the elements $x_1\gamma, x_2\gamma, \ldots, x_n\gamma$ of V. Furthermore, the elements $x_1\gamma, x_2\gamma, \ldots, x_n\gamma$ are linearly independent, for if

$$k_1(x_1\gamma) + k_2(x_2\gamma) + \ldots + k_n(x_n\gamma) = 0,$$

then $$(k_1 x_1 + k_2 x_2 + \ldots + k_n x_n)\gamma = 0,$$

and, since $0\gamma = 0$ (why?),

$$k_1 x_1 + k_2 x_2 + \ldots + k_n x_n = 0.$$

However, the vectors $x_1, x_2, \ldots, x_n$ are linearly independent, and therefore each $k_i = 0$. This in turn proves that the vectors $x_1\gamma, x_2\gamma, \ldots, x_n\gamma$ are linearly independent, and hence that they constitute a basis of $V(F)$. This proves that isomorphic vector spaces necessarily have the same dimension.

On the other hand, let $U(F)$ and $V(F)$ be any two vector spaces over F having the same dimension n, and let $\{x_1, x_2, \ldots, x_n\}$ be a basis of $U(F)$ and $\{y_1, y_2, \ldots, y_n\}$ be a basis of $V(F)$. Define the mapping γ of U into V as follows: for each $x \in U$, say

$$x = k_1 x_1 + k_2 x_2 + \ldots + k_n x_n, \quad k_i \in F,$$

define the element $x\gamma \in V$ by

$$x\gamma = k_1 y_1 + k_2 y_2 + \ldots + k_n y_n.$$

Let us prove that γ is an isomorphism between $U(F)$ and $V(F)$. First of all, it is quite evident that γ is a 1–1 mapping of U onto V. If y is another element of U, say

$$y = j_1 x_1 + j_2 x_2 + \ldots + j_n x_n, \quad j_i \in F,$$

then

$$(x + y) = (k_1 + j_1)x_1 + (k_2 + j_2)x_2 + \ldots + (k_n + j_n)x_n,$$

and

$$(x + y)\gamma = (k_1 + j_1)y_1 + (k_2 + j_2)y_2 + \ldots + (k_n + j_n)y_n.$$

It is clear that the right side of this equation is just $x\gamma + y\gamma$, and therefore that

$$(x + y)\gamma = x\gamma + y\gamma.$$

Similarly, one proves that

$$(kx)\gamma = k(x\gamma)$$

for each $k \in F$. This proves that γ is an isomorphism, and establishes the following theorem for finite dimensional vector spaces.

7-14 THEOREM. The vector spaces $U(F)$ and $V(F)$ are isomorphic if and only if they have the same dimension.

For each positive integer n, we already have an example of an n-dimensional vector space over the field F, namely $V_n(F)$. We thus have the following corollary of 7-14.

7-15 COROLLARY. If $V(F)$ is a vector space of dimension n, then $V(F)$ is isomorphic to $V_n(F)$.

For example, if $V(F)$ has the basis $\{x_1, x_2, x_3\}$, then the mapping γ,

$$\gamma:\ (k_1 x_1 + k_2 x_2 + k_3 x_3)\gamma = (k_1, k_2, k_3), \qquad k_i \in F,$$

of $V(F)$ onto $V_3(F)$ is an isomorphism. Note that $x_1\gamma = u_1$, $x_2\gamma = u_2$, and $x_3\gamma = u_3$, where the u_i are the unit vectors.

7-16 EXERCISES. In each of Exercises 1 to 6, find a basis of the given vector space that contains the given set of vectors.

1. $\{(1,1,0),(1,0,1)\}$ in $V_3(\boldsymbol{R})$.
2. $\{(1,0,1,0),(0,1,1,0)\}$ in $V_4(\boldsymbol{I}/(2))$.
3. $\{(-3,1,-1,2),(4,2,-2,4),(2,5,-2,2)\}$ in $V_4(\boldsymbol{R})$.
4. $\{(2,1,0,1),(1,2,0,1)\}$ in $V_4(\boldsymbol{I}/(3))$.
5. $\{1 - i\}$ in $\boldsymbol{C}(\boldsymbol{R}^*)$.
6. $\{(0,i,0,1),(i,1,1,0)\}$ in $V_4(\boldsymbol{C})$.
7. Find all bases of the vector space $V_3(\boldsymbol{I}/(2))$.
8. In the vector space $V_n(F)$, define the *product* $(\cdot)$ of two vectors as follows: $(a_1, a_2, \ldots, a_n) \cdot (b_1, b_2, \ldots, b_n) = (a_1 \cdot b_1, a_2 \cdot b_2, \ldots, a_n \cdot b_n)$. Is $V_n(F)$ a field under the two operations of vector addition and multiplication? If your answer is no, tell precisely what field properties do not hold.
9. Let $V_3(\boldsymbol{I})$ be the set of all 3-vectors (a,b,c) with integers for coordinates. If we define addition and scalar multiplication of vectors

in $V_3(I)$ as previously, how does the resulting algebraic system differ from a vector space?

10. Define linear independence of vectors in $V_3(I)$ (of Exercise 9) just as in a vector space. Prove that the vectors $(2,0,0),(0,3,0),(0,0,1)$ are linearly independent. Do they make up a basis of $V_3(I)$? Is there any basis of $V_3(I)$ containing these three vectors?

11. Prove that every basis of $V_3(I)$ (of Exercise 9) has three vectors in it.

26. Algebra of subspaces of a vector space

Consider now a vector space $V(F)$ of dimension n. One subspace of $V(F)$ is $0(F)$ where 0 contains the single vector 0. This is the *zero subspace* of $V(F)$; it is said to have *dimension zero*. Another trivial subspace of $V(F)$ is $V(F)$ itself; naturally, this subspace has dimension n.

If $S(F)$ is a subspace of $V(F)$ differing from both $0(F)$ and $V(F)$, then $S(F)$ has dimension $d(S)$, where $0 < d(S) < n$. To see this, let $\{x_1, x_2, \ldots, x_m\}$ be a maximal subset of linearly independent vectors of S. Such a maximal subset must exist, since any set of $n + 1$ vectors of S is necessarily linearly dependent. The set $\{x_1, x_2, \ldots, x_m\}$ is a basis of $S(F)$; for if it were not, there would exist some vector $y \in S$ that is not a linear combination of the vectors $x_1, x_2, \ldots, x_m$, and it would follow that the vectors $x_1, x_2, \ldots, x_m, y$ are linearly independent. It is evident that $0 < m < n$.

For any two subspaces $S(F)$ and $T(F)$ of $V(F)$, define the *intersection* of S and T in the usual way (see Section 1):

$$S \cap T = \{x; x \in S \text{ and } x \in T\}.$$

If $x, y \in S \cap T$, then clearly $x + y \in S \cap T$ since both S and T are closed under addition. Also, for each $x \in S \cap T$, $k \in F$, evidently $kx \in S \cap T$. Thus, in view of 7-7, $(S \cap T)(F)$ is a subspace of $V(F)$. In words, the intersection of two subspaces of $V(F)$ also is a subspace of $V(F)$. Naturally, the same is true of the intersection of any number of subspaces of $V(F)$.

The *union* of two subspaces $S(F)$ and $T(F)$ of $V(F)$ is defined in the following way:

$$S + T = \{x + y; x \in S, y \in T\}.$$

Thus $S + T$ is the set of all vectors of the form $x + y$, where $x \in S$

and $y \in T$. If $u,v \in S$ and $x,y \in T$, then $u + v \in S$, $x + y \in T$, and $(u + x) + (v + y) = (u + v) + (x + y)$. Therefore the sum of two elements of $S + T$ is also in $S + T$. Also if $x \in S$ and $y \in T$, then $kx \in S$ and $ky \in T$, and, since $k(x + y) = kx + ky$, $S + T$ is closed under scalar multiplication. It follows by 7-7 that $(S + T)(F)$ is a subspace of $V(F)$.

The relationship between the subspaces S, T, $S \cap T$, and $S + T$ is shown in the following diagram. This indicates that S and T contain $S \cap T$, while S and T are both contained in $S + T$.

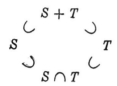

Actually, $S + T$ is the *least upper bound* of S and T in the sense that it is the smallest subspace of $V(F)$ containing both S and T, while $S \cap T$ is the *greatest lower bound* of S and T in the sense that it is the largest subspace of $V(F)$ contained in both S and T. The relationship between the dimensions of these four subspaces of $V(F)$ is given by the following theorem.

7-17 THEOREM. If $S(F)$ and $T(F)$ are subspaces of $V(F)$, then

$$d(S + T) = d(S) + d(T) - d(S \cap T).$$

The theorem is obvious if either S or T is the zero subspace of $V(F)$ (why?), so let us assume that both S and T are nonzero subspaces. If also $S \cap T \neq 0$, let $\{x_1, \ldots, x_p\}$ be a basis of $S \cap T$. Since the vectors $x_1, \ldots, x_p$ are linearly independent and in S, there exists a basis of S containing these vectors. Similar statements also hold for T, and thus there exists a basis of S of the form $\{x_1, \ldots, x_p, y_1, \ldots, y_q\}$ and a basis of T of the form $\{x_1, \ldots, x_p, z_1, \ldots, z_r\}$.

Each element $y \in S$ is a linear combination of the basis elements listed above, and similarly for each $z \in T$. Thus each $y + z \in S + T$ is a linear combination of the elements $x_1, \ldots, x_p, y_1, \ldots, y_q, z_1, \ldots, z_r$. It will follow that the set of these $p + q + r$ elements is a basis of $S + T$ as soon as we show that they are linearly independent. If

$$k_1x_1 + \ldots + k_px_p + j_1y_1 + \ldots + j_qy_q + h_1z_1 + \ldots + h_rz_r = 0,$$

for some k_i, j_i, and h_i in F, then

$$j_1y_1 + \ldots + j_qy_q = -(k_1x_1 + \ldots + k_px_p + h_1z_1 + \ldots + h_rz_r),$$

and therefore $j_1y_1 + \ldots + j_qy_q \in T$. Since this element is also in S, evidently it is in $S \cap T$, and hence is a linear combination of the x's,

$$j_1y_1 + \ldots + j_qy_q = c_1x_1 + \ldots + c_px_p.$$

However, the elements $y_1, \ldots, y_q, x_1, \ldots, x_p$ are linearly independent, and therefore all j_i must be zero. A similar argument shows that all h_i must also be zero, and thus all k_i are zero. This proves that

$$d(S + T) = p + q + r.$$

Since $d(S) = p + q$, $d(T) = p + r$, and $d(S \cap T) = p$, the theorem follows readily.

A slight modification of the proof above disposes of the case when $S \cap T = 0$, and the proof of 7-17 is completed.

Consider now the set L of all subspaces of the vector space $V(F)$. The elements of L are the subspaces of $V(F)$. The order relation $\subset$ is introduced naturally on L: thus for each $S,T \in L$, $S \subset T$ if and only if the subspace $S(F)$ is contained in (or equal to) the subspace $T(F)$. We have already seen how to define operations of intersection ($\cap$) and union ($+$) on L. The set L together with the order relation $\subset$ and the operations $\cap$ and $+$ is an example of an algebraic system called a *lattice*. This is the lattice of all subspaces of a vector space.

7-18 EXERCISES

1. If $S(\boldsymbol{R})$ and $T(\boldsymbol{R})$ are subspaces of $V_3(\boldsymbol{R})$, and S has basis $\{(0,1,0),(0,2,1)\}$ and T has basis $\{(1,0,-1),(0,1,1)\}$, find bases for $S + T$ and $S \cap T$. Illustrate 7-17 with this exercise.

2. If $S(\boldsymbol{R})$ and $T(\boldsymbol{R})$ are subspaces of $V_4(\boldsymbol{R})$, and S has basis $\{(0,1,0,0),(1,0,1,-1),(1,0,0,1)\}$ and T has basis $\{(0,0,2,-3),(1,1,0,-1),(0,0,0,1)\}$, find bases for $S + T$ and $S \cap T$.

3. List all the subspaces of $V_2(\boldsymbol{I}/(2))$. Make a diagram indicating the order relation existing between these subspaces.

4. Do the same as in Exercise 3 for $V_3(\boldsymbol{I}/(2))$.

5. Let $S(\boldsymbol{C})$ be the subspace of $V_4(\boldsymbol{C})$ generated by the vectors $(1,0,i,0)$ and $(1,-i,0,0)$. Find a subspace $T(\boldsymbol{C})$ such that $S + T = V_4(\boldsymbol{C})$, $S \cap T = 0$. Is the subspace $T(\boldsymbol{C})$ unique?

6. Let L be the set of all subspaces of the vector space $V(F)$. Prove the following properties of the lattice $\{L;\subset,\cap,+\}$:

    (i) $\subset$ is reflexive and transitive.

    (ii) $\cap$ is associative and commutative.

    (iii) $+$ is associative and commutative.

    (iv) there exist identity elements relative to both $\cap$ and $+$.

    (v) if $S,T,U \in L$, and if $S \subset U$, then

$$S + (T \cap U) = (S + T) \cap U.$$

CHAPTER VIII

Linear Transformations and Matrices

Starting with a vector space $V(F)$, it is possible to build another algebraic system, the so-called algebra of linear transformations of $V(F)$. This chapter will be devoted to a discussion of this algebra of linear transformations, and of the related algebra of matrices.

27. Elementary properties of linear transformations

The vector spaces encountered in this chapter all are assumed to have a finite, nonzero dimension. Our principal concern now is not with vector spaces, but with certain mappings of vector spaces into themselves. Mappings of one set into another have been designated by small Greek letters up to this point. However, we shall not use Greek letters for the special mappings, called "linear transformations," discussed in the present chapter, but rather shall use capital italic letters such as "A," "C," . . . .. Thus if $V(F)$ is a vector space and if A is a mapping of V into V, then corresponding to each $x \in V$ is an element $xA \in V$.

8-1 DEFINITION. If $V(F)$ is a vector space, a mapping A of V into V is a *linear transformation* of $V(F)$ if and only if

(i) $(x + y)A = xA + yA$, and (ii) $(kx)A = k(xA)$

hold for each $x,y \in V$, $k \in F$.

To illustrate this concept, let A be the mapping of $V_2(R^*)$ into itself defined by

$$A: \quad (a,b)A = (a - b, a + 2b), \qquad (a,b) \in V_2(R^*).$$

Thus, for example, if $a = 1$ and $b = 0$, we have

$$(1,0)A = (1,1).$$

170

Other examples are

$$(0,1)A = (-1,2); \qquad (3,\tfrac{1}{2})A = (\tfrac{5}{2},4).$$

In order to show that 8-1, (i), holds, let (a,b) and (c,d) be any two vectors of $V_2(\boldsymbol{R}^*)$. Then $(a,b) + (c,d) = (a + c, b + d)$ and

$$
\begin{aligned}
((a,b) + (c,d))A &= (a + c, b + d)A, \\
&= (a + c - b - d, a + c + 2b + 2d), \\
&= (a - b, a + 2b) + (c - d, c + 2d), \\
&= (a,b)A + (c,d)A.
\end{aligned}
$$

This proves that 8-1, (i), holds for A. Since $k(a,b) = (k \cdot a, k \cdot b)$ for each $(a,b) \in V_2(\boldsymbol{R}^*)$, $k \in \boldsymbol{R}^*$, evidently

$$
\begin{aligned}
(k(a,b))A &= (k \cdot a, k \cdot b)A, \\
&= (k \cdot a - k \cdot b, k \cdot a + 2k \cdot b), \\
&= k(a - b, a + 2b), \\
&= k((a,b)A).
\end{aligned}
$$

This shows that 8-1, (ii), holds, and completes the proof that A is a linear transformation of $V_2(\boldsymbol{R}^*)$.

So that the reader will not think that every mapping of a vector space into itself is a linear transformation, we give now an example of a mapping of $V_2(\boldsymbol{R}^*)$ into itself that is not a linear transformation. Let the mapping B of $V_2(\boldsymbol{R}^*)$ into itself be defined by

$$B: \quad (a,b)B = (3 + b, a), \qquad (a,b) \in V_2(\boldsymbol{R}^*).$$

For example,

$$(1,0)B = (3,1), \qquad (0,1)B = (4,0), \qquad (1,1)B = (4,1).$$

Since $\qquad ((1,0) + (0,1))B = (1,1)B = (4,1),$

while $\qquad (1,0)B + (0,1)B = (3,1) + (4,0) = (7,1),$

evidently $((1,0) + (0,1))B \neq (1,0)B + (0,1)B$. Thus B is not a linear transformation of $V_2(\boldsymbol{R}^*)$.

8-2 Exercises. Which of the following mappings A of $V_2(R^*)$ into itself are linear transformations? Describe each mapping geometrically, considering $V_2(R^*)$ as the set of all points in a plane.

1. A: $(a,b)A = (a + 2,b)$.
2. A: $(a,b)A = (-a,-b)$.
3. A: $(a,b)A = (a,0)$.
4. A: $(a,b)A = (a,1)$.
5. A: $(a,b)A = ((a + b)/\sqrt{2}, (-a + b)/\sqrt{2})$.
6. A: $(a,b)A = (b,2a)$.

If A is a linear transformation of the vector space $V(F)$, and if S is a subset of V, then define

$$SA = \{xA; x \in S\}.$$

One may think of the set SA as the image of S under the mapping A.

Let us prove now that if $S(F)$ is a subspace of $V(F)$, then $SA(F)$ also is a subspace of $V(F)$. In view of 7-7, we need only show that SA is closed under addition and scalar multiplication. If $x,y \in S$, then $x + y \in S$ also; hence, if $xA, yA \in SA$, then $xA + yA = (x + y)A \in SA$. Thus SA is closed under addition. If $x \in S$, $k \in F$, then $kx \in S$; hence, if $xA \in SA$, $k(xA) = (kx)A$ is in SA. Thus SA is closed under scalar multiplication, and we have proved that $SA(F)$ is a subspace of $V(F)$. An instance of this result of particular importance is that $VA(F)$ is a subspace of $V(F)$. Here $VA(F)$ is the image of the whole space $V(F)$. If A is a mapping of V onto V, then evidently $VA = V$.

If the subspace $S(F)$ of $V(F)$ has basis $\{x_1, x_2, \ldots, x_m\}$, then each $x \in S$ has the form

$$x = k_1 x_1 + k_2 x_2 + \ldots + k_m x_m,$$

for some $k_i \in F$. Hence each $xA \in SA$ has the form

$$xA = (k_1 x_1 + k_2 x_2 + \ldots + k_m x_m)A,$$
$$= (k_1 x_1)A + (k_2 x_2)A + \ldots + (k_m x_m)A \quad \text{(by 8-1, (i))},$$
$$= k_1(x_1 A) + k_2(x_2 A) + \ldots + k_m(x_m A) \quad \text{(by 8-1, (ii))}.$$

It follows that the vectors $x_1 A, x_2 A, \ldots, x_m A$ generate the subspace $SA(F)$. While the set $\{x_1 A, x_2 A, \ldots, x_m A\}$ is not necessarily a basis of $SA(F)$ (why?), certainly some subset of this set is a basis. Thus the dimension of $SA(F)$ cannot exceed m, the dimension of $S(F)$. We have proved the following theorem.

8-3 THEOREM. If $S(F)$ is a subspace of $V(F)$ and if A is a linear transformation of $V(F)$, then $SA(F)$ also is a subspace of $V(F)$. Furthermore, $d(SA) \leq d(S)$.

A linear transformation A of a vector space $V(F)$ is completely determined by what it does to a basis of $V(F)$. To elaborate on this, let $\{x_1, x_2, \ldots, x_n\}$ be a basis of $V(F)$. Since each $x \in V$ has the form

$$x = k_1 x_1 + k_2 x_2 + \ldots + k_n x_n, \qquad k_i \in F,$$

each xA has the form

$$xA = k_1(x_1 A) + k_2(x_2 A) + \ldots + k_n(x_n A).$$

Thus, knowing what the vectors $x_1 A, x_2 A, \ldots, x_n A$ are, we may find xA for any $x \in V$ by the equation above.

For example, if A is a linear transformation of $V_3(R)$, and if it is known that

$$(1,0,0)A = (1,0,1), \qquad (0,1,0)A = (1,-1,0), \qquad (0,0,1)A = (0,1,0),$$

then it is an easy matter to find xA for any $x \in V_3(R)$: thus

$$(a,b,c)A = a((1,0,0)A) + b((0,1,0)A) + c((0,0,1)A),$$

$$= a(1,0,1) + b(1,-1,0) + c(0,1,0),$$

$$= (a + b, -b + c, a).$$

If $\{x_1, x_2, \ldots, x_n\}$ is a basis of the vector space $V(F)$, and if $\{v_1, v_2, \ldots, v_n\}$ is any set of n elements of V, then the mapping A of the set $\{x_1, x_2, \ldots, x_n\}$ onto the set $\{v_1, v_2, \ldots, v_n\}$ defined by

$$A: \quad x_i A = v_i, \qquad i = 1, \ldots, n,$$

can be extended to a linear transformation of $V(F)$ in a natural way. For each $x \in V$, say

$$x = k_1 x_1 + k_2 x_2 + \ldots + k_n x_n, \qquad k_i \in F,$$

we have only to define

$$xA = k_1 v_1 + k_2 v_2 + \ldots + k_n v_n$$

in order to make A into a linear transformation of $V(F)$. If $k_j = 1$ while $k_i = 0$ for $i \neq j$, then $x = x_i$ and $xA = v_i$ according to this definition. Thus $x_i A = v_i$, and consequently this new mapping agrees with the given mapping of the set $\{x_1, x_2, \ldots, x_n\}$ onto the set $\{v_1, v_2, \ldots, v_n\}$.

To prove that this newly defined mapping A of V into V is a linear transformation, let $x, y \in V$,

$$x = k_1 x_1 + \ldots + k_n x_n, \qquad y = j_1 x_1 + \ldots + j_n x_n.$$

Then $\qquad x + y = (k_1 + j_1) x_1 + \ldots + (k_n + j_n) x_n,$

and hence

$$(x + y)A = (k_1 + j_1) v_1 + \ldots + (k_n + j_n) v_n.$$

However,

$$xA = k_1 v_1 + \ldots + k_n v_n, \qquad yA = j_1 v_1 + \ldots + j_n v_n,$$

and therefore

$$xA + yA = (k_1 + j_1) v_1 + \ldots + (k_n + j_n) v_n.$$

Thus we see that

$$(x + y)A = xA + yA$$

for each $x, y \in V$. One proves similarly that

$$(kx)A = k(xA)$$

for each $k \in F$, $x \in V$, which proves that A is a linear transformation of $V(F)$. Clearly A is unique, for if B is any linear transformation of $V(F)$ such that $x_i B = v_i$, then necessarily $xB = (k_1 x_1 + \ldots + k_n x_n)B = k_1(x_1 B) + \ldots + k_n(x_n B) = k_1 v_1 + \ldots + k_n v_n = xA$ for each $x \in V$, and it follows that $B = A$. This proves 8-4.

8-4 THEOREM. If $\{x_1, x_2, \ldots, x_n\}$ is a basis of $V(F)$ and if $\{v_1, v_2, \ldots, v_n\}$ is any set of n elements of $V(F)$, then the mapping $A : x_i A = v_i$, $i = 1, \ldots, n$, uniquely defines a linear transformation of $V(F)$.

As an illustration, consider the vector space $V_3(R^\#)$ with its usual basis $\{u_1, u_2, u_3\}$ of unit vectors. The three vectors $(0,1,1)$, $(1,1,1)$, $(1,0,0)$ define the mapping A as follows:

$$(1,0,0)A = (0,1,1), \qquad (0,1,0)A = (1,1,1), \qquad (0,0,1)A = (1,0,0).$$

The mapping A uniquely defines a linear transformation of $V_3(R^\#)$. Thus, for example,

$$(3,-1,2)A = (3(1,0,0) - (0,1,0) + 2(0,0,1))A,$$
$$= 3((1,0,0)A) - (0,1,0)A + 2((0,0,1)A),$$
$$= 3(0,1,1) - (1,1,1) + 2(1,0,0),$$
$$= (1,2,2).$$

In general

$$(a,b,c)A = a(0,1,1) + b(1,1,1) + c(1,0,0),$$

$$= (b + c, a + b, a + b).$$

If $V(F)$ has basis $\{x_1, x_2, \ldots, x_n\}$, and if A is a linear transformation of $V(F)$, then, as was seen above, $VA(F)$ is generated by $\{x_1A, x_2A, \ldots, x_nA\}$. The number of elements in a basis of $VA(F)$ is of sufficient importance to be given a special name as in the following definition.

8-5 Definition. The *rank* of a linear transformation A of a vector space $V(F)$ is the dimension of the subspace $VA(F)$. Using the notation $r(A)$ for the rank of A, $r(A) = d(VA)$. If $r(A) = d(V)$, A is a *nonsingular* linear transformation, while if $r(A) < d(V)$, A is a *singular* linear transformation.

In the example above, $VA(F)$ is generated by the vectors $(0,1,1)$, $(1,1,1)$, $(1,0,0)$. Since $(1,0,0) + (0,1,1) = (1,1,1)$, these three vectors are linearly dependent. However, $\{(0,1,1), (1,0,0)\}$ is a basis of $VA(F)$, and hence $d(VA) = 2$. Thus $r(A) = 2$, and A is singular.

8-6 Theorem. The linear transformation A of $V(F)$ is singular if and only if there exists a nonzero $x \in V$ such that $xA = 0$.

Let $V(F)$ have basis $\{x_1, x_2, \ldots, x_n\}$. If A is singular, then the n generators $x_1A, x_2A, \ldots, x_nA$ of $VA(F)$ must be linearly dependent (why?). Thus there exist $k_i \in F$, not all zero, such that

$$k_1(x_1A) + k_2(x_2A) + \ldots + k_n(x_nA) = 0.$$

Hence, letting

$$x = k_1x_1 + k_2x_2 + \ldots + k_nx_n,$$

we have $xA = 0$ as desired.

Conversely, if $xA = 0$ for some nonzero $x \in V$, and if $x = k_1x_1 + k_2x_2 + \ldots + k_nx_n$, $k_i \in F$, then $k_1(x_1A) + k_2(x_2A) + \ldots + k_n(x_nA) = 0$ and the vectors $x_1A, x_2A, \ldots, x_nA$ are linearly dependent. Therefore $d(VA) < n$ and A is singular. This concludes the proof of 8-6.

8-7 Theorem. Let A be a linear transformation of $V(F)$. Then A is nonsingular if and only if A is a 1–1 mapping of V onto V.

If A is not a 1–1 mapping, say $xA = yA$ with $x \neq y$, then $(x - y)A = 0$ and A is singular by 8-6. Conversely, if A is singular, then $xA = 0$ for some nonzero $x \in V$. However, $0A = 0$ (why?), and therefore $xA = 0A$. Thus A is not a 1–1 mapping. This proves that A is nonsingular if and only if A is a 1–1 mapping of V into V. That the word "into" may be replaced by "onto" is evident, and the proof of 8-7 is complete.

8-8 EXERCISES. In each of the following exercises, find the rank of the given linear transformation of $V_3(\boldsymbol{R}^\#)$. If A is singular, find a nonzero vector $x \in V_3(\boldsymbol{R}^\#)$ for which $xA = 0$.

1. $(1,0,0)A = (2,1,-1)$, $(0,1,0)A = (1,1,2)$, $(0,0,1)A = (1,0,-3)$.
2. $(1,0,0)A = (1,1,0)$, $(0,1,0)A = (0,1,1)$, $(0,0,1)A = (1,0,1)$.
3. $(1,0,0)A = (1,-1,1)$, $(0,1,0)A = (2,-2,2)$, $(0,0,1)A = (-3,3,-3)$.
4. $(1,0,0)A = (1,0,2)$, $(0,1,0)A = (0,-1,1)$, $(0,0,1)A = (2,-3,7)$.
5. $(1,0,0)A = (0,3,2)$, $(0,1,0)A = (1,1,1)$, $(0,0,1)A = (0,0,1)$.
6. $(1,0,0)A = (1,1,1)$, $(0,1,0)A = (1,1,0)$, $(0,0,1)A = (2,2,-1)$.

28. The algebra of linear transformations

Consider now any two linear transformations A and B of a given vector space $V(F)$. The *sum* $A + B$ of these two linear transformations is the mapping of V into V defined as follows:

8-9 $A + B$: $x(A + B) = xA + xB$, $x \in V$.

Actually, $A + B$ is again a linear transformation of $V(F)$, as we shall now show. For each $x,y \in V$, $k \in F$,

$$(x + y)(A + B) = (x + y)A + (x + y)B \qquad \text{(by 8-9)},$$

$$= (xA + yA) + (xB + yB) \qquad \text{(by 8-1, (i))},$$

$$= (xA + xB) + (yA + yB),$$

$$= x(A + B) + y(A + B) \qquad \text{(by 8-9)};$$

$$(kx)(A + B) = (kx)A + (kx)B \qquad \text{(by 8-9)},$$

$$= k(xA) + k(xB) \qquad \text{(by 8-1, (ii))},$$

$$= k(xA + xB),$$

$$= k(x(A + B)) \qquad \text{(by 8-9)}.$$

Thus the mapping $A + B$ has properties 8-1, (i) and (ii), and therefore it is a linear transformation of $V(F)$.

Let us designate by "L" the set of all linear transformations of $V(F)$. If $A,B \in L$, then $A + B \in L$ also; that is, $+$ is an operation on L. Clearly $+$ is commutative, since $x(A + B) = x(B + A)$ for each $x \in V$. This operation is also associative, for if $A,B,C \in L$, then for each $x \in V$,

$$x((A + B) + C) = x(A + B) + xC = xA + xB + xC,$$

$$x(A + (B + C)) = xA + x(B + C) = xA + xB + xC,$$

and $(A + B) + C = A + (B + C)$.

The mapping that carries each element of V into the zero element is quite naturally called the *zero mapping*, and is designated by "0." Thus

$$0: \quad x0 = 0, \qquad x \in V.$$

It is evident that $0 \in L$. Since $x(A + 0) = xA + x0 = xA$ for each $x \in V$, necessarily $A + 0 = A$ for each $A \in L$. Hence 0 is the additive identity element of L.

For each $A \in L$, the mapping $-A$ is defined by

$$-A: \quad x(-A) = -(xA), \qquad x \in V.$$

It is left as an exercise for the reader to verify that $-A \in L$, and that $-A$ is the additive inverse of A. We have proved the following theorem.

8-10 THEOREM. The set L of all linear transformations of a vector space $V(F)$ forms an abelian group under addition.

The *product* $A \cdot B$ of two linear transformations of $V(F)$ is defined to be the usual product of mappings (1-5); thus

8-11 $\qquad\qquad A \cdot B: \quad x(A \cdot B) = (xA)B, \qquad x \in V.$

That $A \cdot B$ is also a linear transformation follows from the equations below;

$$\begin{aligned}
(x + y)(A \cdot B) &= ((x + y)A)B & \text{(by 8-11),} \\
&= (xA + yA)B & \text{(by 8-1, (i)),} \\
&= (xA)B + (yA)B & \text{(by 8-1, (i)),} \\
&= x(A \cdot B) + y(A \cdot B) & \text{(by 8-11);} \\
(kx)(A \cdot B) &= ((kx)A)B & \text{(by 8-11),} \\
&= (k(xA))B & \text{(by 8-1, (ii)),} \\
&= k((xA)B) & \text{(by 8-1, (ii)),} \\
&= k(x(A \cdot B)) & \text{(by 8-11).}
\end{aligned}$$

Thus L has two operations on it, namely $+$ and $\cdot$. The product operation (8-11) is obviously associative. In general, $A \cdot B$ and $B \cdot A$ are not equal; that is, the product operation is not commutative.

The mapping I defined by

$$I: \quad xI = x, \qquad x \in V,$$

is evidently a linear transformation of $V(F)$. This is the *identity mapping* of V, and, as such, it acts as the identity element relative to the product operation, that is,

$$I \cdot A = A \cdot I = A$$

for each $A \in L$. Since $VI = V$, I is nonsingular.

The usual distributive laws hold in L. Thus for each $A, B, C \in L$,

$$A \cdot (B + C) = A \cdot B + A \cdot C,$$

$$(B + C) \cdot A = B \cdot A + C \cdot A.$$

In order to prove the first of these laws, we must establish that

$$x(A \cdot (B + C)) = x(A \cdot B + A \cdot C)$$

for each $x \in V$. This is proved as follows:

$$\begin{aligned}
x(A \cdot (B + C)) &= (xA)(B + C) & \text{(by 8-11)}, \\
&= (xA)B + (xA)C & \text{(by 8-9)}, \\
&= x(A \cdot B) + x(A \cdot C) & \text{(by 8-11)}, \\
&= x(A \cdot B + A \cdot C) & \text{(by 8-9)}.
\end{aligned}$$

The other distributive law is established in a similar way.

An operation of *scalar multiplication* may be introduced on L in a natural way. Thus for each $A \in L$, $k \in F$, kA is the mapping of V into V defined as follows:

8-12 $$kA: \quad x(kA) = (kx)A, \qquad x \in V.$$

It is left as an exercise for the reader to prove that kA is a linear transformation of $V(F)$. The properties of scalar multiplication are listed below. For each $j, k \in F$, $A, B \in L$,

$$k(A + B) = kA + kB; \qquad (j + k)A = jA + kA;$$

8-13 $$k(A \cdot B) = (kA) \cdot B = A \cdot (kB); \qquad (j \cdot k)A = j(kA);$$

$$0A = k0 = 0; \qquad 1A = A.$$

Since L is an abelian group under addition (8-10), and L has scalar multiplication with properties 8-13, it follows that L itself is a vector space over F. The properties of the various operations of L described in this section are collected together in the following theorem.

8-14 Theorem. Let $V(F)$ be a vector space and L be the set of all linear transformations of $V(F)$. Then the following properties hold for the algebraic system composed of L and the operations of addition, multiplication, and scalar multiplication:

(i) L is a vector space over F under addition and scalar multiplication;

(ii) multiplication is associative, and is distributive relative to addition; also there exists a multiplicative identity element I.

8-15 Exercises. Let L be the set of all linear transformations of some vector space $V(F)$.

1. Prove the second distributive law, namely that $(B + C) \cdot A = B \cdot A + C \cdot A$ for each $A, B, C \in L$.

2. Verify that for each linear transformation A of $V(F)$, $-A$ also is a linear transformation, and $A + (-A) = 0$.

3. Prove that for each $k \in F$, $A \in L$, kA also is in L.

4. Prove 8-13.

5. Prove that for each $A, B \in L$, $r(A + B) \leq r(A) + r(B)$. (Hint: $V(A + B) \subset VA + VB$.)

6. Prove that for each $A \in L$ and each nonzero $k \in F$, $r(kA) = r(A)$.

7. Prove that for each $A, B \in L$, $r(A \cdot B) \leq r(A)$ and $r(A \cdot B) \leq r(B)$.

Some of the linear transformations of $V(F)$ are nonsingular; for example I is nonsingular. Let us designate by *"G" the set of all nonsingular linear transformations of $V(F)$*. Then G is a subset of L containing the multiplicative identity element I.

If $A, B \in G$, so that $VA = V$ and $VB = V$, then $V(A \cdot B) = (VA)B = VB = V$, and we conclude that $A \cdot B$ is nonsingular, that is, that $A \cdot B \in G$. Thus G is closed under multiplication. We prove now the following theorem.

8-16 Theorem. The set G of all nonsingular linear transformations of a vector space $V(F)$ forms a group under multiplication.

We need only prove that each $A \in G$ has a multiplicative inverse to complete the proof of 8-16. By 8-7, A is a 1–1 mapping of V onto V, that is, A is a permutation of V (6-1). As such, A has an *inverse* A^{-1} defined as follows (6-5):

$$A^{-1}: \quad (xA)A^{-1} = x, \qquad x \in V.$$

Remember $VA = V$, and hence each element of V may be written in the form xA. Let us prove that $A^{-1} \in G$. For each $xA, yA \in V$, $k \in F$,

$$(xA + yA)A^{-1} = ((x + y)A)A^{-1} = x + y = (xA)A^{-1} + (yA)A^{-1},$$

$$(k(xA))A^{-1} = ((kx)A)A^{-1} = kx = k((xA)A^{-1}),$$

which prove that $A^{-1} \in L$. From the very definition of $A^{-1}, VA^{-1} = V$ and A^{-1} is nonsingular. By 6-9,

$$A \cdot A^{-1} = A^{-1} \cdot A = I$$

for each $A \in G$. This completes the proof of 8-16.

8-17 EXERCISES. For the vector space $V(F)$, L and G are as defined above.

1. Show that G is closed under scalar multiplication by nonzero elements of F. In what ways does G fail to be a vector space?

2. Prove that $r(A \cdot B) = r(B \cdot A) = r(A)$ for each $A \in L$, $B \in G$.

3. Determine the group G relative to the vector space $V_2(I/(2))$. Prove that G is isomorphic to P_3 (6-10).

4. Prove that the mapping $\alpha \colon k \to kI$ of F into a subset of L is an isomorphism between the field F and a subalgebra of L.

29. The algebra of matrices

The results up to this point on linear transformations of a vector space $V(F)$ have in no way depended on a particular choice of a basis of $V(F)$. We shall now show that starting with a given basis of $V(F)$, a linear transformation of $V(F)$ can be associated with a matrix of elements of F. This association will allow us to introduce an algebra of matrices corresponding to the previously defined algebra of linear transformations.

A square array of elements from the field F such as

8-18
$$\begin{bmatrix} a_{11} & a_{12} & \cdots & a_{1n} \\ a_{21} & a_{22} & \cdots & a_{2n} \\ \cdot & \cdot & \cdot & \cdot & \cdot & \cdot \\ \cdot & \cdot & \cdot & \cdot & \cdot & \cdot \\ a_{n1} & a_{n2} & \cdots & a_{nn} \end{bmatrix}$$

is called a *matrix* over F. The matrix 8-18 is made up of n rows and n columns of elements of F, and is called an "$n \times n$ matrix" for this reason. Evidently there are n^2 elements of F appearing in this matrix.

In case $n = 3$, for example, the matrix 8-18 takes on the form

$$\begin{bmatrix} a_{11} & a_{12} & a_{13} \\ a_{21} & a_{22} & a_{23} \\ a_{31} & a_{32} & a_{33} \end{bmatrix}.$$

Note that the first subscript of each element of the matrix indicates the row in which the element appears, while the second subscript tells the column of the element. For example, a_{23} is in the second row and third column of the matrix; a_{31} is in the third row and first column of the matrix. It is convenient to use the shorthand notation "(a_{rs})" for the given matrix, that is,

$$(a_{rs}) = \begin{bmatrix} a_{11} & a_{12} & a_{13} \\ a_{21} & a_{22} & a_{23} \\ a_{31} & a_{32} & a_{33} \end{bmatrix}.$$

We shall use this notation also for the general case of an $n \times n$ matrix.

For each positive integer n we shall designate by "F_n" *the set of all $n \times n$ matrices over F*. Thus each element of F_n is a matrix (a_{rs}) such as given by 8-18. The following matrices, for example, are elements of R_3:

$$\begin{bmatrix} 2 & 0 & 4 \\ -1 & 2 & 1 \\ 0 & 0 & 2 \end{bmatrix}, \quad \begin{bmatrix} 0 & 1 & -1 \\ 3 & 3 & 2 \\ 2 & 7 & -3 \end{bmatrix}.$$

Let us now return to a vector space $V(F)$, and let us fix our attention on some particular basis $\{u_1, u_2, \ldots, u_n\}$ of $V(F)$. The set of all linear transformations of $V(F)$ will be designated by "L_n" (where $n = d(V)$). The first thing we wish to point out is that associated with each $(a_{rs}) \in F_n$ is a unique $A \in L_n$ defined as follows:

$$u_1 A = a_{11}u_1 + a_{12}u_2 + \ldots + a_{1n}u_n$$
$$u_2 A = a_{21}u_1 + a_{22}u_2 + \ldots + a_{2n}u_n$$

8-19 $\qquad \cdot \quad \cdot \quad \cdot \quad \cdot \quad \cdot \quad \cdot \quad \cdot \quad \cdot \quad \cdot \quad \cdot \quad \cdot \quad \cdot$

$\qquad \quad \cdot \quad \cdot \quad \cdot \quad \cdot \quad \cdot \quad \cdot \quad \cdot \quad \cdot \quad \cdot \quad \cdot \quad \cdot \quad \cdot$

$$u_n A = a_{n1}u_1 + a_{n2}u_2 + \ldots + a_{nn}u_n.$$

The elements $a_{11}, \ldots, a_{rs}, \ldots, a_{nn}$ of F appear in the same order as scalars on the right side of 8-19 as they do in the matrix 8-18. In view of 8-4, A is completely determined by 8-19. Conversely, associated with each linear transformation A of $V(F)$ is a unique matrix (a_{rs}). For if A is the linear transformation defined in 8-19, then associated with it is the unique matrix (a_{rs}) of 8-18. Thus there exists a 1–1 mapping

$$\gamma: \quad (a_{rs})\gamma = A,$$

of the set F_n onto the set L_n.

Thus, for example, corresponding to the matrix

$$\begin{bmatrix} 2 & 0 & 4 \\ -1 & 2 & 1 \\ 0 & 0 & 2 \end{bmatrix}$$

of R_3 is the linear transformation A of $V_3(R)$ defined by:

$$(1,0,0)A = 2(1,0,0) + 4(0,0,1) = (2,0,4),$$

$$(0,1,0)A = -(1,0,0) + 2(0,1,0) + (0,0,1) = (-1,2,1),$$

$$(0,0,1)A = 2(0,0,1) = (0,0,2).$$

We note that if we use the unit vectors as a basis of $V_3(R)$, as we did above, then the linear transformation A carries the unit vectors into the row vectors of the given matrix. Thus $(1,0,0)A = (2,0,4)$, the vector made up of the elements of the first row of the given matrix, and so on.

We digress momentarily from matrices to introduce the handy *sigma notation*. If $a_1, a_2, \ldots, a_n$ are elements of an abelian group G, then the notation

$$\sum_{i=1}^{n} a_i$$

is used to designate the sum of the n given elements; that is,

$$\sum_{i=1}^{n} a_i = a_1 + a_2 + \ldots + a_n.$$

We read the left side of this equation as "the sum of a_i from $i = 1$ to $i = n$." The letter i may be replaced by any other letter; the meaning will not be changed. Thus

$$\sum_{i=1}^{n} a_i = \sum_{j=1}^{n} a_j = \sum_{s=1}^{n} a_s.$$

The n equations of 8-19 may be written in the following compact form using the sigma notation:

8-20
$$u_r A = \sum_{s=1}^{n} a_{rs} u_s, \qquad r = 1, \ldots, n.$$

Thus, as r takes on the successive values $1, 2, \ldots, n$, we get the n equations of 8-19.

In the preceding section, an algebra of linear transformations was formed. Since the sets L_n and F_n are in a 1–1 correspondence with each other, the operations of L_n induce operations on F_n. Thus, if $(a_{rs}) \rightarrow A$ and $(b_{rs}) \rightarrow B$, we define

$$(a_{rs}) + (b_{rs})$$

as the unique matrix of F_n corresponding to the linear transformation $A + B$; we define

$$(a_{rs}) \cdot (b_{rs})$$

as the unique matrix of F_n corresponding to $A \cdot B$; and we define

$$k(a_{rs})$$

as the unique matrix of F_n corresponding to kA.

However, if $(a_{rs}) \rightarrow A$ and $(b_{rs}) \rightarrow B$, then A and B are the following linear transformations of $V(F)$:

$$u_r A = \sum_{s=1}^{n} a_{rs} u_s, \qquad r = 1, \ldots, n;$$

$$u_r B = \sum_{s=1}^{n} b_{rs} u_s, \qquad r = 1, \ldots, n.$$

Since (8-9)

$$u_r(A + B) = u_r A + u_r B, \qquad r = 1, \ldots, n,$$

the addition termwise of the right members of the above equations yields

$$u_r(A + B) = \sum_{s=1}^{n} (a_{rs} + b_{rs}) u_s, \qquad r = 1, \ldots, n.$$

We conclude that the matrix $(a_{rs} + b_{rs})$ corresponds to the linear transformation $A + B$. Thus, from our previous definition of $(a_{rs}) + (b_{rs})$, we must have

8-21 $$(a_{rs}) + (b_{rs}) =: (a_{rs} + b_{rs}).$$

In F_3, for example, 8-21 has the form

$$
\begin{bmatrix}
a_{11} & a_{12} & a_{13} \\
a_{21} & a_{22} & a_{23} \\
a_{31} & a_{32} & a_{33}
\end{bmatrix}
+
\begin{bmatrix}
b_{11} & b_{12} & b_{13} \\
b_{21} & b_{22} & b_{23} \\
b_{31} & b_{32} & b_{33}
\end{bmatrix}
=
\begin{bmatrix}
a_{11} + b_{11} & a_{12} + b_{12} & a_{13} + b_{13} \\
a_{21} + b_{21} & a_{22} + b_{22} & a_{23} + b_{23} \\
a_{31} + b_{31} & a_{32} + b_{32} & a_{33} + b_{33}
\end{bmatrix}.
$$

The addition of matrices turns out to be the natural elementwise addition of the two arrays.

In order to see what the product of two matrices is, we first observe that

$$u_r(A \cdot B) = (u_r A)B, \qquad r = 1, \ldots, n,$$

according to 8-11. Hence, for $r = 1, \ldots, n$,

$$u_r(A \cdot B) = \left(\sum_{s=1}^{n} a_{rs} u_s \right) B,$$

$$= \sum_{s=1}^{n} a_{rs}(u_s B) \qquad \text{(by 8-1),}$$

or, on replacing s by k,

$$u_r(A \cdot B) = \sum_{k=1}^{n} a_{rk}(u_k B).$$

However,

$$u_k B = \sum_{s=1}^{n} b_{ks} u_s, \qquad k = 1, \ldots, n,$$

and therefore

$$u_r(A \cdot B) = \sum_{k=1}^{n} a_{rk} \left(\sum_{s=1}^{n} b_{ks} u_s \right),$$

$$= \sum_{s=1}^{n} \left(\sum_{k=1}^{n} a_{rk} b_{ks} \right) u_s, \qquad r = 1, \ldots, n.$$

The matrix $$\left(\sum_{k=1}^{n} a_{rk} b_{ks} \right)$$

corresponds to the linear transformation $A \cdot B$, so that, by our previous definition,

8-22 $$(a_{rs}) \cdot (b_{rs}) = \left(\sum_{k=1}^{n} a_{rk} b_{ks} \right).$$

If, for example, (a_{rs}), $(b_{rs}) \in F_3$, then 8-22 has the form

$$\begin{bmatrix} a_{11} & a_{12} & a_{13} \\ a_{21} & a_{22} & a_{23} \\ a_{31} & a_{32} & a_{33} \end{bmatrix} \cdot \begin{bmatrix} b_{11} & b_{12} & b_{13} \\ b_{21} & b_{22} & b_{23} \\ b_{31} & b_{32} & b_{33} \end{bmatrix} = \begin{bmatrix} c_{11} & c_{12} & c_{13} \\ c_{21} & c_{22} & c_{23} \\ c_{31} & c_{32} & c_{33} \end{bmatrix},$$

where

$$c_{rs} = \sum_{k=1}^{3} a_{rk}b_{ks} = a_{r1}b_{1s} + a_{r2}b_{2s} + a_{r3}b_{3s}.$$

Finally, it is easy to establish that scalar multiplication of a matrix by an element of F is defined by:

8-23 $$k(a_{rs}) = (k \cdot a_{rs}).$$

That is, scalar multiplication of a matrix is effected by multiplying each element of the matrix by the scalar. It is easy to see that the three equations 8-21 to 8-23 are independent of the particular basis $\{u_1, u_2, \ldots, u_n\}$ chosen for $V(F)$.

By the very way in which the operations of addition, multiplication, and scalar multiplication were introduced in F_n, the resulting algebra of matrices is necessarily isomorphic to the algebra of linear transformations introduced in the previous section. Consequently, F_n is a vector space over F under the operations of addition and scalar multiplication, multiplication is associative, and the usual distributive laws hold in F_n. We shall find it convenient henceforth to use the letters "A," "C," ... to designate matrices as well as linear transformations.

The identity elements of L_n relative to $+$ and $\cdot$ are 0 and I respectively. Evidently the matrix corresponding to 0 has all its elements equal to zero. If we also designate this matrix by "0," then

$$0 = \begin{bmatrix} 0 & 0 & \cdots & 0 \\ 0 & 0 & \cdots & 0 \\ \cdot & \cdot & \cdot & \cdot \\ \cdot & \cdot & \cdot & \cdot \\ 0 & 0 & \cdots & 0 \end{bmatrix}.$$

Now

$$u_r I = u_r = 0u_1 + 0u_2 + \ldots + 1u_r + \ldots + 0u_n,$$

for $r = 1, \ldots, n$, and therefore the matrix corresponding to I, which we shall also designate by "I," has the following form:

$$I = \begin{bmatrix} 1 & 0 & 0 & \cdots & 0 \\ 0 & 1 & 0 & \cdots & 0 \\ \cdot & \cdot & \cdot & \cdot & \cdot & \cdot \\ \cdot & \cdot & \cdot & \cdot & \cdot & \cdot \\ 0 & 0 & 0 & \cdots & 1 \end{bmatrix}.$$

The *principal diagonal* of a matrix is the diagonal that runs from the upper left to the lower right corner of the matrix. The matrix I has 1 at every position on the principal diagonal and 0 at every other position in the matrix.

In F_3, for example, the matrices 0 and I are given by:

$$0 = \begin{bmatrix} 0 & 0 & 0 \\ 0 & 0 & 0 \\ 0 & 0 & 0 \end{bmatrix}; \qquad I = \begin{bmatrix} 1 & 0 & 0 \\ 0 & 1 & 0 \\ 0 & 0 & 1 \end{bmatrix}.$$

Naturally, 0 and I are the identity matrices relative to $+$ and $\cdot$ respectively in F_n, since the corresponding linear transformations are the identity elements of L_n.

The product of two matrices can be expressed in terms of a vector multiplication. The *inner product* ($\cdot$) of two vectors $(a_1, a_2, \ldots, a_n)$, $(b_1, b_2, \ldots, b_n) \in V_n(F)$ is defined by

$$(a_1, a_2, \ldots, a_n) \cdot (b_1, b_2, \ldots, b_n)$$

8-24

$$= a_1 \cdot b_1 + a_2 \cdot b_2 + \ldots + a_n \cdot b_n.$$

The operation of inner product is seen to be a mapping of $V_n \times V_n$ onto F, that is, the inner product of two vectors is a scalar.

In $V_3(R)$, for example,

$$(3,1,2) \cdot (-1,2,2) = 3 \cdot (-1) + 1 \cdot 2 + 2 \cdot 2 = 3,$$

$$(4,0,-6) \cdot (2,1,-5) = 4 \cdot 2 + 0 \cdot 1 + (-6) \cdot (-5) = 38.$$

If $A = (a_{rs})$ is in F_n, then A can be thought of as being made up of n row vectors:

$$A = \begin{bmatrix} x_1 \\ x_2 \\ \cdot \\ \cdot \\ \cdot \\ x_n \end{bmatrix}, \quad \text{where} \quad x_r = (a_{r1}, a_{r2}, \ldots, a_{rn}).$$

Thus $x_1 = (a_{11}, a_{12}, \ldots, a_{1n})$, the first row of A; $x_2 = (a_{21}, a_{22}, \ldots, a_{2n})$, the second row of A; and so on. Similarly, the matrix $B = (b_{rs})$ can be thought of as being made up of n column vectors:

$$B = (y_1 \ y_2 \ \ldots \ y_n), \quad \text{where}$$

$$y_1 = \begin{bmatrix} b_{11} \\ b_{21} \\ \cdot \\ \cdot \\ \cdot \\ b_{n1} \end{bmatrix}, \quad y_2 = \begin{bmatrix} b_{12} \\ b_{22} \\ \cdot \\ \cdot \\ \cdot \\ b_{n2} \end{bmatrix}, \quad \ldots, \quad y_n = \begin{bmatrix} b_{1n} \\ b_{2n} \\ \cdot \\ \cdot \\ \cdot \\ b_{nn} \end{bmatrix}.$$

The product of A and B may be written in terms of inner products of vectors in the following way:

$$8\text{-}25 \qquad\qquad A \cdot B = (x_r \cdot y_s).$$

To show that $x_r \cdot y_s$ is the element in the rth row and sth column of the matrix $A \cdot B$, we need only note that, (reading y_s from top to bottom),

$$x_r \cdot y_s = a_{r1} b_{1s} + a_{r2} b_{2s} + \ldots + a_{rn} b_{ns} = \sum_{k=1}^{n} a_{rk} b_{ks}.$$

For example, let

$$A = \begin{bmatrix} 1 & 2 & -1 \\ 3 & 4 & 2 \\ 6 & -1 & 1 \end{bmatrix} \quad \text{and} \quad B = \begin{bmatrix} 0 & 1 & -3 \\ -1 & 4 & 2 \\ 5 & -3 & 6 \end{bmatrix}$$

be elements of R_3. Then the inner products of the first row of A

by the three columns of B are as follows:

$$(1,2,-1)\begin{bmatrix} 0 \\ -1 \\ 5 \end{bmatrix} = -7; \quad (1,2,-1)\begin{bmatrix} 1 \\ 4 \\ -3 \end{bmatrix} = 12; \quad (1,2,-1)\begin{bmatrix} -3 \\ 2 \\ 6 \end{bmatrix} = -5.$$

Therefore $(-7,12,-5)$ is the first row of $A \cdot B$. The second row of $A \cdot B$ is obtained by taking the inner products of $(3,4,2)$ by the three column vectors of B; and the third row of $A \cdot B$ is obtained by taking the inner products of $(6,-1,1)$ by the three column vectors of B. Carrying these out, we get

$$\begin{bmatrix} 1 & 2 & -1 \\ 3 & 4 & 2 \\ 6 & -1 & 1 \end{bmatrix} \cdot \begin{bmatrix} 0 & 1 & -3 \\ -1 & 4 & 2 \\ 5 & -3 & 6 \end{bmatrix} = \begin{bmatrix} -7 & 12 & -5 \\ 6 & 13 & 11 \\ 6 & -1 & -14 \end{bmatrix}.$$

The reader may verify the following products of matrices.

$$\begin{bmatrix} 0 & 1 & -3 \\ -1 & 4 & 2 \\ 5 & -3 & 6 \end{bmatrix} \cdot \begin{bmatrix} 1 & 2 & -1 \\ 3 & 4 & 2 \\ 6 & -1 & 1 \end{bmatrix} = \begin{bmatrix} -15 & 7 & -1 \\ 23 & 12 & 11 \\ 32 & -8 & -5 \end{bmatrix}.$$

$$\begin{bmatrix} 3 & 0 & 2 \\ 2 & 3 & -1 \\ 4 & 2 & 0 \end{bmatrix} \cdot \begin{bmatrix} 3 & 0 & 2 \\ 2 & 3 & -1 \\ 4 & 2 & 0 \end{bmatrix} = \begin{bmatrix} 17 & 4 & 6 \\ 8 & 7 & 1 \\ 16 & 6 & 6 \end{bmatrix}.$$

8-26 EXERCISES

1. If $A,B,C \in R_3$,

$$A = \begin{bmatrix} -1 & 2 & 0 \\ 3 & 1 & 2 \\ -1 & -1 & 2 \end{bmatrix}, \quad B = \begin{bmatrix} -1 & 0 & 2 \\ -3 & 1 & 3 \\ -1 & 0 & 2 \end{bmatrix}, \quad C = \begin{bmatrix} 2 & -1 & 0 \\ 3 & -\frac{3}{2} & 0 \\ 1 & -\frac{1}{2} & 0 \end{bmatrix},$$

find the following products: $A \cdot B$, $B \cdot C$, $C \cdot B$, A^2, B^2, C^2, $(A \cdot B) \cdot C$, $A \cdot (B \cdot C)$.

2. For $A,B \in (I/(3))_4$ as given below, find $A \cdot B$, $B \cdot A$, A^2, B^2, $A \cdot (B \cdot A)$, $B \cdot A^2$:

$$A = \begin{bmatrix} 1 & 1 & 1 & 2 \\ 2 & 0 & 1 & 1 \\ 0 & 1 & 2 & 0 \\ 1 & 2 & 0 & 2 \end{bmatrix}, \quad B = \begin{bmatrix} 1 & 0 & 2 & 1 \\ 1 & 1 & 0 & 2 \\ 1 & 1 & 0 & 2 \\ 0 & 2 & 2 & 2 \end{bmatrix}.$$

3. If $A \in R_3$ has the form

$$A = \begin{bmatrix} 0 & 0 & 0 \\ a & 0 & 0 \\ b & c & 0 \end{bmatrix},$$

prove that $A^3 = 0$. State and prove an analogous result for R_n.

4. If A is a matrix in F_n such that $A^2 = A$, prove that either $A = I$ or the linear transformation corresponding to A is singular. Give examples of matrices of the latter type.

5. Prove that the inner product operation has the following properties: for each $x,y,z \in V_n(F)$, $k \in F$,

(i) $x \cdot (y + z) = x \cdot y + x \cdot z$;   (ii) $x \cdot y = y \cdot x$;

(iii) $(kx) \cdot y = x \cdot (ky) = k(x \cdot y)$.

6. If $x \in V_n(F)$ and $A \in F_n$, say $A = (y_1 \, y_2 \ldots y_n)$ where y_s is the sth column of A, then define the product of x by A as follows: $x \cdot A = (x \cdot y_1, x \cdot y_2, \ldots, x \cdot y_n)$. Thus the product of a vector by a matrix is a vector. Prove that this *vector-matrix* multiplication has the following properties:

(i) $x \cdot (A + B) = x \cdot A + x \cdot B$;   (ii) $x \cdot (A \cdot B) = (x \cdot A) \cdot B$;

(iii) $x \cdot (kA) = (kx) \cdot A = k(x \cdot A)$; (iv) $(x + y) \cdot A = x \cdot A + y \cdot A$.

If A is any matrix of F_n, then the transpose A^T of A is the matrix obtained by interchanging the rows and columns of A. In F_3, for example,

$$\begin{bmatrix} a_{11} & a_{12} & a_{13} \\ a_{21} & a_{22} & a_{23} \\ a_{31} & a_{32} & a_{33} \end{bmatrix}^T = \begin{bmatrix} a_{11} & a_{21} & a_{31} \\ a_{12} & a_{22} & a_{32} \\ a_{13} & a_{23} & a_{33} \end{bmatrix}.$$

The unary operation T on F_n has the following properties: for each $A,B \in F_n$, $k \in F$,

$$(A + B)^T = A^T + B^T; \quad (A \cdot B)^T = B^T \cdot A^T;$$

8-27

$$(kA)^T = kA^T; \quad (A^T)^T = A.$$

All of these are obvious with the possible exception of the equation $(A \cdot B)^T = B^T \cdot A^T$. To prove this, let $A = (a_{rs})$ and $B = (b_{rs})$. Then $A^T = (a_{sr})$ and $B^T = (b_{sr})$, and (8-22)

$$B^T \cdot A^T = \left(\sum_{k=1}^{n} b_{kr} a_{sk} \right).$$

Interchanging r and s in 8-22, we have

$$(A \cdot B)^T = \left(\sum_{k=1}^{n} a_{sk} b_{kr} \right).$$

Clearly $B^T \cdot A^T = (A \cdot B)^T$ as desired.

30. Further properties of matrices

We now restrict our attention to the n-dimensional vector space $V_n(F)$ over the field F, and to its basis of unit vectors $\{u_1, u_2, \ldots, u_n\}$. If A is a linear transformation of $V_n(F)$ that has the following effect on the unit basis,

$$u_r A = \sum_{s=1}^{n} a_{rs} u_s = (a_{r1}, a_{r2}, \ldots, a_{rn}), \qquad r = 1, \ldots, n,$$

then
$$\overline{A} = (a_{rs})$$

is the matrix of F_n corresponding to A. We note that $u_r A$ is just the rth row vector of the matrix $\overline{A}$. Using the concept of vector-matrix multiplication introduced in 8-26, Exercise 6, in which $x \cdot \overline{A}$ is defined to be the vector whose coordinates are successively $x \cdot y_1, x \cdot y_2, \ldots, x \cdot y_n$, where $y_1, y_2, \ldots, y_n$ are the column vectors of $\overline{A}$, it is clear that

$$u_r A = u_r \cdot \overline{A}, \qquad r = 1, \ldots, n.$$

More generally, if x is any vector of $V_n(F)$, then

$$xA = x \cdot \overline{A}.$$

This is so since
$$x = k_1 u_1 + k_2 u_2 + \ldots + k_n u_n$$

for some $k_i \in F$, and

$$xA = \sum_{i=1}^{n} k_i(u_i A) = \sum_{i=1}^{n} k_i(u_i \cdot \overline{A}) = \left(\sum_{i=1}^{n} k_i u_i \right) \cdot \overline{A} = x \cdot \overline{A}.$$

Having found the matrix $\overline{A}$ corresponding to a given linear transformation A, the fact that $xA = x \cdot \overline{A}$ gives a convenient way of finding the effect of A on a vector of $V_n(F)$.

For example, let the linear transformation $A \in V_3(R)$ be given by:

$$(1,0,0)A = (2,-1,1), \quad (0,1,0)A = (-1,3,4), \quad (0,0,1)A = (0,-1,3).$$

Then

$$\overline{A} = \begin{bmatrix} 2 & -1 & 1 \\ -1 & 3 & 4 \\ 0 & -1 & 3 \end{bmatrix}$$

is the matrix of R_3 corresponding to A. The usual way of finding $(4,-1,2)A$, for example, is as follows:

$$\begin{aligned} (4,-1,2)A &= 4(1,0,0)A - (0,1,0)A + 2(0,0,1)A, \\ &= (8,-4,4) + (1,-3,-4) + (0,-2,6), \\ &= (9,-9,6). \end{aligned}$$

However, finding the inner products of $(4,-1,2)$ by the column vectors of $\overline{A}$, we find immediately that

$$(4,-1,2) \cdot \begin{bmatrix} 2 & -1 & 1 \\ -1 & 3 & 4 \\ 0 & -1 & 3 \end{bmatrix} = (9,-9,6),$$

and therefore that $(4,-1,2)A = (9,-9,6)$.

We shall find it convenient in the remainder of this section to identify the linear transformation A of $V_n(F)$ with its matrix $\overline{A}$. Thus the linear transformations of $V_n(F)$ will be the elements of F_n.

If $x_1, x_2, \ldots, x_n$ are the row vectors of the matrix A, so that

$$A = \begin{bmatrix} x_1 \\ x_2 \\ \cdot \\ \cdot \\ \cdot \\ x_n \end{bmatrix}, \quad \text{where} \quad x_r = (a_{r1}, a_{r2}, \ldots, a_{rn}),$$

then $u_r A = u_r \cdot A = x_r$ and the subspace $V_n A$ of $V_n(F)$ is generated by the vectors $x_1, x_2, \ldots, x_n$. Hence the rank of A (8-5) is the maximal number of linearly independent row vectors of A. If we define the *row-rank* of the matrix A to be the maximal number of linearly independent row vectors of A, then we see that the rank of the linear transformation A equals the row-rank of the matrix A.

A matrix A may also be considered as being made up of n column vectors $y_1, y_2, \ldots, y_n$,

$$A = (y_1 \ y_2 \ \ldots \ y_n).$$

It is natural to define the *column-rank* of A to be the maximal number of linearly independent column vectors of A. We shall show a little later that the column-rank and the row-rank of a matrix are equal.

8-28 Definition. For each $A \in F_n$, the *null space* of A, $N(A)$, is the set of all vectors $x \in V_n$ such that $xA = 0$, that is,

$$N(A) = \{x; x \in V_n, xA = 0\}.$$

The *nullity* of A, $n(A)$, is the dimension of $N(A)$, that is,

$$n(A) = d(N(A)).$$

Implicit in this definition is the statement that $N(A)$ is a subspace of $V_n(F)$. Let us prove that this is so; if $x, y \in N(A)$, then $xA = 0$, $yA = 0$, and therefore $(x + y)A = 0$. Furthermore, for each $k \in F$, $(kx)A = k(xA) = 0$. Thus $N(A)$ is closed under addition and scalar multiplication, and is a subspace of $V_n(F)$.

It is clear from 8-6 that the null space $N(A) \neq 0$ if and only if A is singular. Thus $n(A) = 0$ if and only if A is a nonsingular linear transformation. This is a special case of the following important theorem.

8-29 Theorem. For each $A \in F_n$, the rank of A plus the nullity of A is n, that is, $r(A) + n(A) = n$.

This is true if $n(A) = 0$ in view of our previous remarks, since then $r(A) = n$. So let us assume that A is singular and that $n(A) = k > 0$. Let $\{x_1, x_2, \ldots, x_k\}$ be a basis of the null space $N(A)$. This set of linearly independent vectors can be extended to a basis of $V_n(F)$, say $\{x_1, \ldots, x_k, x_{k+1}, \ldots, x_n\}$.

By definition, $r(A)$ equals the dimension of $V_n A(F)$, and hence $r(A)$ equals the maximal number of linearly independent vectors in the set $\{x_1 A, x_2 A, \ldots, x_n A\}$. The vectors $x_1 A, x_2 A, \ldots, x_k A$ are all 0, while the nonzero vectors $x_{k+1} A, x_{k+2} A, \ldots, x_n A$ are actually linearly independent. To see this, note that if

$$c_1(x_{k+1} A) + \ldots + c_{n-k}(x_n A) = 0, \qquad c_i \in F,$$

then $c_1 x_{k+1} + \ldots + c_{n-k} x_n \in N(A)$. However, this is possible only if all $c_i = 0$ since the vectors $x_1, x_2, \ldots, x_n$ are linearly independent. It is therefore clear that $r(A) = n - k$. Thus $r(A) + n(A) = n$ and 8-29 is proved.

For example, consider the following matrix of R_3:

$$A = \begin{bmatrix} -1 & 2 & 1 \\ 1 & 4 & -3 \\ 5 & 2 & -9 \end{bmatrix}.$$

The row vectors of A are

$$x_1 = (-1,2,1), \qquad x_2 = (1,4,-3), \qquad x_3 = (5,2,-9).$$

Clearly x_1 and x_2 are linearly independent so that $r(A) \geq 2$ and $n(A) \leq 1$. Is there a nonzero vector $(a_1,a_2,a_3) \in V_3$ such that $(a_1,a_2,a_3)A = 0$? To answer this question, note that

$$(a_1,a_2,a_3)A = (-a_1 + a_2 + 5a_3, 2a_1 + 4a_2 + 2a_3, a_1 - 3a_2 - 9a_3);$$

thus the answer is yes provided that the linear equations

$$-a_1 + a_2 + 5a_3 = 0$$
$$2a_1 + 4a_2 + 2a_3 = 0$$
$$a_1 - 3a_2 - 9a_3 = 0$$

have a simultaneous nonzero solution. One easily verifies that $a_1 = -3$, $a_2 = 2$, $a_3 = -1$ is such a solution. Hence $(-3,2,-1)A = 0$ and $(-3,2,-1) \in N(A)$. Since we have already established that $n(A) \leq 1$, evidently $n(A) = 1$ and $r(A) = 2$. Clearly $N(A)$ is the subspace of $V_3(R)$ generated by the vector $(-3,2,1)$, while $V_3A(R)$ is generated by the vectors $(-1,2,1)$ and $(1,4,-3)$.

8-30 EXERCISES

1. Find the rank, nullspace, and nullity of the following matrices over R:

(i) $A = \begin{bmatrix} 1 & 0 & 0 \\ 0 & 1 & 0 \\ 0 & 0 & 0 \end{bmatrix}$; 　　(ii) $B = \begin{bmatrix} 2 & -1 & 3 \\ 1 & 2 & -1 \\ 0 & 1 & -1 \end{bmatrix}$;

(iii) $C = \begin{bmatrix} 1 & 0 & 1 & 1 \\ 1 & 1 & 2 & 0 \\ 0 & 1 & 1 & -1 \\ 1 & 0 & 1 & 1 \end{bmatrix}$; 　　(iv) $D = \begin{bmatrix} -1 & 1 & -1 & 0 \\ 2 & 0 & 4 & 2 \\ 1 & 2 & 4 & 3 \\ 3 & -1 & 5 & 2 \end{bmatrix}$.

2. For each $A,B \in F_n$, prove that $n(A \cdot B) \geq n(A)$ and $n(A \cdot B) \geq n(B)$. (Hint: use 8-15, Exercise 7.)

3. If $A,B \in F_n$ and $A \cdot B = 0$, prove that $r(A) + r(B) \leq n$.

If A is a nonsingular matrix (linear transformation), then there exists a matrix A^{-1} such that $A \cdot A^{-1} = I$, the identity matrix. On the other hand, if A is singular it has no inverse matrix. However, as we shall soon see, there do exist matrices P and Q in this case such that PAQ is "almost" the identity matrix.

Let us define the matrix $J_m \in F_n$ to be the matrix with m successive 1's down the main diagonal and 0's elsewhere. If $m < n$, then the main diagonal of J_m will consist of m 1's and $n - m$ 0's. For example, $J_3 \in F_4$ is as follows:

$$J_3 = \begin{bmatrix} 1 & 0 & 0 & 0 \\ 0 & 1 & 0 & 0 \\ 0 & 0 & 1 & 0 \\ 0 & 0 & 0 & 0 \end{bmatrix}.$$

Naturally $J_0 = 0$, while $J_n = I$, the identity matrix.

As a linear transformation, J_m acts as follows on the unit basis $\{u_1, u_2, \ldots, u_n\}$ of $V_n(F)$:

$$u_i \cdot J_m = u_i, \qquad i = 1, \ldots, m,$$

$$u_i \cdot J_m = 0, \qquad i = m + 1, \ldots, n.$$

8-31 Theorem. If A is a matrix in F_n of rank m, then there exist nonsingular matrices P and Q in F_n such that

$$P \cdot A \cdot Q = J_m.$$

If $m = n$, this theorem follows by letting $P = I$ and $Q = A^{-1}$. If, on the other hand, $m < n$, then $n(A) = n - m > 0$. Let a basis

$$\{x_1, x_2, \ldots, x_n\} \tag{1}$$

be chosen for $V_n(F)$, (as in the proof of 8-29), so that $n - m$ of these vectors generate the null space $N(A)$. For certain reasons soon to be clear, we choose

$$\{x_{m+1}, \ldots, x_n\}$$

as a basis of $N(A)$. And as in the proof of 8-29, the vectors $x_1 A, x_2 A, \ldots, x_m A$ are easily shown to be linearly independent. Let this set be extended to a basis of $V_n(F)$, say

$$\{x_1A, \ldots, x_mA, y_{m+1}, \ldots, y_n\} \tag{2}$$

is such a basis of $V_n(F)$.

There exist unique linear transformations P and Q of $V_n(F)$ defined as follows (by 8-4):

$$u_iP = x_i, \qquad i = 1, \ldots, n, \tag{3}$$

where $\{u_1, \ldots, u_n\}$ is the usual basis of unit vectors;

$$\begin{aligned}
(x_iA)Q &= u_i, \qquad i = 1, \ldots, m, \\
y_jQ &= u_i, \qquad j = m + 1, \ldots, n.
\end{aligned} \tag{4}$$

Since P takes the unit basis into basis (1), while Q takes basis (2) into the unit basis, both P and Q are nonsingular linear transformations.

Now, by (3),

$$u_i(P \cdot A \cdot Q) = x_i(A \cdot Q), \qquad i = 1, \ldots, n,$$

and, by (4),

$$x_i(A \cdot Q) = u_i, \qquad i = 1, \ldots, m.$$

If $i > m$, then $x_iA = 0$ since $x_i \in N(A)$; thus

$$x_i(A \cdot Q) = 0, \qquad i = m + 1, \ldots, n.$$

Combining these results, we have that

$$\begin{aligned}
u_i(P \cdot A \cdot Q) &= u_i, \qquad i = 1, \ldots, m, \\
u_i(P \cdot A \cdot Q) &= 0, \qquad i = m + 1, \ldots, n.
\end{aligned}$$

Clearly $P \cdot A \cdot Q$ is the same mapping as J_m, that is,

$$P \cdot A \cdot Q = J_m.$$

This concludes the proof of 8-31.

An important corollary of this theorem is as follows:

8-32 COROLLARY. The row-rank and column-rank of each matrix $A \in F_n$ are equal.

Since the columns of A are the rows of its transpose A^T, all we must show is that A and A^T have the same row-rank. If $r(A) = m$ and

$$P \cdot A \cdot Q = J_m,$$

then $(P \cdot A \cdot Q)^T = J_m^T = J_m$, and, in view of 8-27,

$$Q^T \cdot A^T \cdot P^T = J_m.$$

Now Q^T and P^T are nonsingular (what are their inverses?), and since $r(Q^T \cdot A^T \cdot P^T) = r(A^T)$ (see 8-17, Exercise 2), evidently $r(A^T) = m = r(A)$. This proves 8-32.

8-33 EXERCISES

1. Prove that if the matrices A and B have the same rank, then there exist nonsingular matrices P and Q such that $P \cdot A \cdot Q = B$.

2. Prove that if A is a matrix and k is an integer less than $r(A)$, then there exist matrices P and Q such that $P \cdot A \cdot Q = I_k$. Show that either P or Q can be chosen as a nonsingular matrix.

3. Use Exercise 2 to prove that if A and B are any matrices such that $r(B) < r(A)$, then there exist matrices P and Q such that $P \cdot A \cdot Q = B$.

CHAPTER IX

Linear Equations and Determinants

The solution of a mathematical problem frequently involves finding the simultaneous solution of several linear equations. Thus, for example, the point of intersection of two lines in a coordinate plane is found by solving simultaneously the equations of these two lines. If the equations of these lines are

$$x - 3y + 4 = 0 \quad \text{and} \quad 2x - y + 3 = 0,$$

then the simultaneous solution of these equations may be found by multiplying both sides of the first equation by 2 and subtracting it, side by side, from the second equation:

$$2x - y + 3 = 0$$
$$- \quad \underline{2x - 6y + 8 = 0}$$
$$5y - 5 = 0$$
$$y = 1.$$

On substituting 1 for y in either equation, we find $x = -1$. We conclude that $x = -1$ and $y = 1$ is the unique simultaneous solution of the given equations, and hence that $(-1,1)$ is the point of intersection of the given lines.

It might happen that a given set of equations has no simultaneous solution. For example, the three equations

$$x - y + 2z = 3$$
$$2x + y - z = 4$$
$$4x - y + 3z = -1$$

have no simultaneous solution. If we try to solve these equations in the usual way, say by adding the first two equations to eliminate y and then adding the last two equations also to eliminate y, we obtain the two equations

$$3x + z = 7$$

$$6x + 2z = 3.$$

On multiplying the first equation by 2 and subtracting it from the second one, we end up with the obviously false equation

$$0 = -11.$$

We can arrive at no other conclusion than that the equations have no simultaneous solution. Considering the three given equations as equations of planes in a three-dimensional coordinate space, our conclusion means that the line of intersection of any two of these planes is parallel to the third plane.

On the other hand, a given set of equations might have many simultaneous solutions. The three equations

$$x - y + 2z = 3$$

$$2x + y - z = 4$$

$$4x - y + 3z = 10$$

form such a set. Eliminating y from these three equations as before, we obtain the two equations

$$3x + z = 7$$

$$6x + 2z = 14.$$

Clearly each solution of one of these equations is also a solution of the other. Thus $z = 7 - 3x$ is a solution of these equations for each choice of x, and, in turn, x, $y = 11 - 5x$, $z = 7 - 3x$ is a simultaneous solution of the given three equations for each choice of x. In particular, $x = 0$, $y = 11$, $z = 7$ and $x = 2$, $y = 1$, $z = 1$ are simultaneous solutions. Geometrically speaking, this means that the three given planes have a common line of intersection.

This chapter will be devoted to the problem of finding all the simultaneous solutions of any given set of linear equations. First, we shall give a theoretical solution of the problem, then we shall show how one may use determinants to carry out the actual work of solving the given system of equations.

31. Systems of linear equations

Let F be a given field, and $x_1, x_2, \ldots, x_n$ be n symbols. An expression such as

$$x_1 a_1 + x_2 a_2 + \ldots + x_n a_n, \qquad a_i \in F,$$

is called a *linear form* over F in the n symbols $x_1, x_2, \ldots, x_n$. If the n symbols in this linear form are replaced by elements of F, say x_1 by k_1, x_2 by k_2, $\ldots$, x_n by k_n, then the resulting expression

$$k_1 \cdot a_1 + k_2 \cdot a_2 + \ldots + k_n \cdot a_n$$

is just an element of F. We shall call an equation of the form

$$x_1 a_1 + x_2 a_2 + \ldots + x_n a_n = b, \qquad a_i, b \in F,$$

a *linear equation* in the n symbols $x_1, x_2, \ldots, x_n$. It is only formally an equation, since the two sides of the equation are not actually equal to each other. However, if $k_1 \cdot a_1 + \ldots + k_n \cdot a_n$ actually equals b, that is, if

$$k_1 \cdot a_1 + k_2 \cdot a_2 + \ldots + k_n \cdot a_n = b,$$

then the set $(k_1, k_2, \ldots, k_n)$ of n elements of F is called a *solution* of the given linear equation.

We turn now to the case of m linear equations over F in n symbols $x_1, x_2, \ldots, x_n$:

$$x_1 a_{11} + x_2 a_{21} + \ldots + x_n a_{n1} = b_1$$
$$x_1 a_{12} + x_2 a_{22} + \ldots + x_n a_{n2} = b_2$$

9-1

$$\qquad \cdot \qquad \cdot \qquad \cdot \qquad \cdot \qquad \cdot \qquad \cdot \qquad \cdot \qquad \cdot \qquad \cdot \qquad \cdot$$

$$\qquad \cdot \qquad \cdot \qquad \cdot \qquad \cdot \qquad \cdot \qquad \cdot \qquad \cdot \qquad \cdot \qquad \cdot \qquad \cdot$$

$$x_1 a_{1m} + x_2 a_{2m} + \ldots + x_n a_{nm} = b_m.$$

The set $(k_1, k_2, \ldots, k_n)$ of elements of F is called a *solution* of the system 9-1 of linear equations provided that it is a solution of each of the m linear equations, that is, provided that

$$k_1 \cdot a_{1i} + k_2 \cdot a_{2i} + \ldots + k_n \cdot a_{ni} = b_i$$

for $i = 1, \ldots, m$. Thus $(k_1, k_2, \ldots, k_n)$ is a simultaneous solution of all the given m linear equations. Note that the first subscript i of a_{ij} in 9-1 indicates that a_{ij} is a coefficient of x_i while the second subscript j indicates that a_{ij} appears in the jth equation. Clearly b_j also is in the jth equation.

The problem presented to us is to give conditions under which the system of linear equations 9-1 has a solution, and, if 9-1 has a solution, to give methods for finding all solutions.

We are going to assume that $m = n$ in our discussion of 9-1. While this appears at first glance to restrict our problem, a little reflection convinces us that this is not the case. For any system of linear equations has the same solutions as some system of n linear equations in n symbols. The new system is formed from the old by introducing new equations or new symbols having all zeros for coefficients. For example, the system

$$x - 3y + z = 4$$
$$x + 2y + 2z = 1$$

of two equations in three symbols x, y, z has the same solutions as the system

$$x - 3y + z = 4$$
$$x + 2y + 2z = 1$$
$$0x + 0y + 0z = 0$$

of three equations in three symbols.

So let us discuss the solving of the following system of n linear equations over F in n symbols:

$$x_1a_{11} + x_2a_{21} + \ldots + x_na_{n1} = b_1$$
$$x_1a_{12} + x_2a_{22} + \ldots + x_na_{n2} = b_2$$

9-2

$$x_1a_{1n} + x_2a_{2n} + \ldots + x_na_{nn} = b_n.$$

Using the sigma notation, this system may be written in the form

9-3 $$\sum_{i=1}^{n} x_ia_{ij} = b_j, \qquad j = 1, \ldots, n.$$

Another useful way of writing 9-2 is in the vector-matrix notation of the preceding chapter. If we let x be the "vector"

$$x = (x_1, x_2, \ldots, x_n),$$

a vector with the n given symbols as coordinates, and if we let

$$A = (a_{rs}),$$

a matrix in F_n, and

$$y = (b_1, b_2, \ldots, b_n),$$

a vector in $V_n(F)$, then 9-2 may be written in the form

9-4 $$xA = y.$$

That this (formally) is so may be seen by finding the "inner product" of the vector x and the jth column of A:

$$(x_1, x_2, \ldots, x_n) \begin{bmatrix} a_{1j} \\ a_{2j} \\ \cdot \\ \cdot \\ \cdot \\ a_{nj} \end{bmatrix} = \sum_{i=1}^{n} x_i a_{ij}.$$

Since the jth element of y is b_j, and

$$\sum_{i=1}^{n} x_i a_{ij} = b_j$$

is the jth equation of 9-2, clearly 9-4 and 9-2 are equivalent. The reader should note that the matrix A is the transpose of the matrix obtained by deleting the x_i's on the left side of 9-2.

Having written 9-2 in the form 9-4, it is clear that our original problem of finding all solutions of 9-2 is equivalent to the problem of finding all vectors.

$$v = (k_1, k_2, \ldots, k_n)$$

in $V_n(F)$ such that

$$v \cdot A = y.$$

The case of most importance from a practical standpoint is that in which the matrix A is nonsingular. Then there exists a unique matrix A^{-1} such that $A^{-1} \cdot A = A \cdot A^{-1} = I$, the identity matrix. The theorem following gives the solution in this case.

9-5 THEOREM. If A is nonsingular, then 9-4 has the unique solution $x = y \cdot A^{-1}$.

Clearly $(y \cdot A^{-1}) \cdot A = y \cdot I = y$, so that $y \cdot A^{-1}$ is a solution of 9-4. This solution is unique since A, as a linear transformation of $V_n(F)$, is a 1–1 mapping of $V_n(F)$ onto $V_n(F)$.

In order to attack the case in which A is singular, we turn to Theorem 8-31, where it was proved that there exist nonsingular matrices $P, Q \in F_n$ such that

9-6 $$P \cdot A \cdot Q = J_m, \qquad m = r(A).$$

We recall that J_m is the matrix with m consecutive ones down the main diagonal and zeros elsewhere.

9-7 THEOREM. Equation 9-4 has a solution if and only if the vector $y \cdot Q$ has the form

$$y \cdot Q = (c_1, c_2, \ldots, c_m, 0, \ldots, 0)$$

for some $c_i \in F$.

If $y \cdot Q$ has the form above, then $(y \cdot Q) \cdot J_m$ will be equal to $y \cdot Q$. Thus

$$(y \cdot Q) \cdot P \cdot A \cdot Q = y \cdot Q,$$

and since Q is nonsingular,

$$(y \cdot Q \cdot P) \cdot A = y.$$

Clearly $y \cdot Q \cdot P$ is a solution of 9-4.

Conversely, if there exists a vector $v \in V_n(F)$ such that $v \cdot A = y$, then

$$(v \cdot P^{-1}) \cdot P \cdot A \cdot Q = y \cdot Q,$$

$$(v \cdot P^{-1}) \cdot J_m = y \cdot Q,$$

and, since $u \cdot J_m$ has the form $(c_1, c_2, \ldots, c_m, 0, \ldots, 0)$ for any $u \in V_n(F)$, $y \cdot Q$ must also have this form. This proves 9-7.

Let us assume now that 9-4 has a solution, that is, that the vector $y \cdot Q$ has the form

9-8 $$y \cdot Q = (c_1, c_2, \ldots, c_m, 0, \ldots, 0).$$

Then the following theorem gives all solutions of 9-4.

9-9 THEOREM. If Equation 9-4 has a solution, and if P, Q, and $y \cdot Q$ are as given in 9-6 and 9-8, then the vector $v \in V_n(F)$ is a solution of 9-4 if and only if

$$v = (c_1, c_2, \ldots, c_m, t_1, \ldots, t_{n-m})P$$

for some $t_1, \ldots, t_{n-m} \in F$.

If v is a solution of 9-4, then we saw above that

$$(v \cdot P^{-1}) \cdot J_m = y \cdot Q,$$

which implies that $v \cdot P^{-1}$ and $y \cdot Q$ have the same first m coordinates. Thus

$$v \cdot P^{-1} = (c_1, c_2, \ldots, c_m, t_1, \ldots, t_{n-m})$$

for some $t_i \in F$ and v has the desired form.

Conversely, if v is any vector of the given form, then

$$(v \cdot P^{-1}) \cdot J_m = y \cdot Q,$$

$$(v \cdot P^{-1}) \cdot P \cdot A \cdot Q = y \cdot Q,$$

and $v \cdot A = y$. This completes the proof of 9-9.

In 9-5 and 9-9 we have a complete theoretical solution of our problem of finding all solutions of a given system of linear equations. However, we have as yet given no practical way of finding the inverse of a nonsingular matrix, nor of finding the matrices P and Q satisfying 9-6. The next section will be devoted to these practical problems.

Let us give an example at this point, even though we shall have to leave out some of the computational steps. Consider the following system of linear equations over the rational number field R.

$$x_1 + x_2 + x_3 + x_4 = 1$$
$$-x_1 \qquad + x_3 + 2x_4 = 1$$
$$3x_1 + 2x_2 \qquad - x_4 = 1$$
$$x_1 + x_2 + 2x_3 + 2x_4 = 1.$$

For this system, $A \in R_4$ and $y \in V_4(R)$ are given by

$$A = \begin{bmatrix} 1 & -1 & 3 & 1 \\ 1 & 0 & 2 & 1 \\ 1 & 1 & 0 & 2 \\ 1 & 2 & -1 & 2 \end{bmatrix}, \qquad y = (1,1,1,1).$$

The matrix A has rank 3, and the reader may verify that

$$\begin{bmatrix} 1 & 0 & 0 & 0 \\ 0 & 1 & 0 & 0 \\ 0 & 0 & 1 & 0 \\ 1 & -1 & -1 & 1 \end{bmatrix} \cdot \begin{bmatrix} 1 & -1 & 3 & 1 \\ 1 & 0 & 2 & 1 \\ 1 & 1 & 0 & 2 \\ 1 & 2 & -1 & 2 \end{bmatrix} \cdot \begin{bmatrix} 2 & -3 & 2 & -3 \\ -2 & 3 & -1 & 1 \\ -1 & 2 & -1 & 1 \\ 0 & 0 & 0 & 1 \end{bmatrix} = \begin{bmatrix} 1 & 0 & 0 & 0 \\ 0 & 1 & 0 & 0 \\ 0 & 0 & 1 & 0 \\ 0 & 0 & 0 & 0 \end{bmatrix}.$$

This equation gives us the matrices P and Q. Now

$$y \cdot Q = (1,1,1,1) \cdot \begin{bmatrix} 2 & -3 & 2 & -3 \\ -2 & 3 & -1 & 1 \\ -1 & 2 & -1 & 1 \\ 0 & 0 & 0 & 1 \end{bmatrix} = (-1,2,0,0),$$

so that we know that the given system of linear equations has a solution according to 9-7. All solutions are given by

$$(-1,2,0,t) \cdot \begin{bmatrix} 1 & 0 & 0 & 0 \\ 0 & 1 & 0 & 0 \\ 0 & 0 & 1 & 0 \\ 1 & -1 & -1 & 1 \end{bmatrix} = (-1 + t, 2 - t, -t, t)$$

according to 9-9. Thus the solutions of the given system are

$$x_1 = -1 + t, \qquad x_2 = 2 - t, \qquad x_3 = -t, \qquad x_4 = t,$$

where t is any rational number.

9-10 Exercises

1. Let A be the matrix of the example above. Find all solutions of the following systems of linear equations:

    (i) $xA = (2,-1,3,4)$;   (ii) $xA = (0,0,1,-1)$;

    (iii) $xA = (0,0,0,0)$;   (iv) $xA = (1,2,-1,4)$;

    (v) $xA = (0,1,-1,0)$;   (vi) $xA = (0,0,0,1)$.

2. Let $A,B \in R_3$,

$$A = \begin{bmatrix} 2 & 4 & -3 \\ -1 & 0 & 1 \\ 3 & 5 & 2 \end{bmatrix}, \qquad B = \begin{bmatrix} -5 & -23 & 4 \\ 5 & 13 & 1 \\ -5 & 2 & 4 \end{bmatrix}.$$

Verify that $A \cdot B = B \cdot A = 25I$. Use this fact to solve the following systems of equations over R.

$$
\begin{array}{ll}
2x_1 - x_2 + 3x_3 = 6 & -x_1 + x_2 - x_3 = 7 \\
\text{(i)}\quad 4x_1 \qquad\quad + 5x_3 = -1; & \text{(ii)}\ -23x_1 + 13x_2 + 2x_3 = -3. \\
-3x_1 + x_2 + 2x_3 = 2 & 4x_1 + x_2 + 4x_3 = -5
\end{array}
$$

3. Let A, B, C be the following 4×4 matrices over the field $I/(3)$:

$$A = \begin{bmatrix} 0 & 2 & 1 & 2 \\ 1 & 0 & 0 & 2 \\ 2 & 1 & 1 & 2 \\ 0 & 2 & 0 & 2 \end{bmatrix}, \quad B = \begin{bmatrix} 1 & 0 & 0 & 0 \\ 2 & 1 & 0 & 0 \\ 2 & 0 & 1 & 0 \\ 1 & 2 & 2 & 1 \end{bmatrix}, \quad C = \begin{bmatrix} 2 & 2 & 0 & 1 \\ 1 & 1 & 1 & 2 \\ 0 & 1 & 1 & 0 \\ 0 & 0 & 0 & 1 \end{bmatrix}.$$

Find $A \cdot B \cdot C$, $B \cdot A \cdot C$, and $C \cdot A \cdot B$. Solve the following systems of linear equations:

(i) $xA = (2,0,1,1)$,   (ii) $xA = (2,1,1,2)$,

(iii) $xA = (1,1,1,1)$,   (iv) $xA = (0,1,2,1)$.

4. If, in 9-2, $b_1 = 0$, $b_2 = 0$, . . ., $b_n = 0$, then this system is called a *homogeneous* system of linear equations. A *trivial solution* of this system is $x_1 = 0$, $x_2 = 0$, . . ., $x_n = 0$. Prove that this system has a nontrivial solution if and only if A is singular.

5. Let $A \in F_n$ have rank m and P be a nonsingular matrix of F_n such that $P \cdot A = (c_{rs})$, where

$$c_{rs} = 0 \quad \text{if} \quad r > s; \qquad c_{rr} = 1 \quad \text{if} \quad r \leq m.$$

Thus the elements below the main diagonal of $P \cdot A$ are all zeros, while the first m elements down the main diagonal are all ones. Prove that $v \in V_n(F)$ is a solution of the homogeneous system of linear equations

$$xA = 0$$

if and only if v has the form $v = (t_1, t_2, . . ., t_n)P$ where $t_i = 0$ for $i = 1, . . ., m$.

32. Determinants

Let F be any field and F_n be the set of all $n \times n$ matrices with elements from F. We shall soon define the determinant of a matrix of F_n. However, before doing this, let us briefly review some needed facts about permutations.

We recall that the symmetric group P_n is the group of all permutations of a set $S = \{1, 2, . . ., n\}$ made up of n elements. Thus for each $\alpha \in P_n$, $\alpha: 1 \to 1\alpha$, $2 \to 2\alpha$, . . ., $n \to n\alpha$ is a 1-1 mapping of S onto itself. The permutations of P_n are divided into two classes, namely the even and the odd permutations. A permutation is even or odd depending on whether it can be factored as a product of an even or an odd number of transpositions. In P_n, $n!/2$ of the permutations are even and $n!/2$ of the permutations are odd. For each $\alpha \in P_n$, let us define ϵ_α as follows:

$$\epsilon_\alpha = 1 \text{ if } \alpha \text{ is even}; \qquad \epsilon_\alpha = -1 \text{ if } \alpha \text{ is odd}.$$

9-11 DEFINITION. The *determinant* of the matrix $A = (a_{rs})$ of F_n, $|A|$, is defined as follows:

$$|A| = \sum_{\alpha \in P_n} \epsilon_\alpha a_{1\,1\alpha} \cdot a_{2\,2\alpha} \cdot \ \ldots \ \cdot a_{n\,n\alpha}.$$

Clearly $A \to |A|$ is a mapping of F_n into F; $|A|$ is a sum of $n!$ elements of F of the form

$$\pm a_{1\,1\alpha} \cdot a_{2\,2\alpha} \cdot \ \ldots \ \cdot a_{n\,n\alpha},$$

with the sign $+$ or $-$ depending on whether the permutation α is even or odd. Each of these $n!$ terms of A is in turn a product of n elements of the matrix A, and, since both the first and the second subscripts of these n elements range from 1 to n, evidently precisely one of these n elements is from each row and one is from each column of A. Consequently, if some row or column of A is made up of zeros, the determinant of A also is zero.

If $A \in F_2$, say

$$A = \begin{bmatrix} a_{11} & a_{12} \\ a_{21} & a_{22} \end{bmatrix},$$

then the corresponding permutation group P_2 has 2 elements, namely

$$\alpha = (1)(2) \quad \text{and} \quad \beta = (12).$$

Since α is the identity permutation, $\epsilon_\alpha = 1$; and since β is an odd permutation, $\epsilon_\beta = -1$. Thus $1\alpha = 1$ and $2\alpha = 2$, while $1\beta = 2$ and $2\beta = 1$, and

$$|A| = a_{11} \cdot a_{22} - a_{12} \cdot a_{21}.$$

For example, if F is the rational field,

$$\begin{vmatrix} 3 & 1 \\ -4 & 2 \end{vmatrix} = 3 \cdot 2 - 1 \cdot (-4) = 10.$$

Next, consider $A \in F_3$, say

$$A = \begin{bmatrix} a_{11} & a_{12} & a_{13} \\ a_{21} & a_{22} & a_{23} \\ a_{31} & a_{32} & a_{33} \end{bmatrix}.$$

The six elements of P_3 (6-2) are listed below:

$$\alpha_1 = (1)(2)(3), \qquad \alpha_2 = (23), \qquad \alpha_3 = (13),$$
$$\alpha_4 = (12), \qquad \alpha_5 = (123), \qquad \alpha_6 = (132).$$

Of these, α_2, α_3, and α_4 are odd while α_1, α_5, and α_6 are even. Thus $\epsilon_2 = \epsilon_3 = \epsilon_4 = -1$, $\epsilon_1 = \epsilon_5 = \epsilon_6 = 1$, and

$$|A| = a_{11}\cdot a_{22}\cdot a_{33} - a_{11}\cdot a_{23}\cdot a_{32} - a_{13}\cdot a_{22}\cdot a_{31} - a_{12}\cdot a_{21}\cdot a_{33}$$
$$+ a_{12}\cdot a_{23}\cdot a_{31} + a_{13}\cdot a_{21}\cdot a_{32}.$$

For example, if F is the rational field,

$$\begin{vmatrix} 1 & 2 & -1 \\ 3 & 2 & 4 \\ 2 & 1 & 3 \end{vmatrix} = \begin{aligned} &1\cdot 2\cdot 3 - 1\cdot 4\cdot 1 - (-1)\cdot 2\cdot 2 - 2\cdot 3\cdot 3 \\ &+ 2\cdot 4\cdot 2 + (-1)\cdot 3\cdot 1, \end{aligned}$$

$$= 6 - 4 + 4 - 18 + 16 - 3 = 1.$$

If the matrix A is in F_n with $n > 3$, it is apparent that much labor is needed to find $|A|$ from the definition. Thus, for example, $|A|$ has 120 terms if A is a 5×5 matrix. Fortunately, there are certain general properties of determinants that greatly simplify the actual computation of the determinant of any given matrix. These properties will now be developed.

9-12 THEOREM. For each $A \in F_n$, $|A| = |A^T|$.

If $A = (a_{rs})$, then $A^T = (a_{sr})$, and, according to 9-11,

$$|A^T| = \sum_{\alpha \in P_n} \epsilon_\alpha a_{1\alpha\,1}\cdot a_{2\alpha\,2}\cdot \,\ldots\, \cdot a_{n\alpha\,n}.$$

Since $\qquad a_{k\alpha\,k} = a_{k\alpha\,(k\alpha)\beta}, \quad$ and $\quad \epsilon_\alpha = \epsilon_\beta$

if $\beta = \alpha^{-1}$, it follows that

$$a_{1\alpha\,1}\cdot a_{2\alpha\,2}\cdot \,\ldots\, \cdot a_{n\alpha\,n} = a_{1\,1\beta}\cdot a_{2\,2\beta}\cdot \,\ldots\, \cdot a_{n\,n\beta}.$$

Thus $\qquad\qquad |A^T| = \sum_{\beta \in P_n} \epsilon_\beta a_{1\,1\beta}\cdot a_{2\,2\beta}\cdot \,\ldots\, \cdot a_{n\,n\beta},$

and since this sum is just $|A|$, 9-12 follows.

9-13 THEOREM. If every element of some row (column) of a matrix A of F_n is multiplied by an element c of F, and if B is the resulting matrix, then $|B| = c\cdot|A|$.

If
$$B = \begin{bmatrix} a_{11} & a_{12} & \cdots & a_{1n} \\ \cdot & \cdot & \cdot \cdot \cdot \cdot \cdot & \cdot \\ c \cdot a_{i1} & c \cdot a_{i2} & \cdots & c \cdot a_{in} \\ \cdot & \cdot & \cdot \cdot \cdot \cdot \cdot & \cdot \\ a_{n1} & a_{n2} & \cdots & a_{nn} \end{bmatrix},$$

then, by 9-11,

$$|B| = \sum_{\alpha \in P_n} \epsilon_\alpha a_{1\,1\alpha} \cdot \, \ldots \, \cdot (c \cdot a_{i\,i\alpha}) \cdot \, \ldots \, \cdot a_{n\,n\alpha}.$$

Clearly c is a factor of the right side of this equation, and the other factor evidently is $|A|$. This proves 9-13.

9-14 THEOREM. If the matrix B is the same as the matrix A except that two rows (columns) have been interchanged, then $|B| = -|A|$.

We shall prove this only for the case that the first two rows of A are interchanged to yield B; the general case is no more difficult. Thus

$$B = \begin{bmatrix} a_{21} & a_{22} & \cdots & a_{2n} \\ a_{11} & a_{12} & \cdots & a_{1n} \\ a_{31} & a_{32} & \cdots & a_{3n} \\ \cdot & \cdot & \cdot \cdot \cdot \cdot \cdot & \cdot \\ \cdot & \cdot & \cdot \cdot \cdot \cdot \cdot & \cdot \\ a_{n1} & a_{n2} & \cdots & a_{nn} \end{bmatrix},$$

and
$$|B| = \sum_{\alpha \in P_n} \epsilon_\alpha a_{2\,1\alpha} \cdot a_{1\,2\alpha} \cdot a_{3\,3\alpha} \cdot \, \ldots \, \cdot a_{n\,n\alpha}.$$

If $\gamma = (12)\alpha$, then $\epsilon_\gamma = -\epsilon_\alpha$ and

$$\epsilon_\alpha a_{2\,1\alpha} \cdot a_{1\,2\alpha} \cdot a_{3\,3\alpha} \cdot \, \ldots \, \cdot a_{n\,n\alpha} = -\epsilon_\gamma a_{1\,1\gamma} \cdot a_{2\,2\gamma} \cdot \, \ldots \, \cdot a_{n\,n\gamma}.$$

Since every permutation γ of P_n may be written in the form $\gamma = (12)\alpha$ for a unique α in P_n, clearly

$$|B| = -\sum_{\gamma \in P_n} \epsilon_\gamma a_{1\,1\gamma} \cdot a_{2\,2\gamma} \cdot \, \ldots \, \cdot a_{n\,n\gamma}.$$

This proves 9-14.

9-15 THEOREM. If two rows (columns) of the matrix A are identical, then $|A| = 0$.

This is evident from the previous theorem, for if the two identical rows of A are interchanged the matrix is unchanged while the determinant of A changes sign. Clearly this implies that $|A| = -|A|$, which yields $2|A| = 0$ or $|A| = 0$.

The above proof of 9-15 fails if the field F has characteristic two (why?). However, 9-15 may be proved directly much as was 9-14, and the proof will hold for any characteristic of F.

9-16 THEOREM. If a constant c times one row (column) of a matrix A is added to another row (column) of A resulting in the matrix B, then $|B| = |A|$.

If, for example, c times the second row of A is added to the first row of A, the resulting matrix B is as follows:

$$B = \begin{bmatrix} a_{11} + ca_{21} & a_{12} + ca_{22} & \cdots & a_{1n} + ca_{2n} \\ a_{21} & a_{22} & \cdots & a_{2n} \\ \cdot & \cdot & \cdots & \cdot \\ \cdot & \cdot & \cdots & \cdot \\ a_{n1} & a_{n2} & \cdots & a_{nn} \end{bmatrix}$$

Evidently

$$|B| = \sum_{\alpha \in P_n} \epsilon_\alpha (a_{1\,1\alpha} + c \cdot a_{2\,1\alpha}) \cdot a_{2\,2\alpha} \cdot \ldots \cdot a_{n\,n\alpha},$$

$$= |A| + c \cdot \sum_{\alpha \in P_n} \epsilon_\alpha a_{2\,1\alpha} \cdot a_{2\,2\alpha} \cdot \ldots \cdot a_{n\,n\alpha}.$$

Since this last sum is just the determinant of a matrix with its first two rows equal, it equals zero. Thus $|B| = |A|$ as desired. The proof for the case when a constant times the ith row of A is added to the jth row of A is entirely similar, and hence is omitted.

While Theorems 9-13 to 9-16 were stated both for row operations and column operations on A, they were proved only for row operations. Thus, for example, we proved that $|B| = -|A|$ if the matrix B is obtained from the matrix A by interchanging two rows of A. That these theorems also apply to column operations is a consequence of 9-12. For the columns of A are the rows of A^T, and column operations on A are equivalent to row operations on A^T. Since $|A^T| = |A|$, these theorems obviously hold for column operations on A.

How many of the terms of $|A|$ contain the factor a_{11}? The answer clearly is $(n-1)!$, since there are $(n-1)!$ permutations α of P_n

such that $1\alpha = 1$. If a_{11} is factored out of these terms, the resulting sum a'_{11} is as follows:

$$a'_{11} = \sum \epsilon_\alpha a_{2\,2\alpha} \cdot a_{3\,3\alpha} \cdot \ \ldots \ \cdot a_{n\,n\alpha},$$

where the sum is taken over all $\alpha \in P_n$ for which $1\alpha = 1$. It is evident that a'_{11} is precisely the determinant of the matrix A_{11} of F_{n-1} obtained from A by striking out the first row and first column of A:

$$A_{11} = \begin{bmatrix} a_{22} & a_{23} & \cdots & a_{2n} \\ a_{32} & a_{33} & \cdots & a_{3n} \\ \cdot & \cdot & \cdot\ \cdot\ \cdot & \cdot \\ \cdot & \cdot & \cdot\ \cdot\ \cdot & \cdot \\ a_{n2} & a_{n3} & \cdots & a_{nn} \end{bmatrix}.$$

More generally, we have the following result.

9-17 Theorem. If all the terms of $|A|$ containing a_{rs} are collected, and if a_{rs} is factored out of these terms yielding a'_{rs},

$$a'_{rs} = \sum \epsilon_\alpha a_{1\,1\alpha} \cdot \ \ldots \ \cdot a_{r-1\,(r-1)\alpha} \cdot a_{r+1\,(r+1)\alpha} \cdot \ \ldots \ \cdot a_{n\,n\alpha},$$

with the sum taken over all $\alpha \in P_n$ for which $r\alpha = s$, then

$$a'_{rs} = (-1)^{r+s} |A_{rs}|,$$

where A_{rs} is the matrix in F_{n-1} obtained from A by striking out the rth row and sth column of A.

The number a'_{rs} associated with a_{rs} is called the *cofactor* of a_{rs} in A. As we see by the theorem above, the cofactor of a_{rs} is either plus or minus the determinant of the matrix A_{rs}.

In order to prove 9-17, let B be the following matrix:

$$B = \begin{bmatrix} a_{rs} & a_{r1} & \cdots & a_{r\,s-1} & a_{r\,s+1} & \cdots & a_{rn} \\ a_{1s} & a_{11} & \cdots & a_{1\,s-1} & a_{1\,s+1} & \cdots & a_{1n} \\ \cdot & \cdot\ \cdot\ \cdot\ \cdot & \cdot & \cdot\ \cdot\ \cdot & \cdot & \cdot\ \cdot\ \cdot & \cdot \\ a_{r-1\,s} & a_{r-1\,1} & \cdots & a_{r-1\,s-1} & a_{r-1\,s+1} & \cdots & a_{r-1\,n} \\ a_{r+1\,s} & a_{r+1\,1} & \cdots & a_{r+1\,s-1} & a_{r+1\,s+1} & \cdots & a_{r+1\,n} \\ \cdot & \cdot\ \cdot\ \cdot\ \cdot & \cdot & \cdot\ \cdot\ \cdot & \cdot & \cdot\ \cdot\ \cdot & \cdot \\ a_{ns} & a_{n1} & \cdots & a_{n\,s-1} & a_{n\,s+1} & \cdots & a_{nn} \end{bmatrix}$$

This matrix is obtained from A by moving the rth row of A until it is the first row of B and the sth column of A until it is the first column of B. It takes an interchange of $r - 1$ rows of A to move the rth row of A until it becomes the first row. Thus one first interchanges the rth and r-1st rows; then the r-1st and the r-2nd rows of the new matrix; and so on. Similarly, it takes an interchange of s-1 columns of A to move the sth column of A until it becomes the first column as in B. Since for each interchange of two rows or two columns of A, the determinant of the new matrix is $-|A|$ by 9-14, evidently

$$|B| = (-1)^{r+s-2} |A| = (-1)^{r+s} |A|.$$

Now if the first row and first column of B are struck out, the resulting matrix is just A_{rs}. Hence if the terms containing a_{rs} (which is b_{11} in B) are collected and if a_{rs} is factored out, yielding b'_{11}, then clearly $b'_{11} = |A_{rs}|$ by our previous remarks. However, the terms of $|B|$ containing a_{rs} are precisely the terms of $(-1)^{r+s}|A|$ containing a_{rs}; therefore $b'_{11} = (-1)^{r+s}a'_{rs}$. Thus $|A_{rs}| = (-1)^{r+s}a'_{rs}$, or $a'_{rs} = (-1)^{r+s}|A_{rs}|$, as desired.

Each term of $|A|$ has precisely one of the elements $a_{r1}, a_{r2}, \ldots, a_{rn}$ in it as a factor. Therefore, for any fixed r,

9-18 $$|A| = a_{r1} \cdot a'_{r1} + a_{r2} \cdot a'_{r2} + \ldots + a_{rn} \cdot a'_{rn}.$$

Similarly, for any fixed s,

9-19 $$|A| = a_{1s} \cdot a'_{1s} + a_{2s} \cdot a'_{2s} + \ldots + a_{ns} \cdot a'_{ns}.$$

Expression 9-18 is called the *expansion of $|A|$ by minors of the rth row*; 9-19 is called the *expansion of $|A|$ by minors of the sth column*.

For example, the following determinant is expanded by minors of the second row:

$$\begin{vmatrix} 3 & -1 & 2 \\ 2 & 1 & 4 \\ -1 & 3 & 1 \end{vmatrix} = 2 \cdot (-1)^3 \begin{vmatrix} -1 & 2 \\ 3 & 1 \end{vmatrix} + 1 \cdot (-1)^4 \begin{vmatrix} 3 & 2 \\ -1 & 1 \end{vmatrix}$$

$$+ 4 \cdot (-1)^5 \begin{vmatrix} 3 & -1 \\ -1 & 3 \end{vmatrix},$$

$$= -2 \cdot (-1 - 6) + 1 \cdot (3 + 2) - 4 \cdot (9 - 1) = -13.$$

Formulas 9-13 to 9-19 when used together can considerably reduce the work involved in evaluating the determinant of a given matrix. The scheme is to use 9-16 to get all the elements in some row (column) with the exception of one equal to zero (without changing the determinant) and then use 9-18 (9-19) on this row (column). Obviously, the expression 9-18 (9-19) will have at most one nonzero term on the right side. We now illustrate this procedure in the example that follows.

To evaluate the determinant of the matrix $A \in R_5$, where

$$A = \begin{bmatrix} -1 & 2 & -1 & 3 & 4 \\ 2 & 1 & -1 & 2 & 1 \\ 0 & 1 & 4 & -1 & 5 \\ 1 & -3 & 2 & 0 & 3 \\ 3 & -2 & 0 & -5 & -7 \end{bmatrix},$$

multiply the first row of A by 2 and add it to the second row; also multiply the first row by 1 and add it to the fourth row; and multiply the first row by 3 and add it to the fifth row. These operations do not change $|A|$. Thus

$$|A| = \begin{vmatrix} -1 & 2 & -1 & 3 & 4 \\ 0 & 5 & -3 & 8 & 9 \\ 0 & 1 & 4 & -1 & 5 \\ 0 & -1 & 1 & 3 & 7 \\ 0 & 4 & -3 & 4 & 5 \end{vmatrix}.$$

Now use 9-19 with $s = 1$, that is, expand $|A|$ by minors of the first column:

$$|A| = - \begin{vmatrix} 5 & -3 & 8 & 9 \\ 1 & 4 & -1 & 5 \\ -1 & 1 & 3 & 7 \\ 4 & -3 & 4 & 5 \end{vmatrix}.$$

If we hold the third row of this new 4×4 matrix fixed, and multiply it in turn by 5, 1, and 4 and add the resulting vector to the first, second, and fourth rows respectively, we obtain

$$|A| = - \begin{vmatrix} 0 & 2 & 23 & 44 \\ 0 & 5 & 2 & 12 \\ -1 & 1 & 3 & 7 \\ 0 & 1 & 16 & 33 \end{vmatrix}.$$

Again using 9-19 with $s = 1$, we have

$$|A| = -(-1) \cdot (-1)^{3+1} \begin{vmatrix} 2 & 23 & 44 \\ 5 & 2 & 12 \\ 1 & 16 & 33 \end{vmatrix}.$$

Holding the first column of this new 3×3 matrix fixed, and then multiplying it in turn by -16 and -33 and adding the resulting vector to the second and third columns respectively, we have

$$|A| = \begin{vmatrix} 2 & -9 & -22 \\ 5 & -78 & -153 \\ 1 & 0 & 0 \end{vmatrix}.$$

Thus, upon expanding this determinant by minors of the third row, we finally obtain

$$|A| = \begin{vmatrix} -9 & -22 \\ -78 & -153 \end{vmatrix} = -339.$$

9-20 EXERCISES. In each of Exercises 1 to 4, find the determinant of the given matrix over R.

1. $\begin{bmatrix} -1 & 3 & 2 \\ 4 & 5 & -6 \\ 2 & 0 & 3 \end{bmatrix}.$

2. $\begin{bmatrix} 2 & 1 & 1 & 2 \\ 4 & -1 & 3 & -2 \\ 0 & 2 & -1 & 3 \\ 3 & 0 & 4 & 2 \end{bmatrix}.$

3. $\begin{bmatrix} 4 & -1 & 2 & 3 \\ 2 & 4 & -2 & -4 \\ 3 & 5 & 1 & -6 \\ 5 & 2 & -3 & 1 \end{bmatrix}.$

4. $\begin{bmatrix} 2 & 3 & -2 & 4 & 3 \\ 3 & -3 & 3 & -3 & 6 \\ 0 & 4 & 2 & 3 & -4 \\ 0 & 0 & 2 & 5 & -4 \\ 2 & 4 & 0 & 3 & 5 \end{bmatrix}.$

5. Prove that if the matrix $A = (a_{rs})$ of F_n is in triangular form, that is, if all the elements of A above (or below) the main diagonal are zero, then $|A| = a_{11} \cdot a_{22} \cdot \ldots \cdot a_{nn}$.

6. Show that for any a,b,c in a given field F,

$$\begin{vmatrix} 1 & a & a^2 \\ 1 & b & b^2 \\ 1 & c & c^2 \end{vmatrix} = (b - c)(c - a)(a - b).$$

7. Show that for any a,b,c in a given field F,

$$\begin{vmatrix} 0 & 1 & 1 & 1 & 1 \\ 1 & 0 & 1+a & 1+b & 1+c \\ 1 & 1+a & 0 & a+b & a+c \\ 1 & 1+b & a+b & 0 & b+c \\ 1 & 1+c & a+c & b+c & 0 \end{vmatrix} = 8 \begin{vmatrix} 1+a & 1 & 1 \\ 1 & 1+b & 1 \\ 1 & 1 & 1+c \end{vmatrix}.$$

8. If A in $(R[x])_4$ is given by*

$$A = \begin{bmatrix} x & 1 & 1 & 1 \\ 1 & x & 1 & 1 \\ 1 & 1 & x & 1 \\ 1 & 1 & 1 & x \end{bmatrix},$$

show that $|A| = (x - 1)^3 (x + 3)$.

9. Show that for any a,b,c in a given field F,

$$\begin{vmatrix} 0 & 1 & 1 & 1 \\ 1 & 0 & c^2 & b^2 \\ 1 & c^2 & 0 & a^2 \\ 1 & b^2 & a^2 & 0 \end{vmatrix} = \begin{vmatrix} 0 & a & b & c \\ a & 0 & c & b \\ b & c & 0 & a \\ c & b & a & 0 \end{vmatrix}.$$

Express either as a product of four factors linear in a,b,c.

*While the matrices of the preceding chapter were assumed to be over a field, it is possible to have a matrix algebra S_n over any integral domain S. If F is the quotient field of S, then S_n may be thought of as a subalgebra of F_n.

10. Show that for any a,b,c in a given field F,

$$\begin{vmatrix} (a+b)^2 & c^2 & c^2 \\ a^2 & (b+c)^2 & a^2 \\ b^2 & b^2 & (c+a)^2 \end{vmatrix} = 2abc(a+b+c)^3.$$

11. Find the roots of the following polynomial $p(x)$ in $R[x]$:

$$p(x) = \begin{vmatrix} x & 1 & 2 & 3 \\ 1 & x & 3 & 2 \\ 2 & 3 & x & 1 \\ 3 & 2 & 1 & x \end{vmatrix}.$$

12. The matrix $A \in F_n$ is called *symmetric* if $A^T = A$; *skew-symmetric* if $A^T = -A$. Prove that for any skew-symmetric matrix $A \in R_n$, n an odd integer, $|A| = 0$.

13. Let $A \in F_n$ have zeros down the main diagonal and ones elsewhere. Prove that $|A| = n - 1$ if n is an odd integer and $|A| = 1 - n$ if n is an even integer. (See, for example, Exercise 8 with $x = 0$.)

14. Let $f(x) = (x - a)(x - b)(x - c)(x - d) \in R^*[x]$. Prove that

$$\begin{vmatrix} a & x & x & x \\ x & b & x & x \\ x & x & c & x \\ x & x & x & d \end{vmatrix} = f(x) - xf'(x),$$

where $f'(x)$ is the usual derivative of $f(x)$.

15. Let $A \in F_n$ have the following properties: (1) the first row is made up of ones; (2) each element of every other row is the sum of the elements directly above it and to the left of it in the preceding row. Prove that $|A| = 1$.

33. Further properties of determinants

Again we let F be any field and F_n be the set of all $n \times n$ matrices over F. It is clear that for the identity matrix I, $|I| = 1$. We shall prove presently that $|A| \neq 0$ if and only if A is a nonsingular matrix. Before doing this, let us look more closely at 9-18 and 9-19, the expansions of $|A|$ by minors of some row or column.

If in the matrix $A = (a_{rs})$ we replace the rth row-vector by the vector $(k_1, k_2, \ldots, k_n)$ thus yielding the matrix B, then, by 9-18,

$$|B| = k_1 \cdot a'_{r1} + k_2 \cdot a'_{r2} + \ldots + k_n \cdot a'_{rn}.$$

Here a'_{ri} is the cofactor of a_{ri} in A. In particular, if $k_1 = a_{j1}$, $k_2 = a_{j2}, \ldots, k_n = a_{jn}$, where j is any integer between 1 and n different from r, then the jth and rth row of B are equal. Hence $|B| = 0$ by 9-15. We conclude therefore that

9-21 $a_{j1} \cdot a'_{r1} + a_{j2} \cdot a'_{r2} + \ldots + a_{jn} \cdot a'_{rn} = 0$ if $j \neq r$.

Similarly, using 9-19, we can prove that

9-22 $a_{1j} \cdot a'_{1s} + a_{2j} \cdot a'_{2s} + \ldots + a_{nj} \cdot a'_{ns} = 0$ if $j \neq s$.

The *adjoint* of the matrix A, adj A, is defined as follows:

$$\mathbf{adj}\ A = \begin{bmatrix} a'_{11} & a'_{21} & \cdots & a'_{n1} \\ a'_{12} & a'_{22} & \cdots & a'_{n2} \\ \cdot & \cdot & \cdot & \cdot \\ \cdot & \cdot & \cdot & \cdot \\ a'_{1n} & a'_{2n} & \cdots & a'_{nn} \end{bmatrix} = (a'_{sr}).$$

Note that adj A is just the transpose of the matrix (a'_{rs}) made up of the cofactors of the elements of A. The importance of the adjoint stems from the following theorem.

9-23 THEOREM.   For each $A \in F_n$,

$$A \cdot \text{adj}\ A = \text{adj}\ A \cdot A = |A|I.$$

Since $A \cdot \text{adj}\ A = (a_{rs}) \cdot (a'_{sr}) = \left(\sum_{k=1}^{n} a_{rk} \cdot a'_{sk} \right),$

while

$$\sum_{k=1}^{n} a_{rk} \cdot a'_{sk} = \begin{cases} |A| & \text{if}\ \ r = s & \text{by 9-18,} \\ 0 & \text{if}\ \ r \neq s & \text{by 9-21,} \end{cases}$$

clearly $A \cdot \text{adj}\ A$ is a matrix having the element $|A|$ along the main diagonal and zeros elsewhere, that is, $A \cdot \text{adj}\ A = |A|I$. Similarly, one proves that adj $A \cdot A = |A|I$, and 9-23 follows.

If $|A| \neq 0$, then this theorem gives us a way to compute A^{-1}. For then

$$A \cdot (|A|^{-1}\ \text{adj}\ A) = (|A|^{-1}\ \text{adj}\ A) \cdot A = I,$$

and the inverse A^{-1} of A must be given by

9-24 $A^{-1} = |A|^{-1}\ \text{adj}\ A.$

Incidentally, the fact that A has an inverse implies that A is nonsingular. Thus if $|A| \neq 0$ evidently A is nonsingular. We give now some examples of this method of computing the inverse of a matrix.

If $A \in R_2$ is as follows,

$$A = \begin{bmatrix} 2 & 3 \\ 1 & 3 \end{bmatrix},$$

then the cofactors of A are easily computed to be:

$$a'_{11} = 3, \quad a'_{12} = -1, \quad a'_{21} = -3, \quad a'_{22} = 2.$$

Hence

$$\text{adj } A = \begin{bmatrix} 3 & -3 \\ -1 & 2 \end{bmatrix},$$

and

$$A \cdot \text{adj } A = \text{adj } A \cdot A = \begin{bmatrix} 3 & 0 \\ 0 & 3 \end{bmatrix}.$$

This is as expected from 9-23, since $|A| = 3$. The inverse of A is obtained by dividing each element of adj A by 3. Thus

$$A^{-1} = \begin{bmatrix} 1 & -1 \\ -\frac{1}{3} & \frac{2}{3} \end{bmatrix}.$$

As another example, let $A \in R_3$ be given by

$$A = \begin{bmatrix} 1 & 1 & 1 \\ 1 & 2 & 1 \\ -3 & 0 & 1 \end{bmatrix}.$$

The cofactors of A are as follows:

$$a'_{11} = \begin{vmatrix} 2 & 1 \\ 0 & 1 \end{vmatrix} = 2, \qquad a'_{12} = -\begin{vmatrix} 1 & 1 \\ -3 & 1 \end{vmatrix} = -4,$$

$$a'_{13} = \begin{vmatrix} 1 & 2 \\ -3 & 0 \end{vmatrix} = 6, \qquad a'_{21} = -\begin{vmatrix} 1 & 1 \\ 0 & 1 \end{vmatrix} = -1,$$

$$a'_{22} = \begin{vmatrix} 1 & 1 \\ -3 & 1 \end{vmatrix} = 4, \qquad a'_{23} = -\begin{vmatrix} 1 & 1 \\ -3 & 0 \end{vmatrix} = -3,$$

$$a'_{31} = \begin{vmatrix} 1 & 1 \\ 2 & 1 \end{vmatrix} = -1, \qquad a'_{32} = -\begin{vmatrix} 1 & 1 \\ 1 & 1 \end{vmatrix} = 0,$$

$$a'_{33} = \begin{vmatrix} 1 & 1 \\ 1 & 2 \end{vmatrix} = 1.$$

Hence
$$\text{adj } A = \begin{bmatrix} 2 & -1 & -1 \\ -4 & 4 & 0 \\ 6 & -3 & 1 \end{bmatrix}.$$

The reader may easily verify that $A \cdot \text{adj } A = \text{adj } A \cdot A = 4I$. Clearly $|A| = 4$, and

$$A^{-1} = \begin{bmatrix} \frac{1}{2} & -\frac{1}{4} & -\frac{1}{4} \\ -1 & 1 & 0 \\ \frac{3}{2} & -\frac{3}{4} & \frac{1}{4} \end{bmatrix}.$$

9-25 EXERCISES. Find the inverse of each of the following matrices over R.

1. $\begin{bmatrix} 6 & 1 & 3 \\ 2 & -1 & 2 \\ 1 & 2 & -1 \end{bmatrix}.$

2. $\begin{bmatrix} 0 & 1 & 1 \\ 1 & 0 & 1 \\ 1 & 1 & 0 \end{bmatrix}.$

3. $\begin{bmatrix} 5 & 1 & 3 \\ 0 & -2 & 1 \\ 1 & 1 & 0 \end{bmatrix}.$

4. $\begin{bmatrix} 3 & 1 & -1 \\ 2 & 0 & -3 \\ 4 & 1 & 1 \end{bmatrix}.$

5. $\begin{bmatrix} 1 & 0 & 2 & 0 \\ 2 & 1 & 0 & 0 \\ 0 & 0 & 1 & -1 \\ 3 & 0 & 0 & 1 \end{bmatrix}.$

6. $\begin{bmatrix} 1 & 1 & 1 & 1 \\ 1 & 2 & 3 & 4 \\ 1 & 3 & 6 & 10 \\ 1 & 4 & 10 & 20 \end{bmatrix}.$

From a given matrix A of F_n many submatrices can be formed by deleting some of the rows and columns of A. For example, if

$$A = \begin{bmatrix} 2 & 1 & -4 & 3 \\ 0 & 1 & 2 & -1 \\ 3 & 0 & 1 & 2 \\ 2 & 2 & 0 & 1 \end{bmatrix},$$

A in R_4, then
$$B = \begin{bmatrix} 0 & -1 \\ 3 & 2 \end{bmatrix}$$

is the submatrix of A formed by striking out the first and fourth rows, and second and third columns of A. We prove now the following important theorem about the rank of a matrix A.

9-26 THEOREM. If, for the matrix $A \in F_n$, k is the largest integer such that some $k \times k$ submatrix of A has nonzero determinant, then k equals the rank of A.

If $k = n$, then $|A| \neq 0$ and, as we remarked previously, A is nonsingular and hence has rank n. Thus the theorem has to be proved only for the case $k < n$. If $k < n$, we might as well assume that the $k \times k$ submatrix in the upper left corner of the matrix A has nonzero determinant. For, by interchanging some rows and some columns of A, the known $k \times k$ submatrix of A with nonzero determinant can be moved into the upper left corner of the resulting matrix. Since the procedure of interchanging rows (columns) of a matrix does not affect the rank of the matrix (why?), we need to prove the theorem only for the new matrix thus formed. So let

$$
B = \begin{bmatrix}
a_{11} & a_{12} & \cdots & a_{1k} \\
a_{21} & a_{22} & \cdots & a_{2k} \\
\cdot & \cdot & \cdot & \cdot \\
\cdot & \cdot & \cdot & \cdot \\
a_{k1} & a_{k2} & \cdots & a_{kk}
\end{bmatrix},
$$

with $|B| \neq 0$. Form the matrix C_i of F_{k+1} as follows:

$$
C_i = \begin{bmatrix}
a_{11} & a_{12} & \cdots & a_{1k} & a_{1i} \\
a_{21} & a_{22} & \cdots & a_{2k} & a_{2i} \\
\cdot & \cdot & \cdots & \cdot & \cdot \\
\cdot & \cdot & \cdots & \cdot & \cdot \\
a_{k1} & a_{k2} & \cdots & a_{kk} & a_{ki} \\
a_{k+1\,1} & a_{k+1\,2} & \cdots & a_{k+1\,k} & a_{k+1\,i}
\end{bmatrix}.
$$

If $i \leq k$, $|C_i| = 0$ since two columns of C_i are equal; if $i > k$, $|C_i| = 0$ since C_i is a $(k + 1) \times (k + 1)$ submatrix of A and k is the largest integer for which any $k \times k$ submatrix has nonzero determinant.

Let us expand $|C_i|$ by minors of the last column to obtain

9-27 $c_1 \cdot a_{1i} + c_2 \cdot a_{2i} + \ldots + c_k \cdot a_{ki} + c_{k+1} \cdot a_{k+1\,i} = 0,$

$$i = 1, \ldots, n.$$

Here $c_1, \ldots, c_{k+1}$ are the respective cofactors of $a_{1i}, \ldots, a_{k+1\,i}$ in C_i. Clearly the numbers $c_1, \ldots, c_{k+1}$ do not depend on i; they are the same for any choice of i between 1 and n.

If we let $x_1, x_2, \ldots, x_n$ be the row vectors of A, so that

$$x_j = (a_{j1}, a_{j2}, \ldots, a_{jn}),$$

then the n equations of 9-27 may be written in the form

$$c_1 x_1 + c_2 x_2 + \ldots + c_k x_k + c_{k+1} x_{k+1} = 0.$$

We need only compute the ith coordinates of the above vectors to obtain 9-27. Since $c_{k+1} = |B| \neq 0$, the above equation shows that x_{k+1} is a linear combination of the vectors $x_1, x_2, \ldots, x_k$.

In place of the last row of C_i we may just as well put

$$a_{j1}, a_{j2}, \ldots, a_{jk}, a_{ji},$$

where j is any integer greater than k. If we do this, then by precisely the same argument as above, we can show that the vector x_j is a linear combination of the vectors $x_1, x_2, \ldots, x_k$.

Since $|B| \neq 0$, B is nonsingular and the row vectors of B are linearly independent. Consequently, the row vectors $x_1, x_2, \ldots, x_k$ of A also are linearly independent. We proved above that every other row vector of A is a linear combination of the first k row vectors. Thus the maximal number of linearly independent row vectors of A is k, and the rank of A is therefore k. This proves 9-26.

Theorem 9-26 may be used to compute the rank of any given matrix A. One has only to find the largest submatrix of A with nonzero determinant. We illustrate how this is done by the following example. Let

$$A = \begin{bmatrix} 3 & 1 & 4 & 8 \\ -1 & 2 & 0 & 6 \\ 2 & 1 & 3 & 7 \\ 4 & 1 & -1 & -9 \end{bmatrix},$$

a matrix over R. We may add a multiple of a given row (column) of A to another row (column) of A without affecting the determinant of A, or of any submatrix of A containing the given row (column). Holding the second column of A fixed, and adding the proper multiples of it to the other columns of A, we obtain

$$B = \begin{bmatrix} 0 & 1 & 0 & 0 \\ -7 & 2 & -8 & -10 \\ -1 & 1 & -1 & -1 \\ 1 & 1 & -5 & -17 \end{bmatrix}.$$

Since
$$|B| = -\begin{vmatrix} -7 & -8 & -10 \\ -1 & -1 & -1 \\ 1 & -5 & -17 \end{vmatrix} = 0,$$

clearly $r(B) < 4$ and also $r(A) < 4$. Now

$$\begin{vmatrix} 0 & 1 & 0 \\ -7 & 2 & -8 \\ -1 & 1 & -1 \end{vmatrix} = 1,$$

and hence, by the above theorem, $r(B) = 3$. Thus $r(A) = 3$.

34. On solving a system of linear equations

We shall indicate in this section a practical method of solving a system of linear equations over F such as 9-2. We recall that 9-2 may be written in the vector-matrix form

$$xA = y,$$

where $A = (a_{rs})$, $x = (x_1, x_2, \ldots, x_n)$, and $y = (b_1, b_2, \ldots, b_n)$.

Let us define the matrix $A' \in F_{n+1}$ as follows:

$$A' = \begin{bmatrix} a_{11} & a_{12} & \cdots & a_{1n} & 0 \\ a_{21} & a_{22} & \cdots & a_{2n} & 0 \\ \cdot & \cdot & \cdot & \cdot & \cdot \\ \cdot & \cdot & \cdot & \cdot & \cdot \\ a_{n1} & a_{n2} & \cdots & a_{nn} & 0 \\ b_1 & b_2 & \cdots & b_n & 0 \end{bmatrix}.$$

This matrix is called the *augmented matrix* of the given system 9-2 of linear equations. The usefulness of the augmented matrix in deciding whether a system of linear equations does or does not have a solution is shown by the following theorem.

9-28 THEOREM. A system of linear equations $xA = y$ has a solution if and only if the matrix A and the augmented matrix A' have the same rank.

If we let the row vectors of A be $z_1, z_2, \ldots, z_n$, so that

$$z_i = (a_{i1}, a_{i2}, \ldots, a_{in}),$$

then it is possible to write the equation $xA = y$ in the form

9-29 $$x_1 z_1 + x_2 z_2 + \ldots + x_n z_n = y.$$

It is clear from 9-29 that the given system of linear equations has a solution if and only if the vector y is a linear combination of the vectors $z_1, z_2, \ldots, z_n$. In other words, the system $xA = y$ has a solution if and only if the last row of A' is a linear combination of the other rows. This latter condition holds if and only if A and A' have the same rank, which proves 9-28.

Let us actually test the following system of linear equations over R for a solution.

9-30
$$
\begin{aligned}
x_1 + x_2 - 2x_3 + x_4 &= 2 \\
2x_1 + 3x_2 + x_3 - x_4 &= -4 \\
x_1 + 3x_2 + 8x_3 + 2x_4 &= 7 \\
x_1 + 2x_2 + 3x_3 + 5x_4 &= 15.
\end{aligned}
$$

For this system, the matrices A and A' are as follows:

$$
A = \begin{bmatrix} 1 & 2 & 1 & 1 \\ 1 & 3 & 3 & 2 \\ -2 & 1 & 8 & 3 \\ 1 & -1 & 2 & 5 \end{bmatrix}; \qquad
A' = \begin{bmatrix} 1 & 2 & 1 & 1 & 0 \\ 1 & 3 & 3 & 2 & 0 \\ -2 & 1 & 8 & 3 & 0 \\ 1 & -1 & 2 & 5 & 0 \\ 2 & -4 & 7 & 15 & 0 \end{bmatrix}.
$$

The ranks of these matrices are found by the methods of the previous section. Adding the proper multiples of the first row of A' to its other rows, we obtain the matrix

$$A_1' = \begin{bmatrix} 1 & 2 & 1 & 1 & 0 \\ 0 & 1 & 2 & 1 & 0 \\ 0 & 5 & 10 & 5 & 0 \\ 0 & -3 & 1 & 4 & 0 \\ 0 & -8 & 5 & 13 & 0 \end{bmatrix}$$

having the same rank as A'. Next, adding the proper multiples of the second row of A_1' to the last three rows of A_1', we get the matrix

$$A_2' = \begin{bmatrix} 1 & 2 & 1 & 1 & 0 \\ 0 & 1 & 2 & 1 & 0 \\ 0 & 0 & 0 & 0 & 0 \\ 0 & 0 & 7 & 7 & 0 \\ 0 & 0 & 21 & 21 & 0 \end{bmatrix}$$

which also has the same rank as A'. Finally, multiplying the fourth row of A_2' by -3 and adding the result to the fifth row, we obtain

$$A_3' = \begin{bmatrix} 1 & 2 & 1 & 1 & 0 \\ 0 & 1 & 2 & 1 & 0 \\ 0 & 0 & 0 & 0 & 0 \\ 0 & 0 & 7 & 7 & 0 \\ 0 & 0 & 0 & 0 & 0 \end{bmatrix}.$$

This matrix has rank at most 3, since two of its rows are zero vectors. Since the submatrix

$$B = \begin{bmatrix} 1 & 2 & 1 \\ 0 & 1 & 2 \\ 0 & 0 & 7 \end{bmatrix}$$

obtained by striking out the third and fifth rows and the fourth and fifth columns of A_3' has nonzero determinant, the rank of A_3', and therefore of A', is actually 3. The matrix B is actually a submatrix of the part of A_3' derived from the matrix A in the upper left corner of A'. Therefore A also has rank 3, and 9-30 has a solution according to 9-28.

Having verified that the matrices A and A' of a given system of linear equations have the same rank, and, incidentally, having found the rank of A, the next suggested step is to rearrange, if necessary, the given linear equations so that the largest submatrix of A having nonzero determinant is in the upper left corner of the matrix A.

In 9-30, for example, the rank of A is 3; however, the 3×3 submatrix in the upper left corner of A as it stands has a zero determinant, as can be verified by looking at A'_2. In order to get a 3×3 matrix in the upper left corner of the matrix of coefficients, let us interchange the last two terms of the left side of each equation of 9-30 as follows:

9-31

$$x_1 + x_2 + x_4 - 2x_3 = 2$$
$$2x_1 + 3x_2 - x_4 + x_3 = -4$$
$$x_1 + 3x_2 + 2x_4 + 8x_3 = 7$$
$$x_1 + 2x_2 + 5x_4 + 3x_3 = 15.$$

The matrix A of coefficients of 9-31 is given by

$$A = \begin{bmatrix} 1 & 2 & 1 & 1 \\ 1 & 3 & 3 & 2 \\ 1 & -1 & 2 & 5 \\ -2 & 1 & 8 & 3 \end{bmatrix}.$$

The 3×3 submatrix B in the upper left corner of A,

$$B = \begin{bmatrix} 1 & 2 & 1 \\ 1 & 3 & 3 \\ 1 & -1 & 2 \end{bmatrix},$$

has a nonzero determinant $(= 7)$.

So let us assume that the system $xA = y$ of linear equations is written so that the $k \times k$ submatrix B in the upper left corner of A has nonzero determinant, where $k = r(A)$. Now each column vector of the augmented matrix A' is a linear combination of the first k column vectors of A' since $r(A') = r(A) = k$ and the first

k column vectors of B, and hence of A', are linearly independent. Therefore each equation of $xA = y$ is a linear combination of the first k equations of the given system. Thus any solution of the first k equations of the system is a solution of all the equations. The problem of solving the system is therefore reduced to the problem of solving the system

$$x_1a_{11} + x_2a_{21} + \cdots + x_na_{n1} = b_1$$

$$x_1a_{12} + x_2a_{22} + \cdots + x_na_{n2} = b_2$$

9-32

$$\cdot \quad \cdot \quad \cdot \quad \cdot \quad \cdot \quad \cdot \quad \cdot \quad \cdot \quad \cdot \quad \cdot \quad \cdot \quad,$$

$$\cdot \quad \cdot \quad \cdot \quad \cdot \quad \cdot \quad \cdot \quad \cdot \quad \cdot \quad \cdot \quad \cdot \quad \cdot$$

$$x_1a_{1k} + x_2a_{2k} + \cdots + x_na_{nk} = b_k$$

where the $k \times k$ matrix B,

$$B = \begin{bmatrix} a_{11} & a_{12} & \cdots & a_{1k} \\ a_{21} & a_{22} & \cdots & a_{2k} \\ \cdot & \cdot & \cdot & \cdot \\ \cdot & \cdot & \cdot & \cdot \\ a_{k1} & a_{k2} & \cdots & a_{kk} \end{bmatrix},$$

is nonsingular (that is, has nonzero determinant).

System 9-32 is solved by replacing $x_{k+1}, \ldots, x_n$ by arbitrary elements $t_{k+1}, \ldots, t_n$ of F, transposing these terms to the right sides of the equations in 9-32, and then solving the resulting system of k equations in k symbols $x_1, \ldots, x_k$ by 9-5. Thus

$$x_1a_{11} + x_2a_{21} + \cdots + x_ka_{k1} = c_1$$

$$x_1a_{12} + x_2a_{22} + \cdots + x_ka_{k2} = c_2$$

9-33

$$\cdot \quad \cdot \quad \cdot \quad \cdot \quad \cdot \quad \cdot \quad \cdot \quad \cdot \quad \cdot \quad \cdot \quad,$$

$$\cdot \quad \cdot \quad \cdot \quad \cdot \quad \cdot \quad \cdot \quad \cdot \quad \cdot \quad \cdot \quad \cdot$$

$$x_1a_{1k} + x_2a_{2k} + \cdots + x_ka_{kk} = c_k$$

where $$c_i = b_i - \sum_{j=k+1}^{n} t_j a_{ji}, \qquad i = 1, \ldots, k,$$

and the solution of 9-33 is given by

9-34 $$(x_1, x_2, \ldots, x_k) = (c_1, c_2, \ldots, c_k)B^{-1}.$$

To complete the solution of 9-31 using 9-34, we find the adjoint of B to be

$$\text{adj } B = \begin{bmatrix} 9 & -5 & 3 \\ 1 & 1 & -2 \\ -4 & 3 & 1 \end{bmatrix},$$

and since $|B| = 7$,

$$B^{-1} = \tfrac{1}{7}(\text{adj } B).$$

Now replacing x_3 by t, we have

$$c_1 = 2 + 2t, \qquad c_2 = -4 - t, \qquad c_3 = 7 - 8t.$$

Hence

$$(x_1, x_2, x_4) = \tfrac{1}{7}(2 + 2t, -4 - t, 7 - 8t) \begin{bmatrix} 9 & -5 & 3 \\ 1 & 1 & -2 \\ -4 & 3 & 1 \end{bmatrix},$$

$$= (-2 + 7t, 1 - 5t, 3).$$

Thus the solutions of 9-30 are

$$x_1 = -2 + 7t, \qquad x_2 = 1 - 5t, \qquad x_3 = t, \qquad x_4 = 3,$$

where t is any element of F.

9-35 EXERCISES. Find all solutions of the following systems of linear equations. In Exercises 1 to 12, the linear equations are over the real field R^*.

1. $\begin{aligned} 6x_1 + x_2 + 3x_3 &= 2 \\ 2x_1 - x_2 + 2x_3 &= -1 \\ x_1 + 2x_2 - x_3 &= 1. \end{aligned}$

2. $\begin{aligned} x_2 + x_3 &= 4 \\ x_1 + x_3 &= -1 \\ x_1 + x_2 &= 3. \end{aligned}$

3. $\begin{aligned} 3x_1 + x_2 - x_3 &= -1 \\ 2x_1 - 3x_3 &= -4 \\ x_1 + 3x_2 + 9x_3 &= 1. \end{aligned}$

4. $\begin{aligned} 6x_1 + 2x_2 + 3x_3 &= -2 \\ 3x_1 + x_2 + 2x_3 &= 0 \\ 3x_1 + x_2 &= -4. \end{aligned}$

5. $\begin{aligned} x_1 + x_2 + x_3 + x_4 &= -1 \\ x_1 + 2x_2 + 3x_3 + 4x_4 &= 1 \\ x_1 + 3x_2 + 6x_3 + 10x_4 &= 1 \\ x_1 + 4x_2 + 10x_3 \\ + 20x_4 &= -1. \end{aligned}$

6. $\begin{aligned} x_1 + 2x_3 &= 2 \\ 2x_1 + x_2 &= 0 \\ x_3 - x_4 &= 0 \\ 3x_1 + x_4 &= 1. \end{aligned}$

$$-x_1 + x_3 + 2x_4 = -9$$
$$x_1 + x_2 - x_3$$
7. $$\quad + 3x_4 = -17$$
$$4x_1 - x_2 + 2x_3 + x_4 = 4$$
$$4x_1 - 3x_2 + 8x_3$$
$$\quad + 5x_4 = -2.$$

$$x_1 + 2x_2 - x_3 + 2x_4 = 3$$
$$-x_1 - 3x_2 + 2x_3$$
8. $$\quad + x_4 = -1$$
$$-x_1 - 5x_2 + 4x_3 + 7x_4 = 3$$
$$x_1 + 6x_2 - 5x_3$$
$$\quad - 10x_4 = -4.$$

$$x_1 + x_3 = 2$$
$$x_2 + x_4 = -1$$
9. $$x_1 + x_5 = 3$$
$$x_2 + x_5 = 7$$
$$x_3 + x_4 = -5.$$

$$x_1 - x_3 + 2x_5 = 8$$
$$x_2 + 2x_3 + x_4 = 3$$
$$x_1 - 3x_2 - x_5 = -1$$
10. $$x_1 - 8x_2 + 4x_3 + x_4$$
$$\quad - 7x_5 = -16$$
$$4x_1 - 11x_2 - 5x_3 - 2x_4$$
$$\quad - x_5 = -1.$$

$$x_1 + 2x_3 = 0$$
$$x_2 - x_4 = 0$$
11. $$x_3 + x_5 = 0$$
$$x_1 - x_2 = 0$$
$$x_4 - 2x_5 = 0.$$

$$x_1 - x_2 + 4x_3 + 6x_5 = -1$$
$$3x_2 - 3x_3 + x_4 - 6x_5 = -3$$
$$x_1 + 2x_2 + x_3 - x_4$$
12. $$\quad + 6x_5 = 8$$
$$-x_1 - 3x_3 + 2x_4$$
$$\quad - 11x_5 = -12$$
$$3x_1 + x_2 + x_4 - 5x_5 = -5.$$

In Exercises 13 and 14, the linear equations are over the field $I/(3)$. Enumerate all the solutions of these systems.

13. $$\begin{aligned} x_1 + 2x_2 + x_3 + x_4 &= 2 \\ 2x_1 + x_2 + 2x_3 + x_4 &= 0 \\ x_1 + x_2 + 2x_3 + x_4 &= 1 \\ 2x_1 + x_4 &= 2. \end{aligned}$$

14. $$\begin{aligned} x_1 + 2x_3 + x_5 &= 1 \\ x_1 + x_2 + x_5 &= 0 \\ x_1 + x_3 + x_4 &= 0 \\ x_2 + 2x_3 + 2x_4 + x_5 &= 0 \\ x_1 + x_2 + 2x_3 + x_4 &= 2. \end{aligned}$$

CHAPTER X

Other Algebraic Systems

In this the final chapter, we shall give a brief introduction to linear algebras, rings, and Boolean algebras. These are types of algebraic systems frequently encountered in higher mathematics.

35. Linear algebras

Before stating the definition of a linear algebra, let us give an example of such an algebraic system. The symmetric group P_n is a universal group in the sense that all other groups of order n are isomorphic to subgroups of P_n(6-23). In a similar way, as we shall presently see, the algebraic system L of all linear transformations of a vector space $V(F)$ is itself a linear algebra, and this linear algebra contains all other linear algebras of a certain order as subalgebras. As we recall from 8-14, L has operations of addition, multiplication, and scalar multiplication by F. The properties of these operations in L are as stated in the following definition.

10-1 DEFINITION. A set A having operations of addition $(+)$, multiplication $(\cdot)$, and scalar multiplication by a field F is a *linear algebra* over F provided that

    (i) A is a vector space over F under the operations of addition and scalar multiplication,

    (ii) multiplication is associative,

    (iii) multiplication is distributive relative to addition,

    (iv) A has a multiplicative identity element, and,

    (v) for each $a,b \in A$, $k \in F$,

$$(ka)\cdot b = a\cdot(kb) = k(a\cdot b).$$

If A is a linear algebra over F, then the underlying vector space (10-1, (i)) is designated by "$A(F)$." Let us now give some examples of linear algebras.

If A is a field containing a subfield F, then it is an easy matter to verify that A is a linear algebra over F. In this example, scalar multiplication of A by F is taken to be the ordinary multiplication of A.

For example, the complex field C is a linear algebra over the real field R^s. Since each complex number has the form

$$r1 + s{\cdot}i, \qquad r,s \in R^s,$$

it is clear that the underlying vector space $C(R^s)$ has dimension 2. A basis of this vector space is the set $\{1,i\}$.

Since the algebra of all linear transformations of the vector space $V_n(F)$ is a linear algebra, the isomorphic algebra F_n of all $n \times n$ matrices over F also is a linear algebra. The vector space $F_n(F)$ associated with this linear algebra has dimension n^2. Thus, for example, let us prove that the 4 matrices

$$E_{11} = \begin{bmatrix} 1 & 0 \\ 0 & 0 \end{bmatrix}, \quad E_{12} = \begin{bmatrix} 0 & 1 \\ 0 & 0 \end{bmatrix}, \quad E_{21} = \begin{bmatrix} 0 & 0 \\ 1 & 0 \end{bmatrix}, \quad E_{22} = \begin{bmatrix} 0 & 0 \\ 0 & 1 \end{bmatrix}$$

make up a basis of $F_2(F)$. These elements of $F_2(F)$ are linearly independent, since

$$k_{11}E_{11} + k_{12}E_{12} + k_{21}E_{21} + k_{22}E_{22} = \begin{bmatrix} k_{11} & k_{12} \\ k_{21} & k_{22} \end{bmatrix},$$

and this latter matrix is zero if and only if each $k_{ij} = 0$. Clearly every matrix of F_2 is a linear combinations of the E_{ij}. For example,

$$\begin{bmatrix} 3 & -1 \\ 2 & 5 \end{bmatrix} = 3E_{11} - E_{12} + 2E_{21} + 5E_{22}.$$

We are primarily concerned with linear algebras A over F such that $A(F)$ has finite dimension. The preceding two examples were of this nature. A set $\{x_1, x_2, \ldots, x_n\}$ of elements of A is a *basis* of the linear algebra A over F if each element $a \in A$ has a unique representation of the form

$$a = k_1 x_1 + k_2 x_2 + \ldots + k_n x_n, \qquad k_i \in F,$$

that is, if $\{x_1, x_2, \ldots, x_n\}$ is a basis of the vector space $A(F)$.

In much the same way that any abstract group can be shown to be isomorphic to some permutation group (6-24), so can it be shown that any linear algebra is isomorphic to some algebra of linear transformations. Let us prove the following theorem.

10-2 Theorem. Let A be a linear algebra over the field F. Then A is isomorphic to a subalgebra of the algebra of all linear transformations of the vector space $A(F)$. In particular, if $A(F)$ has finite dimension n, then A is isomorphic to a subalgebra of F_n.

Corresponding to each $a \in A$ is the mapping θ_a of A into A defined by

$$\theta_a: \quad x\theta_a = x \cdot a, \qquad x \in A.$$

Remember, x and a are both in A so that $x \cdot a$ is defined. We leave it for the reader to verify that θ_a is a linear transformation of the vector space $A(F)$. Let L be the algebra of all linear transformations of the vector space $A(F)$, and let

$$B = \{\theta_a; a \in A\}.$$

Now B is a subalgebra of L; this is a consequence of the following equations:

10-3 $\qquad \theta_a + \theta_b = \theta_{a+b}; \qquad \theta_a \cdot \theta_b = \theta_{a \cdot b}; \qquad k\theta_a = \theta_{ka}.$

We shall prove the first of these, and leave the rest for the reader to verify. Now

$$x(\theta_a + \theta_b) = x\theta_a + x\theta_b = x \cdot a + x \cdot b = x \cdot (a + b) = x\theta_{a+b}, \qquad x \in A,$$

and therefore the mappings $\theta_a + \theta_b$ and θ_{a+b} are equal.

Next, let us prove that the mapping α,

$$\alpha: \quad a\alpha = \theta_a, \qquad a \in A,$$

of A onto B is an isomorphism. From 10-3 we derive immediately that

$$a\alpha + b\alpha = (a + b)\alpha; \qquad a\alpha \cdot b\alpha = (a \cdot b)\alpha; \qquad k(a\alpha) = (ka)\alpha,$$

that is, that the operations of A and B are preserved by α. We have only to prove that α is a 1–1 mapping of A onto B in order to complete the proof that α is an isomorphism. To this end, assume that $a,b \in A$, $a \neq b$. Then, since $1 \cdot a \neq 1 \cdot b$, evidently $1\theta_a \neq 1\theta_b$ and $\theta_a \neq \theta_b$. Thus α is an isomorphism, and the proof of the first part of 10-2 is completed.

If the vector space $A(F)$ has dimension n, then the algebra A

must be isomorphic to a subalgebra of the algebra of all linear transformations of $V_n(F)$ in view of 7-15. Thus, also, A must be isomorphic to a subalgebra of F_n. This proves 10-2.

A realization of this isomorphism between A and a subalgebra of F_n is as follows. Let $\{x_1, x_2, \ldots, x_n\}$ be a basis of the linear algebra A over F. Then for each $a \in A$ and each integer r, $1 \leq r \leq n$, $x_r \cdot a \; (= x_r \theta_a)$ is a linear combination of the basis elements:

$$10\text{-}4 \qquad x_r \cdot a = \sum_{s=1}^{n} k_{rs} x_s, \qquad r = 1, \ldots, n.$$

This equation is just 8-20 with A of 8-20 replaced by a and a_{rs} replaced by k_{rs}. The mapping β,

$$10\text{-}5 \qquad \beta: \quad a\beta = (k_{rs}), \qquad a \in A, \qquad (k_{rs}) \in F_n,$$

of A onto a subalgebra of F_n is an isomorphism for the simple reason that the mapping $\gamma \colon \theta_a \gamma = (k_{rs})$ of B (defined in the proof of 10-2) onto a subalgebra of F_n is an isomorphism. The operations of F_n were actually defined (8-21 to 8-23) so that γ would be an isomorphism.

Let us illustrate this isomorphism between a linear algebra and an algebra of matrices using, as example, the linear algebra C over $R^\#$. A basis of this algebra is $\{1, i\}$. For each $a \in C$, say $a = r + si$, $r, s \in R^\#$, 10-4 takes on the form

$$1 \cdot (r + si) = r1 + si,$$

$$i \cdot (r + si) = (-s)1 + ri.$$

Thus the mapping β of 10-5 is given by

$$\beta: \quad (r + si)\beta = \begin{bmatrix} r & s \\ -s & r \end{bmatrix}.$$

We conclude that the linear algebra C is isomorphic to the algebra of all matrices of $R_2^\#$ of the form

$$\begin{bmatrix} r & s \\ -s & r \end{bmatrix}.$$

For example,

$$1\beta = \begin{bmatrix} 1 & 0 \\ 0 & 1 \end{bmatrix}, \qquad i\beta = \begin{bmatrix} 0 & 1 \\ -1 & 0 \end{bmatrix}, \qquad (3 - 2i)\beta = \begin{bmatrix} 3 & -2 \\ 2 & 3 \end{bmatrix}.$$

The fact that the field C of complex numbers is a linear algebra of dimension 2 over the real field R^* is of great importance in mathematics, for it allows the coordinatization of the plane by complex numbers as shown in Section 16. This coordinatization is the basis of complex variable theory in mathematics.

It is quite natural to ask if there exist fields that are linear algebras of dimension 3, 4, or higher, over the real field that might be used to coordinatize 3–, 4–, or higher, dimensional space. The answer is no; the only field that is a linear algebra of finite dimension over the real field is the complex field C. However, there is a linear algebra of dimension 4 over the real field that lacks being a field in only one particular, namely, in that multiplication is not commutative. This so-called algebra of real quaternions, first discovered by the Irish mathematician Hamilton in about 1848, will now be described in some detail.

The algebra Q of *real quaternions* has a basis of four elements $\{1,i,j,k\}$ over the real field R^*. Naturally 1 is the multiplicative identity element of Q; the other three elements of the basis combine according to the following rules:

$$i^2 = -1, \qquad j^2 = -1, \qquad k^2 = -1,$$

$$i \cdot j = \quad k, \qquad j \cdot k = \quad i, \qquad k \cdot i = \quad j,$$

$$j \cdot i = -k, \qquad k \cdot j = -i, \qquad i \cdot k = -j.$$

The set Q consists of all elements, called *quaternions*, of the form

10-6 $\qquad a = a_1 + a_2 i + a_3 j + a_4 k, \qquad a_i \in R^*.$

If $\qquad b = b_1 + b_2 i + b_3 j + b_4 k, \qquad b_i \in R^*,$

then $a + b$ and $a \cdot b$ are defined as if the laws of a linear algebra were satisfied: thus

$$a + b = (a_1 + b_1) + (a_2 + b_2)i + (a_3 + b_3)j + (a_4 + b_4)k,$$

$$a \cdot b = (a_1 \cdot b_1 - a_2 \cdot b_2 - a_3 \cdot b_3 - a_4 \cdot b_4) + (a_1 \cdot b_2 + a_2 \cdot b_1$$
$$+ a_3 \cdot b_4 - a_4 \cdot b_3)i + (a_1 \cdot b_3 - a_2 \cdot b_4 + a_3 \cdot b_1 + a_4 \cdot b_2)j$$
$$+ (a_1 \cdot b_4 + a_2 \cdot b_3 - a_3 \cdot b_2 + a_4 \cdot b_1)k.$$

Scalar multiplication is defined in the obvious way:

$$ca = (c \cdot a_1) + (c \cdot a_2)i + (c \cdot a_3)j + (c \cdot a_4)k, \qquad c \in R^*.$$

It can be shown that, with operations defined in this way, Q is a linear algebra over $R^\#$.

The *conjugate* a' of the quaternion a of 10-6 is defined to be:

$$a' = a_1 - a_2 i - a_3 j - a_4 k, \qquad a_i \in R^\#.$$

One easily verifies that

$$a \cdot a' = a' \cdot a = a_1^2 + a_2^2 + a_3^2 + a_4^2.$$

Thus the product of a quaternion and its conjugate is a real number, $N(a)$, called the *norm* of a:

10-7 $$N(a) = a \cdot a' = a' \cdot a.$$

If $a \neq 0$ (so that some $a_i \neq 0$), then $N(a) \neq 0$, and since

$$a \cdot \left[\frac{1}{N(a)} a' \right] = \left[\frac{1}{N(a)} a' \right] \cdot a = 1,$$

evidently a has a multiplicative inverse a^{-1} given by

10-8 $$a^{-1} = \frac{1}{N(a)} a'.$$

The operation of multiplication in Q is not commutative, since, for example, $i \cdot j \neq j \cdot i$. Otherwise, Q has all the properties of a field. Some writers call such an algebra as Q a *non-commutative field* or a *skew-field*.

Since the linear algebra Q is of dimension 4 over the field $R^\#$, there must exist a subalgebra of the matrix algebra $R_4^\#$ that is isomorphic to Q according to 10-5. If $a \in Q$ is given by 10-6, then 10-4 takes on the form

$$1 \cdot a = a_1 1 + a_2 i + a_3 j + a_4 k$$

$$i \cdot a = -a_2 1 + a_1 i - a_4 j + a_3 k$$

$$j \cdot a = -a_3 1 + a_4 i + a_1 j - a_2 k$$

$$k \cdot a = -a_4 1 - a_3 i + a_2 j + a_1 k.$$

Hence the mapping β of 10-5 is given by

10-9 $$\beta: \quad (a_1 + a_2 i + a_3 j + a_4 k)\beta = \begin{bmatrix} a_1 & a_2 & a_3 & a_4 \\ -a_2 & a_1 & -a_4 & a_3 \\ -a_3 & a_4 & a_1 & -a_2 \\ -a_4 & -a_3 & a_2 & a_1 \end{bmatrix}.$$

This mapping β is an isomorphism between Q and the subalgebra B of $R_4^\#$ consisting of all matrices of the form

10-10
$$\begin{bmatrix} a_1 & a_2 & a_3 & a_4 \\ -a_2 & a_1 & -a_4 & a_3 \\ -a_3 & a_4 & a_1 & -a_2 \\ -a_4 & -a_3 & a_2 & a_1 \end{bmatrix}.$$

One way of proving that Q actually is a linear algebra (which we have been assuming all along) is to prove that the set B of all matrices of the form 10-10 is closed under addition, multiplication, and scalar multiplication, and that the correspondence 10-9 preserves the previously defined operations of Q in B. Since any subalgebra B of the known linear algebra $R_4^\#$ is also a linear algebra, and the mapping 10-9 is 1–1 and preserves the operations of Q and B, necessarily Q is a linear algebra.

Given the set A of all linear combinations

$$k_1x_1 + k_2x_2 + \ldots + k_nx_n, \qquad k_i \in F,$$

over a field F of n symbols $x_1, x_2, \ldots, x_n$, this set is easily made into a vector space with basis $\{x_1, x_2, \ldots, x_n\}$ by defining operations of addition and scalar multiplication on A as follows:

$$\sum_{i=1}^n k_ix_i + \sum_{i=1}^n c_ix_i = \sum_{i=1}^n (k_i + c_i)x_i, \qquad c_i,k_i \in F,$$

$$c\left(\sum_{i=1}^n k_ix_i\right) = \sum_{i=1}^n (c \cdot k_i)x_i, \qquad c,k_i \in F.$$

Naturally, $\sum k_ix_i = \sum c_ix_i$ if and only if $k_i = c_i, i = 1, \ldots, n$. As usual, we take

$$1x_i = x_i, \qquad i = 1, 2, \ldots, n.$$

If now a multiplication is defined among the basis elements, so that for every i and j, $x_i \cdot x_j$ is some element of A, then a multiplication can be defined on A itself as follows:

$$\left(\sum_{i=1}^n k_ix_i\right) \cdot \left(\sum_{j=1}^n c_jx_j\right) = \sum_{i=1}^n \sum_{j=1}^n (k_i \cdot c_j)(x_i \cdot x_j).$$

Since $x_i \cdot x_j \in A$, the right side of the above equation is just an element of A.

The question now is whether A with the operations of $+, \cdot$, and scalar multiplication will be a linear algebra. If we assume that $x_1 \cdot x_j = x_j \cdot x_1 = x_j$ for every j, then x_1 will be a multiplicative identity element for A. Multiplication is quite easily seen to be distributive relative to addition. Also property (v) of 10-1 is readily verified. Thus whether or not A is a linear algebra depends on whether or not multiplication is associative. If

$$x_i \cdot (x_j \cdot x_k) = (x_i \cdot x_j) \cdot x_k, \qquad i,j,k = 1, \ldots, n,$$

then clearly

$$\left(\sum_{i=1}^{n} c_i x_i \right) \cdot \left[\left(\sum_{j=1}^{n} d_j x_j \right) \cdot \left(\sum_{k=1}^{n} e_k x_k \right) \right]$$

$$= \left[\left(\sum_{i=1}^{n} c_i x_i \right) \cdot \left(\sum_{j=1}^{n} d_j x_j \right) \right] \cdot \left(\sum_{k=1}^{n} e_k x_k \right).$$

Thus the algebra A will be a linear algebra over F with basis $\{x_1, x_2, \ldots, x_n\}$ if and only if multiplication as defined among the basis elements is associative.

For example, let A be the set of all elements of the form

$$a_1 1 + a_2 x + a_3 y, \qquad a_i \in R^\#.$$

Thus A is the set of all linear combinations of the three symbols 1, x, and y over the real field. Let us define the operation of multiplication among these three symbols so that 1 is the identity element (that is, $1 \cdot x = x \cdot 1 = x$, $1 \cdot y = y \cdot 1 = y$) and

$\cdot$	x	y
x	0	x
y	x	1

Here 0 is really the element $01 + 0x + 0y$, the additive identity element of A. If we identify the element a_1 of $R^\#$ with the element $a_1 1 + 0x + 0y$, then $R^\#$ is a subalgebra of A, and 0 and 1 are the additive and multiplicative identity elements of both $R^\#$ and A.

If $a,b \in A$, say

$$a = a_1 + a_2 x + a_3 y \quad \text{and} \quad b = b_1 + b_2 x + b_3 y,$$

then $a + b$, $a \cdot b$, and ka ($k \in R^{\#}$) are defined, with the aid of the above multiplication table, as follows:

$$a + b = (a_1 + b_1) + (a_2 + b_2)x + (a_3 + b_3)y,$$

$$a \cdot b = (a_1 \cdot b_1 + a_3 \cdot b_3) + (a_1 \cdot b_2 + a_2 \cdot b_1 + a_2 \cdot b_3 + a_3 \cdot b_2)x$$
$$+ (a_1 \cdot b_3 + a_3 \cdot b_1)y,$$

$$ka = (k \cdot a_1) + (k \cdot a_2)x + (k \cdot a_3)y.$$

The set A with the above defined operations will be a linear algebra over $R^{\#}$ provided that the multiplication of the basis elements is associative. Clearly $x_i \cdot (x_j \cdot x_k) = (x_i \cdot x_j) \cdot x_k$ if one of the three factors is the identity element 1; thus one has only to verify that

$$x_i \cdot (x_j \cdot x_k) = (x_i \cdot x_j) \cdot x_k$$

where x_i, x_j, and x_k are either x or y. There are 8 such equations to be verified. We verify the following two of them and leave the other six to be verified by the reader:

$$x \cdot (x \cdot y) = x \cdot x = 0; \qquad (x \cdot x) \cdot y = 0 \cdot y = 0.$$

$$x \cdot (y \cdot y) = x \cdot 1 = x; \qquad (x \cdot y) \cdot y = x \cdot y = x.$$

Since all eight equations are true, the algebra A is linear over $R^{\#}$.

The algebra Q of real quaternions is of some importance in mathematical analysis, although it is not nearly so useful as Hamilton envisioned it would be. The German mathematician Frobenius proved in 1878 that C and Q are the only linear algebras of finite dimension over the real field in which the multiplicative cancellation law holds. One definitely would want to have this cancellation law holding in any algebra used for coordinates in an n-dimensional space. There is an algebra of dimension 8 over the real field, the so-called *Cayley-Dickson algebra*, that fails to be a linear algebra only in that the associative law of multiplication does not hold. It has all the properties of the quaternion algebra Q otherwise. The above example of a linear algebra of dimension 3 does not satisfy the multiplicative cancellation law, since, for example, $x \cdot x = 0 \cdot x$ although $x \neq 0$.

10-11 EXERCISES

1. Find a subalgebra of $R^{\#}_3$ isomorphic to the above linear algebra A of dimension 3 over $R^{\#}$.

2. For any two quaternions a and b, prove that the conjugate of $a + b$ is $a' + b'$; of $a \cdot b$ is $b' \cdot a'$. Also prove $N(a \cdot b) = N(a) \cdot N(b)$.

3. If the mapping α of Q onto Q is defined by α: $a\alpha = a'$, is α an isomorphism? Is α^2 an isomorphism?

4. Let c be a fixed nonzero element of Q and let the mapping γ of Q onto Q be defined by γ: $a\gamma = c \cdot a \cdot c^{-1}$, $a \in Q$. Prove that γ is an isomorphism of Q onto Q.

5. If the product of two vectors of $V_n(F)$ is defined as in 7-16, Exercise 8, prove that the resulting algebraic system is a linear algebra.

6. Prove that the quaternion a of 10-6 is a root of the real polynomial $x^2 - 2a_1 x + N(a)$. Prove that a' is a root of the same polynomial.

7. Prove that there is an infinite number of square roots of -1 in Q. What are the conditions on a_1, a_2, a_3, and a_4 in 10-6 that a be a square root of -1?

8. Prove that the mapping γ defined by

$$\gamma: \quad (a_1 + a_2 i + a_3 j + a_4 k)\gamma = \begin{bmatrix} a_1 + a_2 i & a_3 + a_4 i \\ -a_3 + a_4 i & a_1 - a_2 i \end{bmatrix},$$

is an isomorphism between Q and a subalgebra of C_2.

9. Show that the set A of all elements of the form

$$a_1 + a_2 x + a_3 y + a_4 z, \qquad a_i \in R^*,$$

is a linear algebra of dimension 4 over the real field R^* if the elements x, y, z have the following multiplication table:

$\cdot$	x	y	z
x	1	$-y$	z
y	y	0	0
z	z	0	0.

10. Find the subalgebra of R_4^* isomorphic to the linear algebra of Exercise 9.

11. Prove that there is no field of dimension 3 over the real field. (Hint: If F is such a field and $a \in F$, $a \notin R^*$, then necessarily the four elements 1, a, a^2, a^3 are linearly dependent over R^*. Hence a is a root of some polynomial $f(x) \in R^*[x]$ of degree 3. But $f(x) = g(x) \cdot q(x)$ (by 5-29) where $g(x)$ has degree two and $q(x)$ has degree one. Since $f(a) = g(a) \cdot q(a) = 0$ and $q(a) \neq 0$, evidently $g(a) = 0$.

Thus every element of F not in R^s is the root of a quadratic polynomial in R^s. If $a^2 + c_1 a + c_2 = 0, c_i \in R^s$, then $(k_1 a + k_2)^2 = -1$ for some $k_i \in R^s$. Hence some subfield of F is isomorphic to the complex field C. If $\{1, i, j\}$ is a basis of F over R^s where $i^2 = -1$, and $i \cdot j = e_1 + e_2 i + e_3 j$, $e_i \in R^s$, what must e_3 equal?)

36. Rings

A prominent part is played by the field of scalars in a linear algebra. However, some important algebraic systems have no field of scalars associated with them. An example of such a system is the system of the integers modulo n, $I/(n)$, where n is not a prime number. Such an algebraic system as that of the integers modulo n as well as linear algebras are examples of a general type of algebraic system called a "ring."

10-12 DEFINITION. A *ring* A is an algebraic system having operations of addition $(+)$ and multiplication $(\cdot)$ and satisfying the following conditions:

    (i) A is an abelian group under addition;
    (ii) multiplication is associative;
    (iii) multiplication is distributive relative to addition;
    (iv) there exists a multiplicative identity element in A.

Condition (iv) frequently is omitted from the definition of a ring. However, for simplicity, we have included it in our definition.

We designate the additive and multiplicative identity elements of any ring A by "0" and "1" respectively, and the additive inverse of a by "$-a$" as usual. The properties of the abelian group of A under addition are the same as those of an integral domain, and are assumed to be known without further discussion. It is clear also that

$$a \cdot 0 = 0 \cdot a = 0$$

for each $a \in A$.

Integral domains, fields, and linear algebras have all the properties listed in 10-12, and hence are special kinds of rings. Also, as is shown in Section 9, $I/(n)$ is a ring for any integer n. As a further example, let I_n be the set of all $n \times n$ matrices having integers for coordinates; I_n is a subset of R_n, the set of all $n \times n$ matrices over the rational field R. Evidently I_n is closed under multiplication and forms an abelian group under addition. The matrices 0 and I are the additive and multiplicative identity elements of I_n. Properties (ii) and (iii) of 10-12 hold for I_n simply because they hold in R_n. Thus I_n is a ring. Incidentally, I_n is not a linear algebra.

A ring A is called a *commutative ring* if the commutative law of multiplication holds in A, that is, if

$$a \cdot b = b \cdot a$$

for each $a,b \in A$. An integral domain is a commutative ring, as is the ring $I/(n)$ for any integer n. The ring I_n is a noncommutative ring. For example, in I_2,

$$\begin{bmatrix} 0 & 1 \\ 0 & 0 \end{bmatrix} \cdot \begin{bmatrix} 1 & 0 \\ 0 & 0 \end{bmatrix} = \begin{bmatrix} 0 & 0 \\ 0 & 0 \end{bmatrix},$$

while

$$\begin{bmatrix} 1 & 0 \\ 0 & 0 \end{bmatrix} \cdot \begin{bmatrix} 0 & 1 \\ 0 & 0 \end{bmatrix} = \begin{bmatrix} 0 & 1 \\ 0 & 0 \end{bmatrix}.$$

Just as for an integral domain (3-6), general associative and distributive laws hold in a ring. A general commutative law of addition is also valid, but a general commutative law of multiplication is valid only for a commutative ring.

The properties of multiples and powers listed in 3-7, with the exception of

$$a^n \cdot b^n = (a \cdot b)^n,$$

hold for any ring A. The above property also holds in case the given ring A is commutative.

Each element of a ring A has a characteristic just as in the case of an integral domain. Thus for any $a \in A$, the *characteristic* of a is the least positive integer k, if such exists, for which

$$ka = 0.$$

If all positive multiples $ka \neq 0$, a is said to have *characteristic zero*. In a ring, unlike an integral domain, not all the nonzero elements need have the same characteristic.

In the ring $I/(6)$, for example, 1 and 5 have characteristic 6, 2 and 4 have characteristic 3, and 3 has characteristic 2.

An element a of a ring A is called a *divisor of zero* if $a \cdot b = 0$ or $b \cdot a = 0$ for some nonzero element $b \in A$. A trivial example of a divisor of zero in any ring is the element 0. That a ring can have nonzero divisors of zero is seen by the following product in I_2:

$$\begin{bmatrix} 0 & 1 \\ 0 & 0 \end{bmatrix} \cdot \begin{bmatrix} 1 & 0 \\ 0 & 0 \end{bmatrix} = \begin{bmatrix} 0 & 0 \\ 0 & 0 \end{bmatrix}.$$

Thus both the matrices

$$\begin{bmatrix} 0 & 1 \\ 0 & 0 \end{bmatrix} \quad \text{and} \quad \begin{bmatrix} 1 & 0 \\ 0 & 0 \end{bmatrix}$$

are (nonzero) divisors of zero in I_2. Another example is in the ring $I/(6)$, where $3 \cdot 2 = 0$; thus 3 and 2 are (nonzero) divisors of zero in $I/(6)$.

A ring of special importance is the *division ring*. It is a ring A having the additional property following.

10-13 Each nonzero element of A has a multiplicative inverse.

Thus, in a division ring A, for every nonzero $a \in A$ there exists an $a^{-1} \in A$ such that

$$a \cdot a^{-1} = a^{-1} \cdot a = 1.$$

A field is an example of a commutative division ring. We see by 10-8 that the ring Q of real quaternions is also a division ring. This is an example of a noncommutative division ring. If $a \cdot b = 0$, $a \neq 0$, in a division ring A, then

$$a^{-1} \cdot (a \cdot b) = (a^{-1} \cdot a) \cdot b = 1 \cdot b = b = 0.$$

We conclude that 0 is the only divisor of zero in a division ring.

Starting out with a ring A, we can form the set $A[x]$ of all polynomials

$$a_0 + a_1 x + \ldots + a_n x^n, \qquad a_i \in A,$$

in the symbol x, just as in Chapter IV. If operations are introduced in $A[x]$ just as in 4-4, then $A[x]$ is again a ring, the *polynomial ring over* A. The properties of the ring $A[x]$ may be found in more advanced treatises on algebra.

10-14 EXERCISES

　　1. Which of the following algebraic systems are rings?
　　　　(i) The algebra of all even integers.
　　　　(ii) The subalgebra of C containing all complex numbers of the form $a + bi$, a, b integers.

(iii) The subalgebra of I_3 of all matrices of the form

$$\begin{bmatrix} a & 0 & 0 \\ b & a & 0 \\ c & d & a \end{bmatrix}.$$

(iv) The algebra of all non-negative integers.

(v) The subalgebra of Q containing all quaternions of the form $a_1 + a_2 i + a_3 j + a_4 k$, where the a_i are integers.

(vi) The subalgebra of Q containing all quaternions of the form $a_1 + a_2 i + a_3 j + a_4 k$, where either all the a_i are integers, or all the a_i are halves of odd integers.

(vii) The subalgebra of I_2 of all matrices of the form

$$\begin{bmatrix} a & d \\ c & b \end{bmatrix},$$

where a, b are even and c, d are odd integers.

2. Prove that the matrix $C \in F_n$, F a field, is a divisor of zero if and only if it is singular.

3. Let F be a field, and A be the set of all elements of the form $a_1 + a_2 i + a_3 j + a_4 k$, $a_i \in F$. Show that A is a ring if operations are defined in A just as they were in the algebra Q.

4. Prove that the ring A of Exercise 3 is not a division ring if F is the field $I/(p)$ of integers modulo a prime p. Also prove that A is not a division ring if F is the complex number field C. (Hint: find nonzero divisors of zero.)

For any ring, important subsystems are ideals, as defined below.

10-15 DEFINITION. A subsystem S of a ring A is called an *ideal* of A if
  (i) S is a subgroup of the additive group of A, and
  (ii) for each $a \in A$, $s \in S$, both $a \cdot s$ and $s \cdot a$ are in S.

Consider, for example, the commutative ring I of integers. Let "(n)" designate the set of all integers that are multiples of n, that is,

$$(n) = \{a \cdot n; a \in I\}.$$

We assert that (n) is an ideal of I. Certainly $a \cdot n + b \cdot n = (a + b) \cdot n$ is in (n), $0 = 0 \cdot n$ is in (n), and $-(a \cdot n) = (-a) \cdot n$ is in (n). Thus (n) is a group under addition (and hence is a subgroup of the additive group of I). Also, for each $a \cdot n \in (n)$ and each $b \in I$, $(a \cdot n) \cdot b =$

$(a \cdot b) \cdot n$ is in (n). Since I is a commutative ring, $(a \cdot n) \cdot b = (b \cdot a) \cdot n$. Thus (ii) of 10-15 also is satisfied, and we conclude that (n) is an ideal of I for any integer n.

Actually, there are no other ideals of I. For suppose that S is an ideal of I; S must have at least one element, namely 0. If this is the only element of S, then $S = (0)$. Otherwise, if S has nonzero elements, some of its elements are positive integers (why?). Now let n be the least positive integer in S, and let k be any other integer of S. By the usual division process (2-29), there exist integers q and r such that

$$k = n \cdot q + r, \qquad 0 \leq r < n.$$

However, both $n \cdot q$ and k are in S, and therefore $k - n \cdot q = r$ also is in S. But n is the least positive integer in S, which implies that $r = 0$ and $k = n \cdot q$. Clearly, then, $S = (n)$.

In a similar way, one may prove that the only ideals of $F[x]$, F a field, are the sets $(f(x))$, where

$$(f(x)) = \{g(x) \cdot f(x); g(x) \in F[x]\}.$$

Thus, for example, the set of all polynomials of the form

$$a_1 x + a_2 x^2 + \ldots + a_n x^n, \qquad a_i \in F,$$

is an ideal of $F[x]$ (why?).

If A is a division ring, then A has no ideals except the trivial ones. In any ring A, the set A itself and the set (0) made up of the one element 0 are ideals of A. We call these the *trivial ideals* of A. To see that a division ring A has no nontrivial ideals, let S be an ideal of A with $S \neq (0)$. If $b \in S$, $b \neq 0$, then $b^{-1} \cdot b = 1 \in S$ by 10-15, (ii). Hence $a \cdot 1 = a \in S$ for each $a \in A$, and $S = A$.

Let S be an ideal of the ring A. Since S is in particular a subgroup of the additive group of A, S has *cosets* in A (6-33). The right and left cosets of S coincide, since addition is commutative. We remember that the cosets of S in A are the subsets of A having the form $a + S$, where

$$a + S = \{a + s; s \in S\}.$$

Note that $a \in a + S$ since $0 \in S$, and $a + S = b + S$ if and only if $a - b \in S$. Let us designate by "A/S" the set of all cosets of S in A. We recall that the cosets of S in A partition A into non-overlapping subsets of A. For each two cosets $a + S$ and $b + S$, the *sum* and *product* of these are defined as follows:

10-16
$$(a + S) + (b + S) = (a + b) + S,$$
$$(a + S) \cdot (b + S) = (a \cdot b) + S.$$

It should be verified that these operations are well-defined, since sums and products of sets are defined in terms of particular elements of the sets. We must show that if

$$a + S = a' + S \quad \text{and} \quad b + S = b' + S, \tag{1}$$

then also

$$(a + b) + S = (a' + b') + S \quad \text{and} \quad (a \cdot b) + S = (a' \cdot b') + S. \tag{2}$$

From (1) we derive that $a = a' + s$ and $b = b' + t$ for some $s, t \in S$. Hence

$$a \cdot b = (a' + s) \cdot (b' + t) = a' \cdot b' + (a' \cdot t + s \cdot b' + s \cdot t).$$

Since $(a' \cdot t + s \cdot b' + s \cdot t) \in S$ (why?), also $a \cdot b - a' \cdot b' \in S$. Thus we have that $a \cdot b + S = a' \cdot b' + S$ as desired. The other part of 10-16 may be shown to be well-defined similarly.

10-17 THEOREM. If S is an ideal of the ring A, then the set A/S of all cosets of S in A is a ring under the operations $+$ and $\cdot$ defined in 10-16. The ring A/S is called the *quotient ring* of A by S.

The mapping θ defined by

$$\theta: \quad a\theta = a + S, \quad a \in A,$$

is a homomorphism of A onto A/S by the very definition of the operations on A/S. It is clear that all ring properties are preserved under a homomorphism, and therefore A/S is a ring.

The additive identity element of A/S is S ($= 0 + S$), while the multiplicative identity element is $1 + S$. The additive inverse of $a + B$ is $(-a) + B$.

For example, let us find the cosets of the ideal (6) of the ring I of integers. We recall that the ideal (6) is the set of all multiples of 6. The distinct cosets of (6) in I are: (6), $1 + (6)$, $2 + (6)$, $3 + (6)$, $4 + (6)$, $5 + (6)$. The coset $14 + (6)$, for example, equals the coset $2 + (6)$, since $14 - 2 \in (6)$. As a matter of fact,

$$a + (6) = b + (6) \quad \text{if and only if} \quad a \equiv_6 b.$$

The cosets of (6) are precisely the equivalence sets of the relation $\equiv_6$ on I, and the operations 10-16 are just the operations defined in 3-11 for the integers modulo 6. The quotient ring $I/(6)$ is the ring of integers modulo 6 as defined in Section 9.

As another example, consider the ideal $(x^2 + 1)$ of all multiples of the polynomial $x^2 + 1 \in R^*[x]$. The cosets of the ideal $(x^2 + 1)$ in $R^*[x]$ have the form

$$ax + b + (x^2 + 1), \qquad a,b \in R^*.$$

The quotient ring $R^*[x]/(x^2 + 1)$ is isomorphic to the complex number field C introduced previously, with i corresponding to the coset $x + (x^2 + 1)$. It should be clear to the reader that we are merely using a different language to describe what we did before when we partitioned $R^*[x]$ relative to the equivalence relation $\equiv_s$, where $s(x) = x^2 + 1$. The use of ideals is preferable to that of equivalence relations in ring theory, however, if for no other reason than that it is more natural to speak of the cosets $a + S$ than it is of the equivalence sets $[a]$ related to $\equiv_s$.

We have already noted that for each ideal S of the ring A, the mapping θ: $a\theta = a + S$, $a \in A$, is a homomorphism of A onto A/S. A converse, in a sense, of this is also true. That is, if α is a homomorphism of ring A onto ring B, then there exists an ideal S of A such that ring B is isomorphic to the quotient ring A/S. The ideal S, called the *kernel* of α, is defined as follows:

$$S = \{a; a \in A, a\alpha = 0\}.$$

Thus S consists of all elements $a \in A$ that are mapped by α into the zero element of B. In order to verify that S is an ideal of A, certainly $0 \in S$, and whenever $a \in S$, $-a \in S$ also since $(-a)\alpha = -(a\alpha) = 0$. If $a,b \in S$, then also $a + b \in S$ since $(a + b)\alpha = a\alpha + b\alpha = 0$. Finally, if $a \in A$ and $s \in S$, then

$$(a \cdot s)\alpha = (a\alpha) \cdot (s\alpha) = (a\alpha) \cdot 0 = 0,$$

which proves that $a \cdot s \in S$. Similarly, $s \cdot a \in S$ and S is proved to be an ideal of A.

Let the mapping β of A/S onto B be defined by

$$\beta: \quad (a + S)\beta = a\alpha, \qquad a \in A.$$

This mapping is well-defined, for if $a + S = b + S$, then $a = b + s$ for some $s \in S$ and

$$a\alpha = (b + s)\alpha = b\alpha + s\alpha = b\alpha.$$

Thus $a + S = b + S$ implies that $a\alpha = b\alpha$, which shows that β is well-defined.

That β is a homomorphism of A/S onto B is a consequence of the following computations:

$$((a + S) + (b + S))\beta = ((a + b) + S)\beta,$$
$$= (a + b)\alpha,$$
$$= a\alpha + b\alpha,$$
$$= (a + S)\beta + (b + S)\beta;$$
$$((a + S)\cdot(b + S))\beta = (a\cdot b + S)\beta,$$
$$= (a\cdot b)\alpha,$$
$$= (a\alpha)\cdot(b\alpha),$$
$$= (a + S)\beta\cdot(b + S)\beta.$$

In order to show that β is an isomorphism of A/S onto B, assume that $(a + S)\beta = (b + S)\beta$ for some $a,b \in A$. Then $a\alpha = b\alpha$ and $(a - b)\alpha = 0$. Thus $a - b \in S$, which proves that $a + S = b + S$. Hence β is an isomorphism. We have proved the following theorem.

10-18 Theorem. *If S is an ideal of the ring A, then the mapping $\theta\colon a\theta = a + S$, $a \in A$, of A onto A/S is a homomorphism. Conversely, if α is a homomorphism of ring A onto ring B, and if S is the kernel of α, then the mapping $\beta\colon (a + S)\beta = a\alpha$, $a \in A$, is an isomorphism of A/S onto B.*

A consequence of this important theorem, for example, is that if α is a homomorphism of the ring of integers I onto another ring B, then necessarily B is isomorphic to $I/(n)$ for some integer n. Why? For the simple reason that B is isomorphic to I/S for some ideal S of I by 10-18, and the only ideals of I are those of the form (n). Thus the only homomorphic images of the ring of integers are the rings of integers modulo n.

10-19 Exercises

1. Find all ideals of the ring $I/(6)$; of $I/(8)$. In general, what are the ideals of $I/(n)$?

2. Let F be a field, and F_2 be the ring of all 2×2 matrices over F. Prove that F_2 has no nontrivial ideal. (Hint: if E_{ij} is the matrix

with 1 in the (i,j) position and zeros elsewhere, and if A is a nonzero matrix of F_2, then $E_{ij} \cdot A \cdot E_{mn} = kE_{in} \neq 0$ for some choice of j and m. Hence any nonzero ideal of F_2 contains all E_{ij}.)

3. A subring S of a ring A is called a right ideal of A if $s \cdot a \in S$ for each $s \in S$, $a \in A$. Exhibit some nontrivial right ideals in the ring F_2 of Exercise 2.

4. Let A be a ring, and for each positive integer n, let $A(n) = \{a; a \in A, na = 0\}$. Prove that $A(n)$ is an ideal of A for each choice of n.

5. Let A be a ring, and let S be the set of all elements of A of nonzero characteristic. Prove that S is an ideal of A, and that all elements of A/S have zero characteristic.

6. Let A be a ring, and for each positive integer n, let $nA = \{na; a \in A\}$. Prove that nA is an ideal of A for each choice of n. What can be said about the characteristic of the elements of A/nA?

7. Illustrate Exercise 6 with the ring I_2 of all 2×2 matrices over the integers.

8. Prove that the only ideals of the ring $F[x]$, F a field, are those of the form $(f(x))$.

9. Let A be a ring having the property that for each pair (a,b) of elements of A, with $a \neq 0$, there exists an $x \in A$ such that $a \cdot x = b$. Prove that A is a division ring.

10. If S and T are ideals of the ring A, then prove that $S \cap T$ and $S + T = \{s + t; s \in S, t \in T\}$ also are ideals of A. Let L be the set of all ideals of A. Prove that the algebraic system $\{L; \subset, \cap, +\}$, a lattice, has the following properties:

(i) the operations $\cap$ and $+$ on L are associative and commutative;

(ii) there exist identity elements relative to both $\cap$ and $+$;

(iii) if $S,T,U \in L$ with $S \subset U$, then

$$S + (T \cap U) = (S + T) \cap U.$$

37. Boolean algebras

A type of algebraic system that arises naturally in mathematical logic is the Boolean algebra, named in honor of the English logician Boole. Boole was the first to give, in his book *The Mathematical Analysis of Logic*, published in 1847, an algebraic formulation of logic. We shall discuss the algebraic system that arises from this formulation without showing its relation to logic.

Before giving the formal definition of a Boolean algebra, we shall give what is probably the most important example of such an algebra. Let E be any (nonvoid) set of elements, and $P(E)$ be the set of all subsets of E. Included in $P(E)$ is the subset 0 of E that contains no elements; 0 is the *void set*. Naturally, E is itself an element of $P(E)$.

Three operations can be introduced on $P(E)$, namely the familiar binary operations of *union* ($\cup$) and *intersection* ($\cap$), and the unary operation of *complementation* (′). We recall that for each $A,B \in P(E)$, $A \cup B$ is the set of all elements in either A or B (or in both), while $A \cap B$ is the set of all elements in both A and B. The complement A' of any subset A of E is the set of all elements of E that are not in A.

Clearly

$$A \cup B = B \cup A, \quad A \cap B = B \cap A,$$

$$A \cup (B \cup C) = (A \cup B) \cup C, \quad A \cap (B \cap C) = (A \cap B) \cap C,$$

for each $A,B,C \in P(E)$; that is, the operations $\cup$ and $\cap$ are both commutative and associative. Since

$$A \cup 0 = A, \quad A \cap E = A$$

for each $A \in P(E)$, 0 and E are the identity elements of $P(E)$ relative to the operations of union and intersection respectively. From the very definition of the complement, it is apparent that

$$A \cup A' = E, \quad A \cap A' = 0$$

for each $A \in P(E)$. Also, we see that

$$E' = 0, \quad 0' = E.$$

A noticeable difference between the algebra $P(E)$ and the other algebraic systems we have studied is that $P(E)$ is not a group relative to either binary operation. Thus for any proper subset A of E (that is, $A \neq E$, $A \neq 0$), there is no subset B of E such that $A \cup B = 0$ or such that $A \cap B = E$.

Some of the other properties of the algebra $P(E)$ will now be listed: for each $A,B \in P(E)$,

$$A \cap A = A, \qquad A \cup A = A;$$

$$E \cup A = E, \qquad 0 \cap A = 0;$$

$$(A \cup B)' = A' \cap B', \qquad (A \cap B)' = A' \cup B'.$$

These are obvious with the possible exception of the last pair. Let us prove one of them, namely, that

$$(A \cup B)' = A' \cap B'.$$

To this end, let $a \in (A \cup B)'$; then certainly $a \not\subset A$ and $a \not\subset B$, that is, $a \in A'$ and $a \in B'$ so that $a \in A' \cap B'$. This proves that

$$(A \cup B)' \subset A' \cap B'.$$

On the other hand, if $a \in A' \cap B'$, then $a \in A'$ and $a \in B'$, and therefore $a \not\subset A$ and $a \not\subset B$. Certainly then $a \not\subset A \cup B$, that is, $a \in (A \cup B)'$. This proves that

$$A' \cap B' \subset (A \cup B)',$$

which together with the previous result proves that $(A \cup B)' = A' \cap B'$ as desired.

The final properties of the algebra $P(E)$ that we shall give are the following distributive laws: for each $A, B, C \in P(E)$,

$$A \cap (B \cup C) = (A \cap B) \cup (A \cap C),$$

$$A \cup (B \cap C) = (A \cup B) \cap (A \cup C).$$

In order to prove the first of these, let $a \in A \cap (B \cup C)$. Then $a \in A$, and either $a \in B$ or $a \in C$. Thus $a \in A \cap B$ or $a \in A \cap C$, that is, $a \in (A \cap B) \cup (A \cap C)$. This proves that

$$A \cap (B \cup C) \subset (A \cap B) \cup (A \cap C).$$

On the other hand, if $a \in (A \cap B) \cup (A \cap C)$, then either $a \in A \cap B$ or $a \in A \cap C$. Consequently, $a \in A$ and $a \in B \cup C$, so that $a \in A \cap (B \cup C)$. This proves that

$$(A \cap B) \cup (A \cap C) \subset A \cap (B \cup C),$$

which together with the previous result proves the first of the distributive laws. The proof of the other distributive law is similar.

The definition of a Boolean algebra that we are about to present is that given by the American mathematician Huntington in 1904. This definition contains a minimum number of postulates in the sense that no one of them is deducible from the others.

10-20 DEFINITION. A set B together with two (binary) operations $\cup$ and $\cap$ is called a *Boolean algebra* provided that the following postulates hold:

P_1: the operations $\cup$ and $\cap$ are commutative;

P_2: there exist (distinct) identity elements 0 and 1 relative to the operations $\cup$ and $\cap$ respectively;

P_3: each operation is distributive relative to the other; that is, for each $a,b,c \in B$,

$$a \cup (b \cap c) = (a \cup b) \cap (a \cup c),$$

$$a \cap (b \cup c) = (a \cap b) \cup (a \cap c);$$

P_4: for each $a \in B$ there exists an $a' \in B$ such that

$$a \cup a' = 1, \qquad a \cap a' = 0.$$

We easily verify that the algebra $P(E)$ given previously satisfies all the postulates of a Boolean algebra. Of course, we also note that $P(E)$ has many properties not postulated for a Boolean algebra such as the associative laws, the idempotent laws $A \cap A = A \cup A = A$, and other properties listed above. However, all of these properties are deducible from the postulates given, as we shall presently show.

One of the first things that strikes us when we look at the postulates of a Boolean algebra is that there is a perfect symmetry or "duality" existing between the properties of the two operations. Thus, in P_1, each operation is assumed to be commutative; in P_2, each operation is assumed to have an identity element; in P_3, each operation is assumed to be distributive relative to the other; in P_4, either equation is obtained from the other by interchanging operations and identity elements.

This duality that exists between the operations of B leads to the following *principle of duality*: Any proposition deducible from the postulates of a Boolean algebra remains valid if the operations $\cap$ and $\cup$, and the identity elements 0 and 1, are interchanged throughout the proposition.

Some of the properties of a Boolean algebra that follow from the postulates are given in the theorem below. Dual statements are placed side by side; in view of the principle of duality, only one statement from each dual pair need be proved.

10-21 Theorem. The following properties hold in a Boolean algebra B:

(i) the IDEMPOTENT LAWS: for each $a \in B$,

$$a \cup a = a, \qquad a \cap a = a;$$

(ii) for each $a \in B$,

$$a \cup 1 = 1, \qquad a \cap 0 = 0;$$

(iii) the ABSORPTION LAWS: for each $a,b \in B$,

$$a \cup (a \cap b) = a, \qquad a \cap (a \cup b) = a;$$

(iv) the ASSOCIATIVE LAWS: for each $a,b,c \in B$,

$$a \cup (b \cup c) = (a \cup b) \cup c, \qquad a \cap (b \cap c) = (a \cap b) \cap c;$$

(v) the element a' associated with each $a \in B$ is unique;
(vi) for each $a,b \in B$,

$$(a \cup b)' = a' \cap b', \qquad (a \cap b)' = a' \cup b'.$$

The proof of (i) goes as follows:

$$
\begin{aligned}
a &= a \cup 0 & (P_2), \\
&= a \cup (a \cap a') & (P_4), \\
&= (a \cup a) \cap (a \cup a') & (P_3), \\
&= (a \cup a) \cap 1 & (P_4), \\
&= a \cup a & (P_2).
\end{aligned}
$$

We may prove (ii) as indicated below:

$$
\begin{aligned}
0 &= a \cap a' & (P_4), \\
&= a \cap (a' \cup 0) & (P_2), \\
&= (a \cap a') \cup (a \cap 0) & (P_3), \\
&= 0 \cup (a \cap 0) & (P_4), \\
&= a \cap 0 & (P_2).
\end{aligned}
$$

The proof of (iii) uses (ii), and is as follows:

$$
\begin{aligned}
a &= (b \cap 0) \cup a & ((ii), P_2), \\
&= (b \cup a) \cap (0 \cup a) & (P_3), \\
&= (b \cup a) \cap a & (P_2), \\
&= a \cap (a \cup b) & (P_1).
\end{aligned}
$$

In order to establish the associative law relative to $\cup$, let

$$x = a \cup (b \cup c) \quad \text{and} \quad y = (a \cup b) \cup c.$$

Then

$$a \cap x = (a \cap a) \cup (a \cap (b \cup c)) \qquad (P_3),$$
$$= a \cup (a \cap (b \cup c)) \qquad ((\text{i})),$$
$$= a \qquad ((\text{iii})),$$

and

$$a \cap y = (a \cap (a \cup b)) \cup (a \cap c) \qquad (P_3),$$
$$= a \cup (a \cap c) \qquad ((\text{iii})),$$
$$= a \qquad ((\text{iii})).$$

Thus $a \cap x = a \cap y$. Now

$$a' \cap x = (a' \cap a) \cup (a' \cap (b \cup c)) \qquad (P_3),$$
$$= a' \cap (b \cup c) \qquad (P_2, P_4),$$

while

$$a' \cap y = (a' \cap (a \cup b)) \cup (a' \cap c) \qquad (P_3),$$
$$= (a' \cap b) \cup (a' \cap c) \qquad (P_3, P_4, P_2),$$
$$= a' \cap (b \cup c) \qquad (P_3).$$

Thus $a' \cap x = a' \cap y$. Hence

$$(a \cap x) \cup (a' \cap x) = (a \cap y) \cup (a' \cap y),$$
$$(a \cup a') \cap x = (a \cup a') \cap y,$$
$$1 \cap x = 1 \cap y,$$
$$x = y,$$

and the associative law is proved.

The proof of (v) is effected by assuming that there are two elements b and c for each $a \in B$ such that

$$a \cup b = 1, a \cap b = 0; \quad a \cup c = 1, a \cap c = 0.$$

Then

$$c = (a \cup b) \cap c = (a \cap c) \cup (b \cap c) = b \cap c,$$
$$b = (a \cup c) \cap b = (a \cap b) \cup (c \cap b) = c \cap b,$$

and $c = b$ by P_1. Thus the element a' postulated in P_4 is unique.

Finally, let us sketch the proof of (vi):

$$(a \cup b) \cup (a' \cap b') = ((a \cup b) \cup a') \cap ((a \cup b) \cup b'),$$
$$= (1 \cup b) \cap (1 \cup a),$$
$$= 1,$$

while

$$(a \cup b) \cap (a' \cap b') = (a \cap (a' \cap b')) \cup (b \cap (a' \cap b')),$$
$$= (0 \cap b') \cup (0 \cap a'),$$
$$= 0.$$

Clearly, then, $a' \cap b' = (a \cup b)'$.

Nothing has been said as yet about any order relation on a Boolean algebra B corresponding to the relation $\subset$ that plays such a fundamental role in the Boolean algebra $P(E)$ given at the beginning of this section. Such a relation may be introduced on B, as we now show.

10-22 Definition. The order relation "less than or equal to" ($\leq$) is defined on a Boolean algebra B as follows: for each $a,b \in B$,

$$a \leq b \quad \text{if and only if} \quad a \cup b = b.$$

Since $a \cup a = a$, clearly

$$a \leq a$$

for each $a \in B$. Also, if

$$a \leq b \quad \text{and} \quad b \leq a, \quad \text{then} \quad a = b,$$

since $a \cup b = b$ and $b \cup a = a$ imply that $a = b$. The relation $\leq$ is transitive, since

$$a \leq b \quad \text{and} \quad b \leq c$$

imply that

$$a \cup b = b \quad \text{and} \quad b \cup c = c;$$

and these equations imply that $(a \cup b) \cup c = c$, or $a \cup (b \cup c) = c$. Thus $a \cup c = c$ and

$$a \leq c$$

as desired. These are properties of the relation $\leq$ on B in common with the corresponding relation $\leq$ on I, the system of integers.

In many ways, however, the relation $\leq$ on B is much different from the relation $\leq$ on I. Any two elements $a,b \in I$, for example, are comparable in that either $a \leq b$ or $b \leq a$. That this is not so in B is clear, for if $a \in B$, $a \neq 0,1$, then $a \nleq a'$ and $a' \nleq a$. Another property of the relation $\leq$ on B is as follows:

$$0 \leq a \leq 1 \quad \text{for each} \quad a \in B.$$

This is a consequence of the equations

$$0 \cup a = a, \qquad a \cup 1 = 1.$$

For each $a,b \in B$, $a \cup b$ is the least upper bound of a and b while $a \cap b$ is the greatest lower bound of a and b. To see this, let x be any upper bound of a and b, that is, let

$$a \leq x \quad \text{and} \quad b \leq x.$$

Then $a \cup x = x$, $b \cup x = x$, and $(a \cup b) \cup x = x$, so that

$$a \cup b \leq x.$$

Since $a \leq a \cup b$ and $b \leq a \cup b$ (why?), and $a \cup b \leq x$ where x is any upper bound of a and b, clearly $a \cup b$ is the least upper bound of a and b. Similarly, one proves that $a \cap b$ is the greatest lower bound of a and b.

Many other properties of Boolean algebras are contained in the following set of exercises.

10-23 Exercises

1. Let B be the following subset of the integers, $B = \{1,2,3,5,6, 10,15,30\}$. For each $a,b \in B$, define $a \cup b = [a,b]$, the least common multiple of a and b, and $a \cap b = (a,b)$, the highest common factor of a and b. Show that $\cup$ and $\cap$ are operations on B, and that $\{B; \cup,\cap\}$ is a Boolean algebra.

2. Show that the set $B = \{a,b,c,d\}$, with operations $\cup$ and $\cap$ as defined below, is a Boolean algebra.

$\cup$	a	b	c	d
a	a	b	c	d
b	b	b	b	b
c	c	b	c	b
d	d	b	b	d

$\cap$	a	b	c	d
a	a	a	a	a
b	a	b	c	d
c	a	c	c	a
d	a	d	a	d

3. In a Boolean algebra B, prove that $a \leq b$ if and only if $a \cap b = a$.

4. Prove that if $a,b,c \in B$, a Boolean algebra, with $a \leq b$, then $a \cup c \leq b \cup c$ and $a \cap c \leq b \cap c$.

5. Show that the set $B = \{a,b,c,d,e\}$ with operations $\cup$ and $\cap$

as defined below is not a Boolean algebra. Which postulates of 10-20 are satisfied by the algebraic system $\{B; \cup, \cap\}$?

$\cup$	a	b	c	d	e
a	a	b	c	d	e
b	b	b	b	b	b
c	c	b	c	b	b
d	d	b	b	d	b
e	e	b	b	b	e

$\cap$	a	b	c	d	e
a	a	a	a	a	a
b	a	b	c	d	e
c	a	c	c	a	a
d	a	d	a	d	a
e	a	e	a	a	e

6. Prove that for any $a, b, c \in B$, a Boolean algebra,

$$(a \cap b) \cup (b \cap c) \cup (c \cap a) = (a \cup b) \cap (b \cup c) \cap (c \cup a).$$

7. If for $a, b, c \in B$, a Boolean algebra, $a \cap b = a \cap c$ and $a \cup b = a \cup c$, then prove that $b = c$.

8. Define the operations of addition $(+)$ and multiplication $(\cdot)$ in the Boolean algebra B as follows: for each $a, b \in B$,

$$a + b = (a \cap b') \cup (a' \cap b); \qquad a \cdot b = a \cap b.$$

Prove that the algebraic system $\{B; +, \cdot\}$ is a ring having characteristic 2. This ring has the property that $a^2 = a$ for each $a \in B$; it is called a *Boolean ring*.

Index